EMBRYOGENESIS
IN PLANTS

By the same author

★

MORPHOGENESIS IN PLANTS
PHYLOGENY AND MORPHOGENESIS

EMBRYOGENESIS
IN PLANTS

BY

C. W. WARDLAW

Professor of Cryptogamic Botany, University of Manchester

LONDON: METHUEN & CO. LTD
NEW YORK: JOHN WILEY & SONS, INC.

First published in 1955

55-2425 ✓

CATALOGUE NO. 5733/U (METHUEN)

PRINTED AND BOUND IN GREAT BRITAIN AT THE PITMAN PRESS, BATH

To MAY

Preface

CONTEMPORARY botanical science is characterised by great activity along many different lines. From time to time, therefore, it becomes necessary, certainly desirable, to bring together the observations and conclusions relating to major topics. *Embryogenesis in Plants* is such a theme. The embryology of species from different taxonomic groups has long provided subjects for research by the traditional methods of the anatomist and histologist, the results in the main being regarded as a contribution to comparative morphology. There is still scope for further work along these lines. During recent years, however, new ideas and experimental techniques have been applied to the investigation of embryos, and new evidence, some of it of a fascinating interest, and suggestive of great possibilities for further work, is beginning to accrue. This statement applies not only to the seed plants but to other groups also. In the present comprehensive survey—the first of its kind—the author has described, illustrated, and discussed the embryological development in *all* classes of plants, from Algae to Angiospermae, references to the dynamic aspect and to experimental work being incorporated wherever possible. An attempt has been made to offer some explanation of the visible embryological developments in terms of the genetical, physical, and other factors and relationships which may be involved, and to show how such an approach promotes an understanding of the parallelisms of development, or homologies of organisation, found in all the major taxonomic groups. The traditional theme of the bearing of the evidence from embryology on evolutionary and phyletic theory is also fully considered. It is hoped that the book thus contains matter of interest to all botanists, teachers and research workers alike.

Borrowed illustrations are duly acknowledged and here the author would like to express his thanks to all concerned. Sincere thanks are offered to Professor P. Maheshwari and Messrs McGraw-Hill, New York, for the use of illustrations from *An Introduction to the Embryology of Angiosperms*, to Professor D. A. Johansen and Messrs Chronica Botanica Co., Waltham, Mass., for the use of illustrations from *Plant Embryology*, to Messrs Macmillan & Co. for the use of illustrations from books by the late Professor F. O. Bower and Professor D. H. Campbell, to Professor R. Souèges and Professor A. Lebègue for the use of illustrations from their Memoirs, and to the Editors and Publishers of the following journals for the use of illustrations: *Annals of Botany;*

Journal of the Linnean Society; American Journal of Botany; Botanical Gazette; Journal of the Torrey Botanical Club; Journal of Agricultural Research; Biological Bulletin; Growth; Lloydia; Flora, Biologische Zentralblatt; Botanische Zeitschrift; Revue Générale de Botanique; Phytomorphology; Transactions of the New Zealand Institute; Proceedings of the Linnean Society of New South Wales; and to others with whom the author has been unable to make contact. The author is also much indebted to Mr E. Ashby and Mr P. Dawes for assistance in the reproduction of illustrations and to Mrs M. Lightfoot for secretarial assistance. Dr A. Allsopp and Dr M. G. Calder have been so kind as to read some of the chapters and have given the author valuable criticisms for which he now expresses his gratitude; but the responsibility for the text is his own. Lastly, he is deeply indebted to his publishers, Messrs Methuen & Co. Ltd for all the assistance they have given in the production of this book.

C. W. WARDLAW

The University
Manchester
June 1st 1954

Contents

Chapter I

SCOPE AND OUTLOOK

AN *embryo* was originally defined as 'the offspring of an animal before its birth (or emergence from the egg),' or, as applied to plants, 'the rudimentary plant contained in the seed' (1728) (*Oxford Dictionary*). In ferns, however, there is no seed; nor is there a well-defined resting stage, marking the completion of the embryogeny, such as we find in a dicotyledon. On the contrary, the fern embryo grows and develops without interruption until it emerges from the gametophyte tissue and becomes established as a free-living sporophyte; and similar developments are characteristic of the embryos of other Archegoniatae. Some elasticity in the use of the term is therefore desirable. There are also occasions when it may be useful and desirable to extend the survey of development beyond the strictly embryonic phase. The terms *embryo* and *germ* have come to connote the initial developmental phase in all classes of plants and it is with a comprehensive survey of this kind that this book is concerned. Since germs may develop from spores as well as from fertilised eggs, the scope and flexibility of treatment thus afforded will admit of comparisons being made of the early developments of the sporophyte and gametophyte generations of archegoniate plants, and of thallophytes and vascular plants. Such a survey should both broaden and render more critical our knowledge of embryogenesis, i.e. the inception and formation of the embryo or germ. This may perhaps appear an undesirable extension of the conception of embryology but it is justified by the facts and by the interest of the inferences that can be based on them. This survey, then, is concerned with all classes of plants, and not simply with the *Embryophyta*, i.e. organisms with an enclosed or contained embryo (comprising archegoniate and seed plants), as defined by Engler and by Campbell.

There are many reasons, both general and particular, why such a survey should be made, especially at the present stage in the development of botanical science. In any undertaking, it is wise counsel to begin at the beginning; and so it is in the study of plants. There is, of course, no absolute beginning, for life is essentially a continuous process. But, in all classes of plants, there is a recurring sequence of phases. Those phases which have their inception in the germination of a spore, or in the development of a fertilised ovum, constitute new beginnings and afford the botanist opportunities for investigating the

1

growth, development, assumption of form, differentiation, and functional activities of organisms, from their small and relatively simple unicellular state to their large and complex adult state. Studies of embryos thus provide essential information on the inception of the varied form and structure of plants.

If our aim is to seek unity in the great and wonderful diversity which we find in the Plant Kingdom, and to understand how, and at what point, the divergences between species and higher taxonomic units occur, we must begin with that stage which is common to all, i.e. the single germ cell, and we must study its constitution, environment, growth, assumption of form, and structural differentiation. An adequate study of embryos thus requires an integration of the data of the several main branches of botanical science, i.e. morphology, physiology and genetics. On these grounds, a substantial, indeed a unique, position may be claimed for embryological studies.

During recent years, investigators of morphogenesis have devoted much time to the study of shoot apices. Since this primary morphogenetic region is as yet inadequately investigated, it clearly merits all the attention that can be given to it. But we should not lose sight of the fact that, in experimental morphogenesis, the perennially embryonic shoot apex has often been pressed into service as a substitute for the young embryo, because of the manipulative difficulties which the latter presents by reason of its small size, delicacy and inaccessibility. Even though they may show similar growth developments, the meristematic cell masses of the apex and of a developing zygote are not really strictly comparable: the environmental and histological relationships of the two are vastly different. In this tendency to avoid embryos as experimental materials and to interpret morphogenetic processes in terms of factors considered to be at work in the shoot apex, it may well be that important phenomena are being neglected and important opportunities missed. Studies of embryogenesis, therefore, not only carry their own interest; they should be regarded as the primary approach to the study of morphogenesis.

As an organism develops, its characteristic *organisation* becomes evident. This is seen in its overall size, shape and structure, in the relationships of its members, and not least, in the harmoniously regulated development of the whole. Moreover, the several tissue systems, whether in a vascular plant or a thallophyte, constitute a characteristic and sometimes highly distinctive pattern, e.g. a cross-section of the rhizome of the common bracken (*Pteridium aquilinum*). As a fact, our knowledge of the factors which determine the tissue pattern in plants is still very slight; but this at least can be said: the process has its inception in the embryogeny.

In the post-Darwinian phyletic period—comprising the latter part of the Nineteenth Century and the beginning of the Twentieth Century —many botanists were confident that the genealogical relationships of all classes of plants could be truly represented by a unified and coherent taxonomic system; in short, by a monophyletic classification. A widening knowledge of plant form and structure, however, and a growing appreciation of the prevalence of parallel and convergent evolution, brought the realisation that the evolution of plants might perhaps not be adequately represented by a monophyletic genealogy. Indeed, it seemed that the evolution of the several classes or subdivisions would be more correctly indicated by a system of separate phyletic lines, possibly originating in ancient algal forms. The more comparative morphologists studied this theme, the more they became aware of the difficulty of finding common ancestors for any of the major groups of plants. In fact, gaps occurred at almost every critical point in the record of the evolutionary process; and this was true not only of the major monophyletic system, but also within individual phyletic lines. So impressed was D'Arcy Thompson (1917, 1942) by the prevalence of these 'phyletic gaps' that he remarked that it almost seemed as if a 'principle of discontinuity' was involved. Here it should be said that although the details of plant embryology were certainly not neglected by the evolutionist, many of the conclusions relating to phylogeny were necessarily based on comparisons of the form and structure of adult organisms, especially in the fossils; and it was in these comparisons that the prevalence of phyletic gaps became so evident. Woodger (1945, 1948), however, has indicated that these data may be viewed in another way and that there is great scope for renewed investigations in comparative embryology, provided a new set of concepts can be devised. In his view, organisms which are rather unlike in the adult state may nevertheless have much in common in their early development; and a more adequate study of the factors which are at work in the embryogeny may eventually show that some of the phyletic gaps, which had proved so puzzling to the early investigators, may in reality be considerably less wide than had been thought, or they may even be non-existent. The contemporary botanist may thus feel encouraged to go as deeply as possible into the study of embryogenesis and he should constantly search for new ideas and new techniques. Zoologists have made much greater progress than botanists in their studies of embryos by experimental and other means. Here reference may be made to the remarkably ingenious manipulative investigations of Spemann (1936, 1938), Dalcq (1938, 1941) and others, and to studies of biochemical relationships by Needham (1931, 1942) and Brachet (1950). It is not suggested that botanical investigators should sedulously follow the zoologists—indeed, they should be cautious to a fault when applying zoological concepts to botanical phenomena—but it is evident that they can gain inspiration and valuable techniques from them.

Some early investigators of embryology held the view that ontogeny was a recapitulation of phylogeny. According to the Theory of Recapitulation, the morphological development of the individual affords a record in miniature of the history of the race. This idea has not found much support or favour among botanists and it has been strongly rebutted by some zoologists (*see* de Beer, 1930, 1950). Indeed, it has been regarded more as an interesting general idea than as a fundamental conception which could be fully accepted. There is, of course, some evidence that seems to support the theory. In the contemporary view, the many aspects of development are held to be determined and controlled by factors in the genetic constitution, or genotype, of the species. Since the genotype of a contemporary species comprises ingredients of the hereditary constitution of ancestral forms, a study of the ontogeny may reveal the inception and development of both distant ancestral and more recently evolved characters.

While some major groups of plants afford indisputable evidence of community of origin, there is also abundant evidence of parallel and convergent evolution. The study of the underlying causes of these *homologies of organisation* may be indicated as one of the most interesting and important tasks in biology. The data of embryogenesis may have an important place in the study of this phenomenon.

The initial embryological studies were essentially morphological in inception and outlook, and indeed this was necessarily so. The aim was to provide a demonstration or record of development from the first division of the zygote up to the point where the embryo could maintain itself as a free-living individual. A great deal of careful and painstaking effort has been necessary to obtain this information; and it may be said, with due emphasis, that these anatomical studies not only show us what the embryos of particular species look like: they constitute the basis on which all further work must rest. Nowadays, however, we recognise that embryology need not, and should not, be pursued only by the methods of the anatomist: we want to know about the factors which determine the observed developments. Many new possibilities are opening up. A new outlook and new investigations have been made possible by recent discoveries in genetics, biochemistry and physiology and by new manipulative techniques, e.g. surgical treatments, and the methods of tissue culture. In short, it is the *process of embryogenesis*, culminating in the organisation of the young plant, that is of paramount interest and importance to the contemporary student of embryology; and to this end experimental work should be introduced wherever possible.

In this book the author has attempted: (i) to review the facts of embryogenesis in all classes of plants; (ii) to consider to what extent the observed developments can be referred to genetical, physiological, physical and environmental factors and to spatial relationships; (iii) to inquire how a study of embryos advances our knowledge of morphogenesis; and (iv) to consider what light this study sheds on the problems of phylogeny, parallel and convergent evolution. Such a survey seems timely, for the general advance of botanical science and the elaboration of new techniques during recent years have made feasible new investigations along several lines. Indeed, the main reason and justification for this book is to stimulate this new work. Lastly, the importance of studying the development of the organism as a whole is emphasised, i.e. the integrative aspect is held to be essential if an adequate account of the harmonious development of the individual is to be given.

Chapter II

FACTORS IN EMBRYOGENESIS

THE ZYGOTE OR SPORE AND ITS ENVIRONMENT

IN studying embryogenesis in any plant, our initial concern is with the growth of a single cell, a zygote or a spore, in its particular environment. In some, perhaps in all, developing sporophytes we probably ought to begin with the unfertilised ovum; for some of the orderly changes that take place during the ontogenetic development may already have been determined by the cytoplasmic organisation of the ovum. If we examine the ovum, whether in an embryo-sac or archegonium, there is evidence that it has undergone some specialised development, e.g. in the archegonium it becomes rounded off and lies free in the venter, and it is a reasonable assumption that it may be affected differentially by various biochemical and physical factors in its immediate environment. In naked, fertilised or unfertilised ova, such as those of *Fucus*, there is apparently no specialised cytoplasmic organisation which determines the polarity of the young embryo: the polar axis may be established in any direction and it is not necessarily, or invariably, determined by one particular factor or group of factors (Whitaker, 1940). On the other hand, the extruded but still attached ovum of *Laminaria* gives rise to an embryo whose axis coincides with that of the oogonium.

We still know very little about the organisation either of the unfertilised or the fertilised egg in plants. Nevertheless, the post-fertilisation developments, especially in archegoniate and seed plants, are such as to indicate that the organisation of the ovum and the zygote is affected, and its subsequent development determined, by factors in the immediate environment, i.e. by the enveloping gametophyte tissue, as well as by physical factors such as gravity. In its most fundamental aspect, the organisation of the ovum and the zygote is due to genetical factors; for in so far as the genes determine the chemical constitution of the reaction system, they also determine the kind of cytoplasmic framework or organisation that is possible.

The position of the ovum in the gametophyte tissue may be important. In some pteridophytes the archegonium typically points downwards, in others, laterally, and in yet others, upwards. These several orientations affect the subsequent embryogenic development. It is probably by the action of biochemical factors, however, that the

6

gametophyte tissue exercises its principal effects both on the maturation of the egg and the subsequent growth of the embryo. Before and after fertilisation, the archegonium is a locus of growth and hence there is a translocation of nutrients of all kinds to it from the surrounding tissue. We may therefore assume, as a working hypothesis, that both the ovum and the zygote are liable to be affected by metabolic gradients, and that these may be among the factors which determine polarity and other important developments. In different classes of Embryophyta, then, the environment of the ovum and zygote deserve careful study.

In the germination of a spore, be it of an alga, a bryophyte, or a pteridophyte, the environment of the single propagative unicell is (i) the water, soil, rock, bark or other substratum in or on which the spore has been deposited, and (ii), in the case of subaerial organisms, moist air. In all of these spores, there is no adjacent tissue either to supply nutrients to, or to direct or control the morphogenetic developments in, the germinating cell. The developments on germination are, therefore, determined, or directed, by internal factors, including the cytoplasmic organisation which has already been established, and by factors in the external medium or environment, e.g. light, humidity, solutes in the substratum, gravity etc. Comparisons of the growth and development of naked as compared with enclosed germ cells, and an analysis of the factors at work in them, in fact, yield many points of interest, including some notable homologies of organisation as well as evident dissimilarities.

STATEMENT OF THE PROBLEMS—INITIAL DEVELOPMENT IN DIFFERENT CLASSES

The fertilised egg is usually a spherical or ellipsoidal body and so too are many spores, though spores may exemplify a considerable diversity of shape. In Fig. 1 young embryos from different taxonomic groups have been selected to illustrate the fact that certain developments are of very general occurrence and to provide materials for a consideration of the main problems in embryogenesis.

On spore germination, or at the earliest manifestation of growth in the zygote, there is evidence of polarity and of *filamentous* or *axial* development; in all but the very simplest organisms, there is, from the outset, a distinction of *apex* and *base* (or of *distal* and *proximal* regions, or *poles*). In short, both the sporeling and the very young embryo afford evidence of *orderly* or *organised* development. Each species has its own particular *ontogenetic pattern* from which there are, as a rule, no very marked departures. If, at the outset of development, there is an indeterminate phase, during which the morphogenetic process might be directed into one of several possible channels or trends, that phase

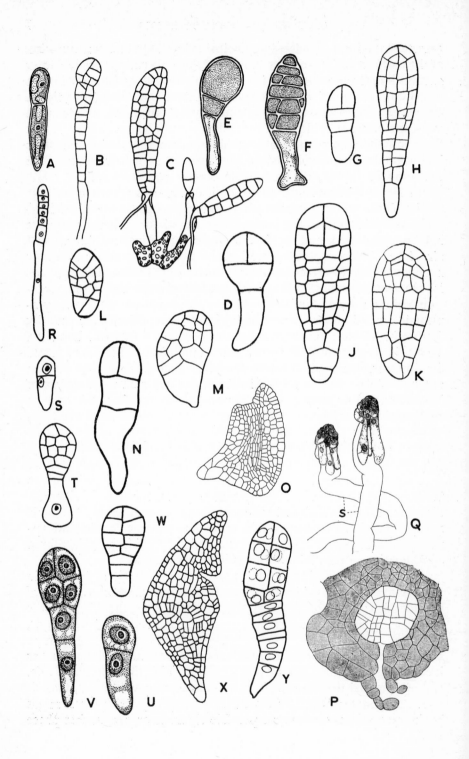

is of brief duration. Such a phase is conceivable and may indeed have a real existence, e.g. in the free-floating zygotes of certain algae such as *Fucus*. Where the embryo is enclosed, as in the Embryophyta, although occasional aberrant developments have been recorded, the normal embryogeny yields evidence of being closely controlled, or *regulated*, from the outset.

The filamentous or axial development, as illustrated in Fig. 1, is characteristic of the embryogeny in all classes of plants and has been described by Bower (1922) as constituting a 'primitive spindle.' This development is attended by cell division and the laying down of partition walls, usually in a very regular and constant manner, so that the embryo has a characteristic *cellular pattern* from the outset. The first partition wall is typically laid down at right-angles to the axis of the embryo, i.e. to the direction of elongation of the primitive spindle or filament. In some embryos several successive transverse divisions take place and an elongated filament results: in others, divisions at right-angles to the first wall take place, and in this we see the inception of a *tissue mass*. In many of the smaller algae the organism never develops beyond the filamentous state; in others, a flat thallus may be formed; but in the larger algae, especially the brown, and in archegoniate and seed plants, the distal region of the filament sooner or later develops into a multi-cellular tissue. At this stage another important general phenomenon becomes evident, namely, that the most distal region is the locus of active growth. This can be observed in many filamentous algae and in all classes of parenchymatous plants: it is a feature of the embryo-geny of *Fucus* and *Polysiphonia* just as it is of *Lycopodium* and *Capsella*. On the further development of these embryos it can be seen that the

---

Fig. 1. Young embryos from different systematic groups

A, *Enteromorpha intestinalis*, a green alga: young plant from zoospore (after Kylin). B, *Fritschiella tuberosa*, a green alga: filament showing beginning of parenchyma formation. C, *Laminaria digitata*, a brown alga: young sporophytes still attached to oogonia. D, *Fucus vesiculosus*, a brown alga (after Thuret and Olt-manns). E, F, *Ceramium areschoughii*, a red alga: young plants from spores (after Oltmanns). G, H, *Radula complanata*, a liverwort (Jungermanniales): young sporo-phytes (after Leitgeb). J, *Aneura multifida*, a liverwort (Jungermanniales): young sporophyte (after Leitgeb). K, *Fegatella* (*Conocephalum*) sp., a liverwort (Mar-chantiales): young sporophyte (after Cavers). L, *Funaria hygrometrica*, a moss: young embryo (after Campbell). M, *Lycopodium annotinum*, a lycopod (after Bruchmann). N, O, *Selaginella spinulosa*, a ligulate lycopod: young and older embryos (after Bruchmann). P, *Adiantum concinnum*, a leptosporangiate fern: embryo in post-octant phase (after Atkinson). Q, *Sequoia sempervirens*, a gymno-sperm: two embryos borne on primary suspensors, with embryonal cells beginning to form secondary suspensors (after Buchholz). R, *Lobelia amoena*, a dicotyledon: filamentous embryo (after Hewitt). S, T, *Sagina procumbens*, a dicotyledon: two stages in the development of the embryo (after Souèges). U, V, *Nicotiana* sp., a dicotyledon (after Souèges). W, X, *Poa annua*, a monocotyledon: two stages in development (after Souèges). Y, *Daucus carota*, a dicotyledon (after Borthwick).

primary *formative activity* is also located in the distal region, this region having become organised as an *apical meristem*. In fact, the subsequent development of the organism is primarily due to the activity of this meristem. It remains in the embryonic state throughout the vegetative development, acts as a self-determining, morphogenetic region, giving rise to the organs and tissues of the enlarging axis (or thallus); and it exercises a physiological dominance over the other parts of the embryo, thus contributing to its regulated, harmonious development. That these observations have a general application is seen in the close parallelism of development (or homology of organisation) exemplified by the apical meristems, and the somata to which they give rise, in *Ascophyllum nodosum* (a brown algae), *Dryopteris aristata* (a fern), and any representative dicotyledon, e.g. *Lupinus albus* or *Primula polyantha* (Wardlaw, 1953).

Each of the successive embryonic phases of any selected species raises its own problems. Our aim is to discover the underlying causes, i.e. the forces determining the sequence of orderly developments characteristic of the species. In particular, we shall have to inquire into the phenomenon of polarity, the predominance of the distal cell group, the mode of nutrition of the embryo, the organisation of the distal apical meristem, the inception and elaboration of the histological pattern, the formation of leaf and root primordia, and the regulated development of the embryo as a whole. The importance of these investigations needs no emphasis: they are of the essence of biological inquiry; and the more we know about factors in the embryogeny, the more adequate will be our understanding of the subsequent developments as the organism grows to the adult state.

GENIC CONTROL OF DEVELOPMENT

Growth from the zygote or spore to the adult state is characterised by an orderly sequence of developments, during which the organism increases in size, becomes structurally complex, and develops the specific characters by which it can be recognised. It may be accepted as a working hypothesis that, in every aspect and phase of development, factors in the hereditary constitution are involved. In that these factors, or genes, determine and control metabolic processes, they are in some way involved in all growth and cellular activity, and therefore in morphogenesis. Such a view is generally accepted by biologists. But how the genes act, individually and collectively, is a problem that is as difficult as it is important. A comprehension of genic action in embryogenesis is clearly a matter of first importance to the biologist.

The *time of action* of particular genes is important in all development, but it has a special interest and importance in embryogenesis.

Thus we may ask: In the developing embryo, how do particular genes become activated at the proper time so that the characteristic orderly development ensues? Haldane (1932) has pointed out that any gene, or other body involved in the transmission of hereditary characters, may affect any of six distinct stages in an organism: (i) the gamete carrying it; (ii) the zygote carrying it; (iii) the endosperm carrying it; (iv) the mother of the zygote carrying it; the former not necessarily carrying it; (v) a gamete (not necessarily carrying it) formed by a zygote carrying it; and (vi) a zygote (not necessarily carrying it) produced by a mother carrying it. Different genes may come into action at different times. Wettstein, for example, was able to observe the effect of one of four genes in *Funaria hygrometrica* in the protonemal stage, whereas the effects of the others did not appear until later.

The embryos of related organisms tend to be more alike than the adults, and this Haldane explains saying that the genes which determine the interspecific differences exercise their chief effect, or come into action, rather late in the individual development. But while this may be so, it should also be pointed out that, as the organism grows to large size, many other factors, not necessarily gene-controlled, may enter into the situation. A common tendency, recognised by students of evolution, is for certain characters to make their appearance progressively earlier in the life-cycle. In such instances, organogenesis is said to be *accelerated*. This may be explained genetically by saying that the first action of particular genes, which normally come into action at a certain stage of development, has taken place at an earlier stage. Again, organs present in an adult ancestor may be reduced to vestiges and appear in the embryo of later evolutionary types. In the genetical explanation, this may often be attributed to acceleration as defined above. The interest of these views for the student of embryology needs no emphasis.

Another tendency, known as *neoteny* or *paedogenesis*, to which Haldane directs attention, consists in a deferment of the action of certain genes, with the result that originally embryonic characters may persist in the adult. Neoteny is, in fact, the opposite of acceleration. The result of neoteny is 'the sudden appearance in an adult form of new characters, which have evolved in ancestral embryos.' De Beer (1930) has described this process, which may have a wide application, as 'clandestine evolution.' In Haldane's view the possibilities of clandestine evolution have probably been underestimated. The same process may simultaneously accelerate or retard the action of a large number of genes. Thus a change in permeability, due to a single gene, would affect the time of action of many genes, with consequential effects on development. Modifications of the time of action of a number of genes will lead to orthogenetic evolution. As Goldschmidt (1927) has pointed out, the sooner a gene begins to act, the more it can do.

According to Goldschmidt (1938), either the genes or their immediate products act as catalysts. Because an enzyme is specific in its action, it will only act if the proper substratum and suitable sustaining conditions are present. When all the conditions are satisfied, the action of the enzyme, which might have been present in the zygote since fertilisation, though perhaps not in sufficient concentration, may begin. This is described as the *activation of the gene*, and, from the metabolic standpoint, embryogenesis may be regarded as a sequence of cytoplasmic states, each of which is initiated under genic control. Thus, as the zygote grows, the original cytoplasmic substratum is transformed into two or more different ones, these providing the substrates suitable for the action of new genes.

Stern (1939) has suggested that there may be specific periods of gene activity. The orderly sequence of developmental processes would then be a direct result of an orderly, timed, genic activity. He also notes that whereas some genes produce phenotypic effects at an early stage in the individual development, others may show a continued activity. To relate the developmental sequence to the hypothetical orderly activity of genes, however, merely restates the problem in other terms, or at most puts it one stage further back: it does not account for the assumption of specific form in a developing organism.

CHEMICAL ASPECTS OF EMBRYOGENY

Textbooks of botany and of plant physiology contain little information on the chemical composition of the zygote, the young embryo, or the surrounding tissues. Nor do they tell us much about the metabolic processes that may be involved in the germination of a spore or the growth and division of a zygote. Equally, they have little to say about the composition and metabolism of the distal meristem that is established at an early stage in the embryogeny and persists throughout the vegetative development. These points are emphasised to remind the reader how much remains to be done before any adequate presentation of what is involved in embryogenesis can be made. Admittedly the magnitude and complexity of the task are formidable. But so too are they in the equivalent field of zoological inquiry; yet zoologists have made some progress, even if thus far only the surface of the problem has been scratched. Here the reader is referred to the books of Needham (1931, 1942) and Brachet (1944, 1950), where the results of a very considerable amount of biochemical and physiological work have been recorded. Thus, they deal with the cytochemistry and histochemistry of the mature and fertilised egg and the factors which may affect them, the environment of the egg, the nutrition of the young embryo, the constitution and effect of the adjacent tissue, and the stimuli and mechanisms which may be involved in the processes of morphogenesis and organisation. Nowhere in the botanical literature has an equivalent body of information been gathered together—indeed the most recent books on plant embryology make virtually no reference to these important and fundamental topics—but some relevant data are available and these will be dealt with in their proper place.

When one contemplates the many distinctive developments that ensue when fertilisation of the ovum has taken place, or when a spore begins to germinate, one cannot fail to realise that, for any adequate understanding of embryogenesis, the existing morphological data must be vastly supplemented by physiological observations. The morphological data merely illustrate the results of embryogenic processes: they tell us little about the underlying causes. But, meanwhile, they constitute the greater part of our information and they are, in fact, the foundation on which the new knowledge must be built.

POLARITY

In thallophytes, bryophytes, pteridophytes and seed plants, the earliest perceptible embryogenic development is the establishment of polarity. As Bowar (1922) has shown, a characteristic, filamentous, axial or spindle-like development is found in the embryogeny of all classes of plants. The formation of this 'primitive spindle' appears to be a fundamental feature in the embryogeny of plants and affords evidence of the early establishment of polarity in the zygote. There is clearly need for a searching inquiry into the phenomenon of polarity; thus far we have little exact information on the factors which determine it. Here it should be noted that a filamentous development, with early establishment of polarity, is to be observed in spore germination just as in the developing zygote (Figs. 1A, B, E, F; 2C; 8A, B, C, D; 9; 10A, B).

The position of the first partition wall in the enlarging zygote has assumed great importance in the literature of embryogeny, for, by the time this wall is laid down, the polarity of the young embryo has been irrevocably determined. Whether polarity is established in the growing but still undivided zygote, and the first dividing wall is consequentially laid down at right angles to what will become the long axis, or whether the position of the first wall is the actual determinant of polarity, cannot yet be decided on the evidence, but several indications favour the former view. In *Psilotum, Tmesipteris, Lycopodium, Selaginella, Equisetum,* some ferns, and in bryophytes, the first division of the zygote is typically at right-angles to the neck of the archegonium; but in leptosporangiate ferns, and in some bryophytes, e.g. *Anthoceros*, the first wall lies in the axis of the archegonium, Fig. 2. These facts suggest that polarity is not determined by structural features of the archegonium itself. In the encapsulated embryo in bryophytes and vascular plants, the establishment of polarity brings the embryo into a particular position in relation to the gametophyte plant (e.g. the moss plant or the pteridophyte

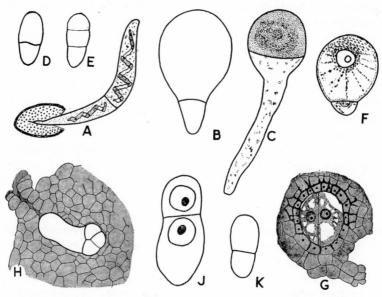

Fig. 2. The first division of the zygote or spore in different groups

A, *Spirogyra velata*, germinating zygospore (after West and Fritsch). B, *Fucus* sp. (after Rostafinski). C, *Polysiphonia atrorubescens*, germinating tetraspore (after Chemin). D, *Targionia hypophylla* (after Campbell). E, *Radula* sp. (after Leitgeb). F, *Osmunda claytoniana*, germinating spore (after Campbell). G, *Adiantum concinnum*, divided zygote (after Atkinson). H, *Lycopodium phlegmaria* (after Treub). J, *Chenopodium bonus-henricus*. K, *Luzula forsteri* (after Souèges).

prothallus) or gametophyte tissue (in seed plants). As this early establishment of a polarised axis has many consequences in the subsequent embryogenic development, it is evident how essential it is to have some knowledge of the factors which may bring it about.

As early as 1878 Vöchting, by dissecting plants into smaller and smaller segments, was able to demonstrate that every fragment possessed definite polarity (Vöchting, 1878, 1884). As polarity was evident in even the smallest fragment this phenomenon would, by implication, extend to the individual cell. However, as later workers (Goebel, 1908; Schwaritz, 1935) were to show, the polarity and morphogenetic behaviour manifested by single cells or groups of cells depend on the fragment as a whole.

In different instances, different factors may assume greater or less importance in determining polarity. In many bryophytes and pteridophytes, for example, the embryo is typically *exoscopic*, i.e. the apex emerges through the neck of the archegonium; but in some, in which a suspensor—a feature which arises in relation to the genetic constitution —is present, the embryo is *endoscopic*, i.e. directed away from the archegonial neck. The embryos of flowering plants may also be regarded as being endoscopic. In each instance the polarity of the embryo is determined by the time the first cleavage of the zygote appears. There is experimental evidence that, in some species, the plane of this first cleavage may be determined by pressures. In a majority of angiosperms, however, since the zygote projects freely into the semi-liquid contents of the embryo sac, pressure cannot be the determining factor. The effects of gravity and light are known to be important and as we have seen, genetical factors, whatever the nature of their action may be, cannot be excluded. The direction of the main gradients of nutrient substances, and in particular of growth-regulating substances, may be important in determining polarity.

Auxins and Polarity. The action of growth-regulating substances, or their precursors, is closely bound up with their polarised movement in the plant. Auxins, for example, typically more basipetally, i.e. from the shoot apex downwards to the root and only to a slight extent in the opposite direction. It has been demonstrated that auxins can move with great rapidity from one part of the plant to other parts. This movement is not, however, equally rapid in all directions, i.e. from the point of origin, or, in experiments, from the point of application. The movement of auxins, which is considerably more rapid than diffusion, may take place through parenchyma, phloem, or, more generally, through vascular tissue. It is a reasonable hypothesis that the polarity of the shoot, or of the organ involved, in some way affects the movement of growth-regulating substances. The suggestion of Czaja (1935) that polarity is due to the movement of auxins and not the cause of it, has not met with general acceptance. The evidence indicates that the polar transmission of stimuli is due to the polar transport of auxins. According to Went and Thimann (1937), polarity in auxin transport is probably determined by some inherent property of the living cells: it is therefore difficult to influence by changing the external environment. The nature of this property is not known. Van der Weij (1934) observed that the direction of transport is quite independent of the gradient of auxin concentration. Went and White (1939) have shown that the polar movement of indoleacetic acid is much more pronounced than earlier workers had realised, only high concentrations being transported acropetally. Great differences in transport velocity have also been found among various other growth-promoting substances.

White (1934) has expressed the view that the methods of tissue culture may be used in the investigation of polarity. He points out that while the formation of specific organs may be due to specific substances, the process may also be affected by concentration gradients of various kinds and 'hence by polar (physical) as well as chemical relationships.' Possible gradients of pH, or of redox, electrostatic or hydrostatic potential, may be involved in different instances; but the primary cause of polarity is still unknown. Gautheret (1945), also using tissue culture data, has advanced a theory of polarity based on experimental observations. He notes as a striking fact that the direction in which buds, formed on the foliar end, or shoot face, of segments of endive root, exercise their effect on root development and inhibition of lateral buds, corresponds with the direction of circulation of auxins. By assuming the existence of a polarised circulation he is able to offer various interesting ideas as to how undifferentiated tissue, growing in culture, becomes organised into an axial structure with an apical bud, leaves and roots; but the basic problem of polarity still remains un-solved and, in his view, must be sought, not at the tissue level of development, but at the cellular level.

Polarity in Fucus Eggs.[1] Whitaker (1940) has discussed the results of a long series of experiments (Whitaker, 1931–1940) on the polarity in the eggs of the brown algae, in particular of the genus *Fucus*, Figs. 3, 4. In these investigations he has attempted to answer the question: In the spherical, free-floating zygote of *Fucus*, what factors determine the axis of growth and differentiation? He has expressed the view that: 'The effects on the living protoplasm of physical and of chemical factors become largely indistinguishable if the physiological analysis can be carried far enough.' Any physical change inevitably affects biochemical processes; moreover, the distinction between physical and chemical properties 'largely disappears at the molecular and sub-molecular levels at which we believe the ultimate, even if mostly unidentified, processes of differentiation and growth take place.'

The fertilised egg of *Fucus* is a spherical and relatively undifferen-tiated body. Growth and differentiation, i.e. a quantitative and a qualitative change, take place simultaneously, the first visible manifesta-tion being the appearance at one point of a rhizoidal outgrowth. The first cell division takes place in the plane at right angles to the emerging rhizoid. The factors which determine the position of this rhizoid therefore determine the polarity of the developing germ. Polarity is

---

[1] In the experiments of Whitaker and others the term 'eggs' usually refers to zygotes. Where unfertilised eggs are indicated, they are so described.

evidently established at a very early phase in the development of the zygote; that is, on the assumption that it was not already present in the unfertilised egg.

A single zygote, kept in darkness and as free as possible from gradients or asymmetry of environmental factors, forms a single rhizoid and develops mormally. Whitaker argues that a very labile and readily

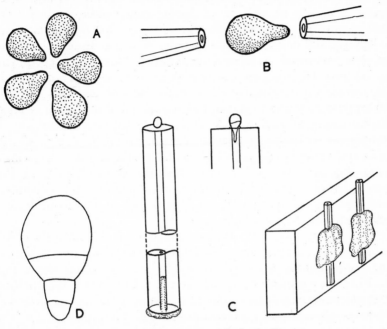

Fig. 3. Experiments on polarity in *Fucus*

A, In a cluster of zygotes, the rhizoidal development is typically centripetal. B, When a fertilised egg is placed in a gradient of pH, i.e. between two pipettes of solution, the rhizoid grows out on the more acid side (A and B, after Whitaker). C, Apparatus for determining the effect of various solutions on the segmentation of *Fucus*; (*see* text pp. 18, 48) (after Olson and DuBuy). D, Segmentation in *Fucus* (after Rostafinski).

altered polarity is either already established (perhaps due to conditions during oogenesis) or that it is established after shedding by 'chance environmental differentials of a minor sort.' Knapp (1931) states that in *Cystoseira*—an alga of *Sargassum* affinity—the rhizoid emerges at the point of entrance of the spermatozoid; and this may also happen in *Fucus*. The important point is that if polarity is thus established, it is readily superseded by the effects of subsequent physical or chemical gradients.

The facts relating to the establishment of polarity may be summarised as follows: Unilateral illumination by white light causes rhizoids to form on the least illuminated side. (Rosenvinge, 1899; Kniep, 1907; Whitaker and Lowrance, 1936). Hurd (1920) has shown that only the shorter wave-lengths of the visible spectrum are effective (violet blue and probably the shorter green). In experiments conducted in the dark, in which eggs were subjected to a direct electric current, rhizoids formed on the side towards the positive pole—at which negative ions including those of auxin presumably accumulated (Lund, 1923). Where eggs are assembled together in groups, the rhizoids point into the centre of the group, Fig. 3. This effect of one cell on another acts over a considerable distance—up to 0·3 mm. of sea water. (Rosenvinge, 1889; Kniep, 1907; Hurd, 1920; Whitaker, 1931). Whitaker observed that two eggs alone in normal sea water did not form rhizoids towards each other, appreciable masses of eggs being necessary. Moreover, the effect was found to be non-specific in that it was produced by un-fertilised eggs of *F. vesiculosus* on developing eggs of *F. evanescens*. The presence of masses of eggs, releasing CO_2 into the sea water, will increase the hydrogen ion concentration; it was found that by acidifying the water to pH 6·0, the 'group effect' in rhizoid formation was greatly increased so that five or even two eggs together would show rhizoids directed towards each other at distances up to four egg diameters. A negative group effect was observed in alkaline sea water (Whitaker and Lowrance, 1940). An egg responds to diffusion gradients from itself as well as to the products of another egg (Whitaker, 1937), the rhizoid forming on the side subjected to the greatest concentration of substances diffusing from the egg.

When individual eggs were placed between two pipettes, one containing normal sea water at pH 8·0, and the other acidified to a pH of 6·0 the rhizoid developed on the acid side (Whitaker, 1938) (Fig. 3). If the acid pipette was at pH 5·6 the rhizoid developed on the other side. Whitaker points out that gradient rather than actual pH is the important consideration.

DuBuy and Olson (1937) succeeded in extracting an auxin (un-determined) from *Fucus* eggs and van Overbeek (1940) has shown that auxin is present in *Macrocystis*. Olson and DuBuy (1937) found that rhizoids form on the side supplied with the greatest concentration of heteroauxin. Whitaker (1940) points out that the presence of auxin in *Fucus* eggs does not prove that it is normally functional there, i.e. it could be a waste product. 'The strong effect of acid on the *Fucus* egg may well be due in part to its activating effect on auxin, but it appears highly probable that so active an agent as the hydrogen ion would also act on other steps in the rhizoid-forming process as well.'

Fucus eggs respond to temperature gradients by forming the rhizoid on the warmer side, provided the gradient across the egg does not exceed 0·4°C., (Lowrance 1937). Respiration and other processes will proceed more rapidly on the warmer side; the pH gradient will also tend to be established with the highest acidity on the warmer side.

Centrifuging and Polarity. The centrifuge method developed about the beginning of the century was taken up by many investigators. The basic idea was that, if the specific organ-forming substances, believed to be present, could be displaced from their positions in the cell, the positions in which new parts developed would be altered. The centrifugal displacement of visible granules, as in gravity experiments, was soon found to have no effect on polarity. Lillie (1909) concluded from his experiments that polarity is a property of the ground substance, i.e. the cytoplasm, while later Conklin (1931) considered that the effects produced by high speed centrifuging in ascidian eggs were due to the displacement of specific areas of cytoplasm. As Schechter (1934, 1935) was able to change polarity in the red alga *Griffithsia bornetiana* by the use of low speeds, he considers it improbable that displacement of cytoplasmic areas took place. Cells of this alga, in which the dense material had been centrifuged to the basal end, developed photosynthetic filaments and not rhizoids at that end. These filaments were not so large as those developed at the apical end, nor was the development of filaments at the apical end precluded. Rhizoids continued to be formed in their normal positions. Schechter does not consider that specific organ-forming substances were necessarily involved in the developments observed, but rather that the formation of the new filaments was due to a stimulus set up by an 'unusual concentration of rather non-specific materials.' Centrifuged eggs of *Cystoseira* became stratified and developed rhizoids at the centrifugal end (Knapp, 1931).

Schechter (1934) showed that *Griffithsia*, when placed in an electric current, formed rhizoids towards the positive pole and also that the chromatophores migrated to that pole. He then centrifuged the chromatophores to the centrifugal end and found that filaments and not rhizoids developed there. Whitaker (1937) has shown that when *Fucus* eggs, embedded in sea-water agar, are centrifuged, they become stratified; and when the eggs develop in normal sea water at pH 8·0, with the stratification still present, the rhizoid develops at the centrifugal pole, Fig. 4. Where the visible contents become redistributed before the formation of rhizoids, the latter develop at random in relation to the previous stratification. Ultra-centrifuging produced essentially the same result. When ultra-centrifuged eggs were kept in sea water, acidified to pH 6·0, the rhizoids formed centripetally, Fig. 4. (For a tentative explanation of this result, *see* Whitaker, 1937).

Beams (1937) and Whitaker (1937) have recorded that the eggs of

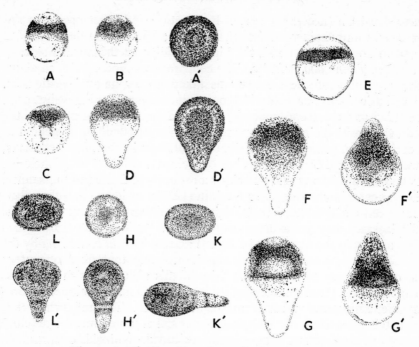

Fig. 4. A–D¹, The effect of centrifuging *Fucus* zygotes

A, A fertilised egg 23 min after being centrifuged for 20 min at 3,000 × g; the centrifugal end is below; the chloroplasts have become aggregated in the dark centripetal band. B, The same egg 15 min later; some dispersion of the dark band is taking place. C, Another similar egg, 3 hr 10 min later; the nucleus has emerged from the dark stratum. D, Another egg from same sample 13 hr 25 min later; the rhizoid has emerged at the centrifugal end. A¹ and D¹ are normal non-centrifuged eggs, corresponding to A and D respectively. All these eggs were reared in the dark at 15°C and at pH 7·9–8·0.

E–G¹, The effect of ultra-centrifuging *Fucus* zygotes.

E, Typical stratified egg soon after being centrifuged for 5 min in normal sea water at 150,000 × g; the centripetal layer is the oil cap; the dense layer includes the plastids and nucleus. F, Similar egg after development in the dark in sea water at pH 8·0; the rhizoid has developed at the centrifugal pole. G, Later stage of same. F¹, Egg similar to that shown in E after developing in sea water acidified to pH 6·0; the rhizoid has developed at the centripetal pole. G¹, Later stage of same.

H–L¹, Effect of shape on the determination of the axis in *Fucus* zygote

H. Normal spherical egg soon after fertilisation. H¹, Similar egg after rhizoid has developed. K, An egg which has been elongated soon after fertilisation. K¹, The rhizoidal development in sea water at pH 8·0. L, An egg which has been elongated soon after fertilisation. L¹, The rhizoidal development at the end of the short axis in acidified sea water at pH 6·0; the rhizoid formed towards the bottom of the culture dish (all after Whitaker).

Fucus can be subjected to centrifugal forces of 150,000 times gravity for several minutes without being killed or even suffering ill effects.

In contrast to these results of Whitaker, when Beams (1937) strongly centrifuged (150,000 × g) the eggs of *Fucus serratus* for various intervals of time, the eggs showed marked stratification but this did not appear to bear any particular relationship to the position in which the rhizoid subsequently developed. He therefore concluded that the stratification of the egg contents had little or no effect on its polarity. (For a general review of the effect of centrifugation on plant cells, *see* Beams and King, 1939).

Unilateral ultra-violet irradiation of *Fucus* eggs resulted in rhizoid development on the side away from the source of light. A sufficiently strong dosage inhibits rhizoid formation without causing cytolysis. Such dosages may act by denaturing proteins, by changing the pH, or by inactivating the auxin (Went and Thimann, 1937).

From the data set out above it appears that in plant zygotes or spores the polarity may be determined to a considerable extent by external factors. Stahl (1885) had already observed that differential exposure to light determined polarity in the spores of *Equisetum*, while the extensive researches of Whitaker and others have shown that the polarity of the fertilised eggs of seaweeds can be modified by factors of very different kinds. Among these, gradients of specific substances are important.

Polarity in Animals. In the zoological field Needham (1942) has referred to the 'difficult question of polarity, perhaps the central puzzle of embryonic development' (p. 656). With a wealth of illustration he shows that the cell protoplasm must be envisaged as possessing organisation: its constituent molecules, of many kinds, are arranged in a particular way, or have a particular orientation, so that the whole has a definite structure which, in morphogenesis, is manifested as polarity. The polarity of the animal egg is in a high degree fixed, and unlike some plant zygotes, e.g. *Fucus*, almost impossible to alter.

Chapter III

FACTORS IN EMBRYOGENESIS (*continued*)

THE FIRST DIVISION OF THE ZYGOTE

THE fertilised ovum is usually seen and depicted as a spherical or ellipsoidal body with no evident regional protoplasmic differentiation. In many archegoniate plants it elongates in the axis of the archegonium and soon reaches a size when cell division becomes necessary. A partition wall is then laid down, the position of this wall being generally, though not invariably, an indicator of the polarity, i.e. the axis of the embryo is at right angles to it. The formation of this first wall is interesting on several counts. According to D'Arcy Thompson (1917, 1942), division is a means of restoring equilibrium within an enlarging cell, and hence, in a considerable measure, the histological pattern can be directly attributed to the action of physical factors, i.e. to internal and surface forces. If an elongating ellipsoidal zygote were of uniform protoplasmic consistency and metabolic activity, with uniform conditions on all sides of it, it would, at a certain critical size, divide into two exactly equal portions by a median transverse wall, i.e. a wall of minimal area. The first wall would thus be at right-angles to the embryo axis, Fig. 5. This is what takes place in many bryophytes and in *Psilotum, Tmesipteris* (Holloway, 1917, 1921, 1939), *Equisetum* and some other pteridophytes. In *Anthoceros*, however, the ovoid zygote is divided by a longitudinal wall, Figs. 5, 14. In leptosporangiate ferns, the spherical zygote is divided into two equal hemispheres, though Atkinson (1894) and others have suggested that the segments may be somewhat unequal. There are, however, many pteridophyte embryos, notably those in which a suspensor (*see* below) is formed, and also flowering plant embryos, where the first wall does not divide the zygote into cells of equal volume, Fig. 5. If, therefore, cell division is a means of maintaining an approximate state of equilibrium in a growing system, it may be inferred that the enlarging zygote, in certain species, must undergo some protoplasmic differentiation; for the first wall separates a relatively large *suspensor* cell from the relatively small *embryo* cell,[1] Fig. 5. In other words, this unequal

---

[1] In pteridophytes in which no suspensor is present, the first partition wall divides the zygote into an *epibasal* cell, which gives rise to the shoot, and a *hypobasal* cell, which gives rise to the root and foot. But in *Lycopodium, Selaginella,* and some eusporangiate ferns, the first wall divides the zygote into a suspensor and an embryonic cell proper. The latter then divides by a wall parallel to the first wall, the cell next the suspensor being recognised as the hypobasal cell and the

division is evidence of differences in metabolic activity at the two poles. Indeed, it may well be that the inception of polarity is due to a drift or trend towards metabolic heterogeneity in an initially homogeneous system. There are many indications that the suspensor and embryonic

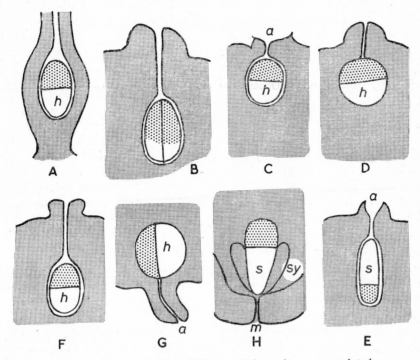

Fig. 5. The first division of the zygote in various encapsulated
embryos (diagrammatic)

A, as in most liverworts and mosses. B, *Anthoceros*. C, *Psilotum*, *Tmesipteris* and *Equisetum*. D, *Isoetes*. E, *Selaginella* and *Lycopodium*. F, *Ophioglossum vulgatum*. G, *Adiantum*, *Onoclea* and other leptosporangiate ferns. H, as in flowering plants. The distal, epibasal, apical or embryonic cell (or embryonic region), is stippled; *s*, suspensor; *h*, hypobasal cell; *sy*, synergids; *a*, archegonium neck; *m*, micropyle.

ends are physiologically different; for whereas the latter continues to grow and divide, yielding the meristematic apical region of the embryo, the suspensor and the cells adjacent to it enlarge and become differentiated as parenchymatous cells (*see* Fig. 7).

distal one as the epibasal cell. As the suspensor is always the cell lying adjacent to the neck of the archegonium, the embryo during its growth thrusts itself into the tissue of the prothallus. Such an embryogeny is said to be *endoscopic*. Where no suspensor is present, as in *Psilotum*, the epibasal cell lies next the neck of the archegonium, the shoot apex grows out through the neck, and the embryogeny is said to be *exoscopic*. The Marattiaceae, however, afford examples of endoscopic embryogeny, even though no suspensor is present. In the embryogenesis of flowering plants a suspensor is of very general occurrence.

There is evidence, which needs to be confirmed and extended, that polarity and the orientation of the first wall dividing the zygote are affected by gravity. Leitgeb (1878), in experiments with *Marsilea*, in which the large megaspores could at will be variously oriented, rotated on a kleinostat, and so on, found that the first partition wall of the zygote was always formed in the axis of the archegonium, no matter what conditions obtained. But the wall could occupy any rotational position round this axis, and, in fact, its position was such that the embryo was always disposed with an upwardly directed shoot-forming half, and a downwardly-directed foot- and root-forming half. This admittedly limited evidence suggests that while gravity may have some effect on the initial phase of development in some species, it is to factors in the fertilised ovum or in the adjacent gametophyte tissue that we should look to explain the observed developments. So far as the writer is aware, it has not been suggested that there is a protoplasmic differentiation in the unfertilised egg or in the zygote in plants comparable with that in certain mozaic eggs known to zoologists. In encapsulated ova it may, however, be inferred that immediately after fertilisation, if not before, protoplasmic differentiation begins to take place. This, indeed, is to be expected when we consider the configuration of the archegonium and its relation to the nutritive prothallial tissue. Somewhat similar considerations will apply to the embryo sac in flowering plants.

While the growth of the encapsulated zygote may be ascribed to biochemical stimuli resulting from the fusion of the male nucleus with that of the ovum, its polarised development seems likely to be determined by auxin or other physiological gradients in the adjacent tissue. In pteridophytes the uptake of nutrients from the prothallus—a process which has been in operation during the maturation of the ovum—is maintained until the embryo becomes a free-living sporophyte; in bryophytes, it continues until the maturation of the sporophyte. Contemplation of the structural details in archegoniate plants suggests that the path of nutrition to the zygote is more likely to be by way of the base and sides of the archegonium than through the region adjoining the neck. If so, the metabolic gradients may determine both the polarity and the position of the first partition wall.

Much importance has been attached to the presence of a suspensor in pteridophytes by comparative morphologists. By them, it is regarded as a primitive feature that has been retained in some modern survivors and it has been suggested by Jeffrey that it is 'useful in pushing the developing embryo deeper down into the prothallial tissue' (Campbell, 1911–40). But, if we look at the matter objectively, two points may be noted: (i) the suspensor undergoes a rapid parenchymatous enlargement, as do the adjacent cells of the foot; (ii) the presence of a suspensor indicates that there are very different physiological conditions at the neck as compared with the basal end of the archegonium. We may also note that a suspensor is consistently present in the embryogeny of seed plants. Whether the very different developments of the suspensor and the embryonic cell in pteridophytes are due to a gene-controlled differentiation in the egg or zygote, to metabolic gradients in the prothallus, to gradients of gaseous concentration, or to some residual effect of fertilisation, must remain open questions. Certainly, there would appear to be some quite fundamental difference between those pteridophytes in which the epibasal cell (destined to become the shoot apex) lies adjacent to the neck of the archegonium, as in *Psilotum*, and those in which it is adjacent to the base of the archegonium, as in *Lycopodium*.[1]

When the comparative morphologist asserts that the suspensor is a primitive organ found in the embryogeny of some modern survivors of ancient stocks, he has probably seized upon a truth, even though he cannot account for the mechanism involved: it is a particular feature of the hereditary constitution which happens to become manifest in the embryogeny. In those genera and families in which a suspensor is known, it occurs with a high degree of regularity. In the contemporary view, the suspensor could be regarded as a gene-determined organ in the inception of which, perhaps, only a few genes are involved; and the genic action leading to its formation would be seen in the differential protoplasmic changes which take place in the elongating zygote. Even if we accept D'Arcy Thompson's view that physical factors determine the way in which the zygote divides, the material on which the relevant forces must work is a specific protoplasm, the metabolism of both the zygote and the surrounding cell matrix being under genic control.

In this, as in all studies of morphogenesis, the basic assumption is that genic action pervades every phase of development, i.e. it is involved in the metabolism which underlies all morphological and histological developments. The distinctive biochemical situations which arise at different stages in the ontogeny have also their biophysical expression. Indeed, at the molecular level, the distinction between chemical and physical properties largely disappears. The action of various extrinsic factors may tend to obscure the primary genic effect, but, as has long been recognised, the basic material on which all morphogenetic factors work is the specific hereditary substance, the ultimate form and structure being the result of both internal and external factors.

This brief survey shows how very little exact information there is on

[1] See p. 103, Fig. 5.

the factors which determine polarity, the position of the first wall, the differentiation of a suspensor, and the positional relationship of the enlarging embryo to the parent prothallus.

THE SEGMENTATION PATTERN

A distinctive segmentation pattern is characteristic of the early embryogeny in all classes of plants. In some instances, as in the simpler algae, this segmentation consists merely in the transverse partitioning of an elongating filament. In other algae there is also an initial filamentous stage, but divisions in other planes soon follow and a regular histological pattern results. In bryophytes, pteridophytes and seed plants the successive segmentations may take place with such a high degree of regularity as to suggest a stepwise (or stage-by-stage) genic control of development.

In pteridophyte species which have no suspensor, and in the further development of the embryonic cell in those with a suspensor, the cell divisions in the enlarging embryo usually conform to one or two very regular and characteristic histological patterns, Fig. 6. At one time, such cellular patterns were thought to be significant as a guide to taxonomic affinities and phylogenetic relationships. To some extent, because ultimately they are determined in a system with a gene-controlled metabolism, it may well be that they do have this significance. A detached scrutiny of the facts, however, would seem to support D'Arcy Thompson's view that the segmentation pattern in a growing tissue is primarily due to physical factors. A growing embryo, like any other physical system, will constantly tend towards a state of minimal free energy. Cell division, by keeping constant the ratio of surface to

---

Fig. 6. The development of the segmentation pattern in the embryogeny in different groups

A–D, *Antithamnion plumula*, germinating spores (after Kylin). E, *Fucus vesiculosus*, young embryo (after Thuret and Oltmanns). F, *Cystoclonium purpurascens*, the subspherical spore has divided into two and then into four equal quadrants (after Kylin). G, *Targionia hypophylla*, early segmentation pattern (after Campbell). H–L, *Lejeunia serphyllifolia* (Jungermanniales), spore germination leading to organisation of an apical cell (after Goebel). M, *Blechnum spicant* (leptosporangiate fern), spore germination, leading to organisation of an apical cell. N, O, P, Diagrams illustrating the ideal segmentation pattern in a dividing sphere (or circle) and its quadrants; each cell is equally divided by a wall of minimal area; I–I, II–II, III–III, IV–IV, the successive partition walls. P, Shows the characteristic readjustment at points of wall conjunction (after D'Arcy Thompson). Q, *Marsilea vestita*, showing a segmentation pattern in the developing embryo that approximates to the ideal pattern illustrated in P (after Campbell). R, *Equisetum arvense*, young embryo; *b–b*, basal wall; *m–m*, first vertical wall; *w*, root initial (after Sadebeck). S, *Epipactis palustris* (Orchidaceae), young and fully formed embryos (after Treub). T, *Drosera rotundifolia* (after Souèges). U, *Chenopodium bonus-henricus* (after Souèges). V, *Scapania nemorosa* (Jungermanniales), young sporophyte (after Leitgeb).

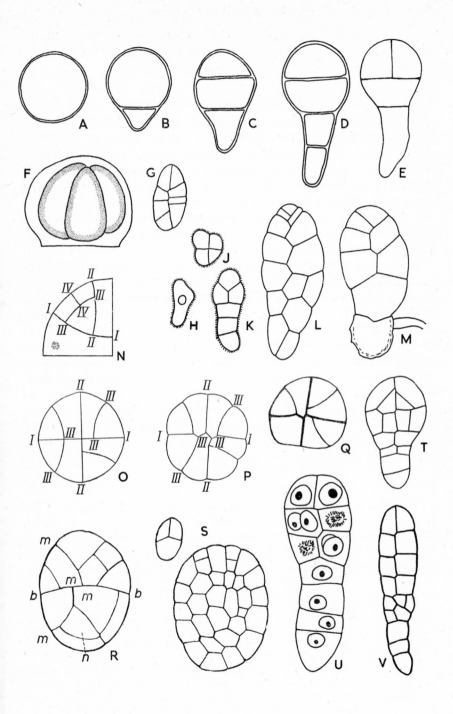

mass, and therefore the ratio of internal to surface free energy, thus tends to maintain equilibrium in the growing organism.

D'Arcy Thompson has argued cogently—though not all observers share his views—that surface forces, in particular surface tension, are important in determining the external shapes of small objects such as embryos, and that they may also account for their characteristic mode of segmentation. A conception of this kind would help to account for the fact that species, which are quite unrelated taxonomically, may nevertheless have comparable segmentation patterns in their embryogeny. His argument is as follows. If equilibrium is to be maintained in a growing embryo, the free surface energy must be reduced to the minimum, i.e. only minimal surfaces must be created by cell division.[1] This conception seems to have an apt application to the segmentation patterns seen in the embryos of plants, Fig. 6. The successive segmentations in the embryogeny of a leptosporangiate fern, for example, are in very close conformity with those which we should expect to find in an ideal growing spherical system, subdividing by walls of minimal area. (*see* D'Arcy Thompson, 1942, pp. 580 *et seq*). Again, in flowering plants, in which the embryo is immersed on all sides in the liquid contents of the embryo-sac (except at the region of attachment of the suspensor), the initial phase of development consists essentially in the enlargement and highly regular segmentation of a subspherical or club-shaped body. After some time, in relation to other factors, differential growth sets in. In general, the segmentation pattern continues to develop in conformity with D'Arcy Thompson's postulates, but it is modified by the different rates of growth in different directions, by the inception of localised growth centres, and so on.

In embryos of quite different systematic affinity, closely comparable cellular patterns are found. As we have seen, these remarkable homologies of organisation seem to be largely determined by physical factors. In other words, the same physical factors may become incident in different, gene-controlled metabolic systems. It also begins to be understandable how a genic change affecting some particular metabolic process may have an effect on the embryonic pattern.

---

[1] This principle of cell division by walls of minimal surface has a wide application in the Plant Kingdom. It was Berthold (1886) who, propounding the principle, compared the forms of many cells and the disposition of their dividing walls with those assumed by a system of weightless films, under the influence of surface tension. In the same year, quite independently, Errera definitely ascribed to the embryonic cell wall the properties of a semi-liquid film and deduced that it must be subject to ordinary physical laws and must accordingly assume a form in conformity with the principle of minimal areas. Another conception which we owe to Errera is that the partition wall formed in a dividing cell tends to be such that its area is the least possible by which the given space-content can be enclosed. In an ovoid body with metabolic homogeneity, the partition wall would be median and transverse; but if there were aggregations of different metabolites at the two poles, with concomitant different energy relationships, the partition wall would separate off two cells of equal energy but they would probably be of different sizes.

POSITION AND NUTRITION

As the embryo grows and develops, its nutrition becomes of ever-increasing importance. The nutrition of an enclosed embryo must stand in some relationship to the position which it occupies in the gametophyte tissue. This question will be considered in greater detail in subsequent chapters. As already noted, the gradients of nutrient supplies to the young embryo may be among the factors determining its polarity. From a very early stage, the distal pole becomes the primary growing and formative region, whereas the proximal or basal pole becomes parenchymatous and functions as the region of uptake of nutrients from the gametophyte. In archegoniate and seed plants, there is also evidence that from an early stage nutrients may not be absorbed over the entire surface of the embryo, as might perhaps be supposed, but are taken up by the basal region and passed on from there to the distal growing region, just as in the adult shoot. Even in filamentous algae there are indications of the same general mechanism of growth.

In bryophytes and in *Psilotum*, *Tmesipteris* and *Equisetum*, where the embryogeny is exoscopic, the hypobasal region remains in contact with the gametophyte tissue and acts as the absorptive foot region, taking up nutrients and passing them on to the actively meristematic epibasal region. We should not, indeed, expect the epibasal cell, which lies in contiguity with the archegonial neck and may soon emerge from the gametophyte tissue, to be the absorptive region of the embryo. All this seems to be straightforward and in conformity with our general knowledge of axial growth. Nevertheless, it is doubtful if such reasoning, based on a consideration of the anatomical data, goes to the root of the matter; for in endoscopic species, e.g. *Lycopodium*, the suspensor and the nutrient-absorbing foot are in contiguity with the archegonium neck and the growing embryo becomes deeply embedded in the fleshy tissue of the prothallus. Hence we may ask: Do these embedded endoscopic embryos absorb nutrients over their entire surface, or is the uptake confined to the foot? While the embryo is still very small, it may be that nutrients are absorbed over the whole of its surface; but, as it enlarges, the indications are that the foot is the main absorptive region. Certainly, from an early stage, there is a marked difference in the development of the basal cells as compared with those at the apical or distal end. The cells of the foot soon become considerably distended; they may extend what appear to be suctorial processes into the tissue of the prothallus; they may contain deposits of starch grains; and they show a gradient of cell-size from the proximal to the distal region. Collectively, these observations suggest that, from a very early stage in the embryogeny, the relation of the distal to the basal region of the embryonic axis is essentially the same as in a normal adult shoot. A growing body of experimental evidence supports the

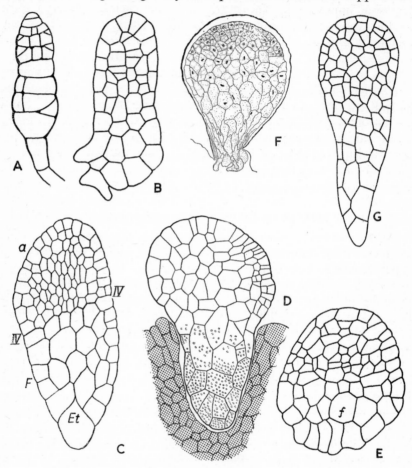

Fig. 7. Gradient of cell size in the embryonic development

A, *Delesseria ruscifolia*, red alga, germling (after Nienburg). *Notothylas* sp., Antho-cerotales, young sporophyte (after Lang). C, *Lycopodium selago*; *et*, suspensor, *f*, foot, *a*, apex (after Bruchmann). D, *Lycopodium cernuum*, the enlarged cells of the foot in contact with the prothallus contain starch grains (after Treub). E, *Os-munda cinnamomea*, showing the large cells of the foot, *f*, and the smaller cells of the embryonic distal region (after Cross). F, *Ginkgo biloba*, young embryo (after Lyon). G, *Zea mays*, young embryo (after Randolph).

view that the shoot apex is a self-determining, morphogenetic region: the data given above indicate that this relationship is established at an early stage in the embryogeny.

On further growth, the apex of an endoscopic embryo bursts out of the prothallus, but the embryo continues for some time to draw upon the prothallus for its nutrition. At this stage there is no longer any question of the nutrients being absorbed over the whole embryonic surface: they must be taken up by way of the foot region; and in this we probably see what is no more than the continuation of a system established at a much earlier stage.

GRADIENT OF CELL SIZE

Closely related to the topic of the preceding section is the fact that the embryos of many different classes show a more or less well marked gradient of cell size from the base or foot into the meristematic shoot region, Fig. 7. Here we have another general phenomenon in embryology for which a physiological explanation is required. The data of tissue culture investigations may in time afford a clue to these characteristic developments.

EFFECTS OF GROWTH AND ENLARGEMENT

As the embryo grows, departs from the filamentous state and becomes a three dimensional tissue system, the spatial relationships of its parts undergo a continuous series of changes. In many of the higher plants the embryo becomes approximately spherical, cylindrical or obconical in shape. There is, accordingly, a continuous diminution in the ratio of surface to bulk or volume. Moreover, we begin to distinguish the outer from the inner tissue layers, these being usually arranged in a concentric manner. In a way, this may be regarded as a kind of differentiation. We do not know how the outer layers differ from the inner layers of an embryo—they may receive more oxygen, or have a lower tension of carbon dioxide, for example—but on further development they are seen to be histologically different. This matter of the distribution in space and the relative positions occupied by tissues certainly merits attention when we try to account for the inception of the several tissue systems. The progressive increase in size of the embryo almost certainly has an effect on its differentiation and organisation: it alters the proportion of surface to bulk and this may be important where surfaces of interchange are involved and also in mechanical relationships. In fact, many developing organisms afford evidence of a size-structure relationship (Bower, 1921, 1930, 1948), and this is seen both in the external configuration and the disposition of the tissues. These relationships have their inception in the embryogeny.

ORGANOGENESIS AND HISTOGENESIS

As the embryo of a vascular plant enlarges, new and critical developments begin to take place. In particular, new organs are formed, usually in a definite relation to the axis and to the distal cell group. Thus, in the embryos of dicotyledons, the spherical cellular mass derived from the distal embryonic cell begins to form two equal lateral lobes: these grow more rapidly than the distal cell group and are recognised as the cotyledons. In lycopods, also, the enlarging embryonic tissue mass gives rise to the first leaf or leaves, the inception of the first root taking place more or less simultaneously. In leptosporangiate ferns, the approximately spherical embryo divides in a very regular manner till it has attained a certain size: thereafter it becomes possible to distinguish one of the quadrants as the shoot apex, one as the first leaf, one as the first root, and the fourth as the formatively inactive but important absorptive foot. These several organogenic developments are usually accompanied by characteristic histogenic changes in the hitherto uniform meristematic cells. It becomes possible to distinguish the elongating cells of the incipient or prevascular tissue from the adjacent incipient parenchyma, and both of these from the cells at the apices of leaf, shoot and root, which remain in the embryonic state. These initial organogenic and histogenic developments, which, as it were, set the pattern for future developments, may well be regarded as being among the most interesting, important and enigmatic phenomena in biology. What factors are involved in the assumption of form, and in the successive changes in form, during the ontogenetic development, and likewise in the differentiation of the increasingly complex tissue systems? These are questions which we must attempt to answer, no doubt very inadequately in the present state of knowledge, in the course of this study. Even if we cannot explain any but a few of the phenomena, it is important for the advancement of botanical science that the relevant problems should be clearly before us; for if we cannot understand something of these phenomena of morphogenesis at their inception in the embryogeny, how can we hope to have any exact knowledge of them in the adult plant?

ORGANISATION IN THE YOUNG EMBRYO

From an early stage the embryos in all classes of plants afford evidence of orderly development or organisation. To understand what constitutes this organisation, which is progressively manifested throughout the ontogeny, is one of the central problems in biology. Here, perhaps, we should note that the inception of the tissue pattern in organisms is a composite effect. Thus, in any elongating organ, such as a shoot or a root, the characteristic tissue pattern can be referred to the axial development that follows the establishment of polarity, to a concentric mode of differentiation in which we can distinguish epidermis, cortex and stele, and to a radiate mode of differentiation which we see exemplified in the distribution of the vascular tissues. How these several components of what we describe as pattern are induced will evidently call for investigations of a most searching kind.

In considering the distinctive organisation of any species, it is evident, as already indicated in Chapter II, that genic action is involved in all the underlying metabolic processes. The characteristic differential or allometric growth of the embryo, i.e. the distribution of growth in different directions which results in the production of a characteristic shape, is also held to be under genic control. Furthermore, at certain stages of development, particular genes appear to be invoked and these in some way bring about the inception and development of particular organs. While it may be accepted that the genes are the primary factors in all morphogenetic processes, an essential scientific task is to ascertain the nature of the underlying mechanism. Even if we assume that genes are biochemical agents, exercising their effects through the control or direction of metabolism, we are still very far from an adequate account of the assumption of form or the differentiation of tissues. Other factors and relationships of an essentially extrinsic character are also involved. In short, the phenomenon of organisation in the embryo is essentially a multi-aspect and integrative one. Some of the things that are involved in this conception are indicated in the descriptive table on p. 332.

THE ORGANISM AS A REACTION SYSTEM

In this book certain assumptions are made as a basis for explaining features of the embryogeny in different classes. These include the following:

(i) A developing zygote is a very complex, specific, diffusion reaction system, which functions in conformity with the laws of physical chemistry. In considering how complex and unique the reaction system of a particular species is, it is well to remember that the constitution of its protoplasm is the result of a long evolutionary process.

(ii) A biochemical pattern, i.e. a patternised distribution of metabolites, always underlies and precedes the visible morphological or histological pattern.

(iii) The mechanism which brings about the patternised distribution of metabolites—which may be described as one of the most important, enigmatic and challenging phenomena in biology—is to be sought in the laws of physical chemistry as applied to the metabolic systems present in embryonic tissues.

(iv) A contemporary diffusion reaction theory of morphogenesis (Turing, 1952; Wardlaw, 1953) postulates that in a zygote or embryonic tissue, in which the metabolic substances may initially be distributed in a homogeneous manner, a regular, patternised distribution of specific metabolites may eventually result, affording the basis for the inception of a morphological or histological pattern. (*see* below).

Turing's Diffusion Reaction Theory of Morphogenesis. This theory is based on a consideration of the diffusibilities and reaction rates of substances which may be involved in growth and morphogenesis. Considerable mathematical knowledge is essential to follow the theory in detail; but its main features can be indicated to, and appreciated by, the non-mathematical biologist without too much difficulty. The theory introduces no new hypotheses: on the contrary, it makes use of well-known laws of physical chemistry, and, as Turing has shown, these seem likely to be sufficient to account for many of the facts of morphogenesis. The underlying point of view, in fact, is closely akin to that expressed by D'Arcy Thompson in *Growth and Form.* It will be appreciated that a theory, based essentially on laws of physical chemistry that must apply to every growing system, is of the kind that may well account for the general occurrence of certain organisational features in plants. An essential feature of the theory is that it deals with the inception of a morphogenetic pattern *as a whole*; but it is not inconsistent with epigenetic development when other organs or parts have already been formed. Not least, it is compatible with the concepts of physiological genetics.

An indication of the theory may be given by assuming that two interacting, pattern-forming substances, or morphogens, X and Y, are essential metabolites in a morphogenetic process; a third substance C, which is in the nature of an evocator and catalyst, is also involved, a pattern only appearing if its concentration is sufficiently great. It is necessary to assume: (i) that both X and Y are diffusible, and at different rates; and (ii) that there is a number of reactions involving X, Y and the catalyst C: these reactions do not merely use up the substances X and Y, but also tend to produce them from other metabolic substances (which might be called 'fuel substances') which are assumed to be abundantly present in the growing region, i.e. to some extent the morphogens are autocatalytic. If a pattern is to be produced, there is a number of conditions relating the diffusibilities and marginal reaction rates which must be satisfied. (By marginal reaction rate is meant the amount by which the reaction rate changes per unit change of concentration.) If we assume that the appropriate conditions are satisfied, and that the concentration of the catalyst-evocator is initially at a low value, but is slowly increasing, the phenomena observed will be as follows:

(i) Initially there is a state of homogeneity: both X and Y are uniformly distributed (i.e. in the embryonic tissue in which a pattern will subsequently appear), apart from some slight deviations due to Brownian movement and to chance fluctuations in the number of the X and Y molecules that have reacted in the various possible ways in various regions.

(ii) The concentrations of X and Y will vary slowly as the system adjusts itself to the changing evocator concentration. This change will also result in the fluctuations of concentration smoothing themselves out more and more slowly, and eventually the point is reached where the system is unstable, i.e. the fluctuations no longer are smoothed out: they become cumulative, and even tend to become exaggerated with the passage of time.

(iii) At this stage the morphogen concentrations form a more or less irregular wave pattern. Later, however (for instance when in some places the concentration of one morphogen is practically zero), the progressive deepening of the waves is arrested. The pattern will then regularise itself, and will eventually reach an equilibrium which is almost perfectly symmetrical. The resulting pattern may be described as a *stationary wave*.

Such a stationary wave, in a biological situation, might take the form of the accumulation of one of the morphogens in several, e.g. 3, 4, 5 or more, evenly distributed loci on a one-dimensional system such as the circumference of a circle: the other morphogen will tend to accumulate at intermediate loci.

A patternised distribution of specific metabolites can thus take place in conformity with the laws of physical chemistry as applied to diffusion-reaction systems; and this will be true whether the morphogenetic substances are held to be specifically gene-determined, or whatever mechanism is assumed to connect such genes with the morphogens. It seems not improbable that reaction systems of the kind indicated in the theory may be of general occurrence in living organisms, but, of course, evidence that this is so is essential. A provisional acceptance of the theory would certainly afford a basis for understanding both the prevalence of homologies of organisation and the diversification of basic kinds of pattern under the impact of genic factors. For, as we have seen, the patternised distribution, or specific location, of metabolites depends on the diffusibility and chemical reaction of the metabolites, some, or many, of which are specifically gene-determined.

That diffusion-reaction systems are present in all growing regions, indeed in all living matter, is basic to studies of metabolism. What is novel in Turing's theory is his demonstration that, under suitable conditions, many different diffusion-reaction systems will eventually give rise to stationary waves; in fact, to a patternised distribution of metabolites. Thus, in the present writer's view, the theory would appear to afford an explanation of the inception of the symmetrical, radiate histological pattern that appears adjacent to the embryonic region of the root apex. Not all kinds of pattern, however, are referable to the development of stationary waves—the major feature of Turing's theory as thus far developed—but all may eventually be related to some kind of diffusion-reaction system. The inception of polarity, i.e. of axial development, in an embryo is probably due to a particular distribution of metabolites in an initially homogeneous system; this could be regarded as a very simple case of a stationary wave. The following may be tentatively indicated as examples of pattern in plants which may perhaps be explained, in whole or in part, as the theory is more fully developed and explored: phyllotactic systems; whorled branching in algae; the distributing of procambial strands in shoots; the radiate pattern in root steles and in lycopod shoots. Turing has indicated how the dappled pattern in the skins of animals and gastrulation in the developing animal embyro can be explained by his theory.

In the general system of ideas incorporated in the theory there are many points of interest to the student of morphogenesis. Thus, with regard to the breakdown of symmetry and homogeneity, attention is directed to the importance of small random changes in the distribution of morphogenetic substances, i.e. irregularities and statistical fluctuations in the numbers of molecules taking part in the various reactions. The determination of polarity in the fertilised ovum of *Fucus*, for example, may be due to random changes, or to factors in the environment. In the enclosed embryos of land plants, in which polarity is determined soon after fertilisation, if not before, quite small gradient effects proceeding from the gametophyte tissue could be the means of initiating the breakdown of homogeneity and the establishment of polarity. Some deviations from homogeneity in a reaction system may be of great importance in the process of differentiation; for the system may reach a state of instability in which the irregularities, or certain components of them, tend to grow. If this happens, a new and stable equilibrium is usually reached, and this may show a considerable departure from the original distribution of metabolites. Thus, in contiguous cells which are initially metabolically identical, a drift from equilibrium may take place in opposite directions as a result of statistical fluctuations in the components of the reaction system, or of small changes induced by neighbouring cells. Changes of this kind could, for instance, account for the very different developments in two adjacent, equivalent embryonic cells—a histological phenomenon of much interest to the botanist.

EXPERIMENTAL INVESTIGATION OF EMBRYOS

Thus far, the facts of plant embryology have been mainly those obtained by the methods of the anatomist and histologist. Much remains to be done in the fields of experimental morphogenesis, genetics, biochemistry and biophysics. Indeed, the new phase of embryology should be characterised by an experimental outlook. The results of experimental investigations of embryos in different systematic groups will be given in the appropriate chapters.

At this point it may be advantageous to consider briefly some of the general ideas and conclusions that have emerged from recent experimental studies of other embryonic regions, e.g. the shoot apex, which exemplifies what has been described as a 'continued embryogeny.' We should not, of course, assume out of hand that these conclusions have a direct application to the small developing embryo, but there may be phenomena common to both which can be more readily studied in the large tissue mass afforded by the adult apex.

Polarity is important in the shoot apex in vascular plants and is closely associated with many of its morphogenetic activities. It is difficult to modify by experimental treatment and has important effects on the movement of metabolites. Thus auxins move rapidly in a basipetal direction but only very slowly in the opposite direction.

The symmetry of the apical region, which is largely due to intrinsic factors, is important in morphogenesis. In typically dorsiventral plants, such as species of *Selaginella*, the dorsiventrality is not readily modified by experimental treatment. But in some species the symmetry shows a certain lability, plants growing in the shade being dorsiventral, whereas those exposed to full light are radially symmetrical. Many species, however, are completely and persistently dorsiventral.

With certain qualifications, the embryonic cells at the shoot apex of a particular species are of a characteristic size. Thus, whereas the apical cell in some ferns may develop to a very large size during the ontogeny, small cells are characteristic of the adult shoot apex in most gymnosperms and flowering plants. A survey of seed plant apices, however, shows how very diverse are the sizes and arrangements of their meristematic cells (Wardlaw, 1953). In diploid and polyploid members of the same species, the latter have consistently larger meristematic cells than the former. It may therefore be concluded that there is a relationship between the genetical constitution of a species and the size of its embryonic cells at the shoot apex. This relationship may be of interest in the study of embryos in the same and in different taxonomic groups.

The shoot apex is recognised as being the primary morphogenetic region of the plant. It may be characterised by a distinctive histological and physiological organisation, as in leptosporangiate ferns such as *Dryopteris* or *Matteuccia*. A comparable organisation is also thought to be present in the apices of gymnosperms and seed plants, though the histological pattern may be considerably less evident. Nevertheless, in all groups of flowering plants and gymnosperms, the shoot apex is characterised by a distinctive arrangement of its meristematic cells. Thus the tunica may consist of one or several layers, it may constitute a very definitely zoned tissue, or the zonation may be rather feebly defined. Again, in some species, a central group of mother-cells may give rise to the various regions of the apex; and there are many other variants of histological pattern. Since these several types of apical organisation have their inception at some stage in the embryogeny, or in the post-embryonic phase, it may well be that the embryologist can both profit by the existing knowledge of apices and contribute to it. Indeed, all too little is known of the inception of the characteristic patterns in the apices of seed plants.

The shoot apex gives rise to lateral members in an orderly fashion, leaves being usually formed in a regular phyllotactic sequence while buds normally occupy characteristic positions on the shoot. It will evidently be a matter of interest to inquire at what stage in the embryogeny this regulated development first becomes apparent.

Studies of the shoot apex have shown that the prevascular tissue typically originates close to the most distal cell group. This can be seen particularly well in the ferns, but also in some flowering plants. A considerable body of experimental evidence supports the view that the inception of the vascular tissue, whether in shoot, leaf or root, is due to the basipetal diffusion of a substance (or substances) from the actively growing apical meristem or distal cell group.

In the contemporary view, the development of an axial structure from a shoot apex is essentially epigenetic in character, i.e. each subsequent development is determined by those that have gone before, and all suggestions of preformation are ruled out. It is assumed here that the development of the zygote to the adult state is also an epigenetic process. Some factors are at work throughout the individual development, others become incident at particular stages, and gradually, as the result of the action of factors of many kinds, the characteristic form and structure of the species become manifest (*see* table, p. 332). Studies of the shoot apex have shown that both extrinsic and intrinsic factors, size-structure and other spatial relationships, and the reciprocal relationships of parts, must all be considered in attempts to explain the observed developments. Similar considerations almost certainly apply to investigations of embryogenesis.

Experimental studies of apices have shown that lateral members such as leaves and buds, and presumably roots, owe their characteristic form and structure, among other considerations, to the positions in which they are formed. That is to say, it is to the genic control and mechanics of growth that we should look for an account for the characteristic form and structure of organs and not to the presence in the race of particular factors which specifically determine these organs.

Lastly, it may be duly emphasised that, if progress is to be made, it is not merely a question of working at apices, or embryos, from the morphological, physiological and genetical points of view, and of bringing the respective data together: a profound effort must be made to effect an actual integration of these data; for only by so doing can we hope to gain an adequate insight into the progressive organisation which is characteristic of development both in the individual and in the race.

Chapter IV

EMBRYOGENESIS IN THE ALGAE

THE plants of the land have been described collectively as the *Embryophyta*, the implication being that in these plants there is a characteristic embryonic phase which is not present in the great aquatic groups of the algae. If, however, we regard as an embryo any small germ which develops from a fertilised egg or from a spore, then it is clearly legitimate to include the algae in this survey. This, indeed, is fully justified by the facts, for in algae such as *Fucus* there are developments which are very similar to those in archegoniate plants. It might perhaps seem permissible to apply the term *embryo* to the young algal plant which develops from a fertilised ovum, but not to the plantling that develops from a spore. This procedure, however, would bring its own difficulties in the isomorphic green, brown and red algae.

The ontogenetic development of the algae affords many points of interest. Thus a majority of the green algae never advance beyond the filamentous stage, whereas others, such as the large brown and red algae, pass through an embryonic phase and proceed to one of considerable somatic elaboration, i.e. their ontogenetic development is comparable with that of land plants. In such comparisons the Chaetophorales are of special interest. It has been suggested (Fritsch, 1939, 1945) that it is from this group of green algae that the plants of the land, i.e. the Embryophyta, have originated.

GREEN ALGAE

Haplobiontic green algae have no embryonic phase that is strictly comparable with that found in organisms in which the sporophyte has its inception in a fertilised egg. In algae like *Spirogyra* or *Oedogonium*, the zygote (zygospore or oospore), after a period of rest, again becomes active, its diploid nucleus undergoes meiosis, and one to four haploid propagative cells are formed. Where these are motile, the zoospore eventually settles down, attaches itself to a substratum, and grows out into a filament. In *Spirogyra*, Figs. 2, 8, a filament grows directly out of the zygospore which has split open. In this, as in other filamentous green algae where the plantling is initially attached to the substratum, the germ shows evidence of polarity from the outset. The distal region is the locus of active growth (though in some species intercalary growth may subsequently supervene), and, as

40

the illustrations in Fig. 8 show, there is evidence of translocation of nutrients to it. The basal or proximal region, which develops as an organ of attachment, soon becomes more or less highly vacuolated and in general appears to be a region in which the metabolism is considerably different from that of the distal region. When a zoospore of *Botrydium*, *Protosiphon* or *Oedogonium* germinates, it elongates and

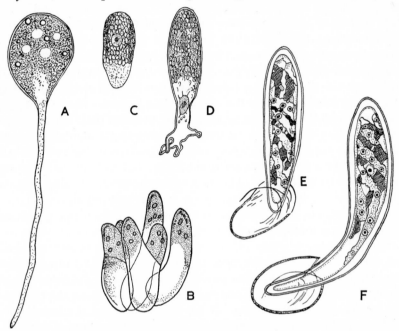

Fig. 8. Green algae: young plants

A, B, *Protosiphon botryoides*. A, Normal plant developed from a zoospore. B, Group of plants, grown from zoospores in a nutrient solution, showing the distal aggregation of dense protoplasmic contents (after Klebs). C, D, *Oedogonium concatenatum*. Germinating zoospores (after Hirn). E, F, *Spirogyra neglecta*. Germinating zygospores (after Tröndle).

gives rise to a polarised, ovoid or filamentous structure, in which there is an evident concentration of the protoplasmic materials in the distal region, Fig. 8. This mode of development, which is general in both septate and siphonaceous species, is not unlike the enclosed young embryo in archegoniate and seed plants. Why the distal region should become the seat of protein synthesis is a problem about which little is known. The phenomenon is common to all classes of plants, and it may be that the same, or closely similar, factors determine the characteristic heterogeneous distribution of protoplasmic materials.

The great majority of green algae might be specified as plants which have never evolved beyond the simple filamentous or embryonic somatic state. There are, however, exceptions, e.g. the development of a thin flat expanse of tissue in *Ulva*, various developments shown by the Chaetophorales (*see* below), the highly complex construction in the Siphonales, and the characteristic axis with whorled branching in the Charales, Fig. 9.

Chaetophorales. According to Fritsch (1945), it is to this order of green algae that we should look for evidence of those developments which may have a bearing on the origin of land plants. Morphological features of special interest in this connection shown by members of the group are the polarised filamentous development of the spore or zygote product, growth by an apical cell, and a characteristic mode of cell division leading to an incipient parenchymatisation, or tissue formation. *Fritschiella* (Fig. 9) shows some of these developments (Iyengar, 1932). *Draparnaldia* and *Draparnaldiopsis* afford evidence of the first steps in cellular specialisation in a simple filamentous organism, in that alternate cells remain short and give rise to the lateral branches. Fritsch has suggested that the higher members of the ancestral Chaetophorales were the plants which successfully colonised the land, giving rise to the Bryophyta and the several classes of vascular plants. However, apart from the general points indicated above, the embryogeny of the Chaetophorales yields no specific clues to that of the Embryophyta.

Among the Chaetophorales, attention is often directed to *Coleochaete* because of its oogamous reproduction and the elaborations which characterise the post-fertilisation phase. These developments, however, like carpospore formation in the red algae, add nothing to our knowledge of embryonic processes.

Volvocales and Chlorococcales. Strictly speaking, these groups have no embryogeny equivalent to that of brown algae, archegoniate and seed plants. Yet the development of the larger colonial forms from the single reproductive cell affords some points of interest that are not without relevance. When colonial species of the Volvocales begin to grow from a germ cell, there is a characteristic phase of repeated cell division. Each of the *Chlamydomonas*-like cells divides longitudinally with the result that a saucer-like multi-cellular body is formed; on further division this assumes the form of a hollow sphere. This sphere now undergoes a curious 'inversion,' i.e. it is turned outside-in, a process which has the effect of bringing the flagella to the outside of the new colony. Some of these developments are not unlike the early stages in the development of an echinoderm from a fertilised egg. In both instances, biochemical, physical and other factors are at work. In echinoderms, the production of a regular segmentation pattern is recognised as a typical embryonic development; it may be that we shall not be entirely wide of the mark if we regard the Volvocales as also

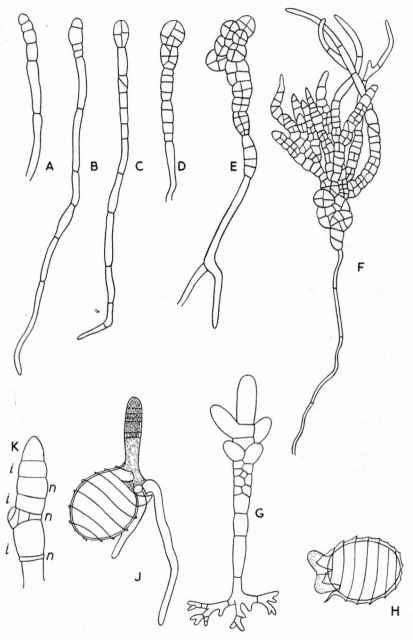

Fig. 9. Green algae: young plants

A–F, *Fritschiella tuberosa* (after Iyengar). G, *Siphonocladus pusillus* (after Schmitz). H, J, *Tolypella glomerata*. Plantling from oospore (after de Bary). K, *Chara fragilis*. Distal region of young filament; *n*, nodes; *i*, internodes (after Pringsheim).

exemplifying a kind of embryogeny, though it is of a somewhat unusual kind for plants. Similar observations apply to the reproduction of organisms such as *Scenedesmus* or *Pediastrum*. Initially the several products of cell division may be distributed at random within the containing wall, but soon, in relation to the forces at work in the system, the cells become arranged in a characteristic symmetrical pattern. This kind of development in the algae reaches its highest expression in the water-net, *Hydrodictyon* (*see* Fritsch, 1935). When the haploid polyhedral resting spore germinates, a phase of abundant cell division ensues, and a very large number of separate cells, actually zoospores, are formed within an enlarged envelope or vesicle. These zoospores are initially distributed at random within the vesicle but after some time they become arranged in a regular pattern; in fact, they form a minute hollow cylinder with a net-like construction. On further growth this structure becomes a new *Hydrodictyon* plant.

BROWN ALGAE

In general, the zoospore or swarmer on settling down grows into a simple filament which may be procumbent or erect; or it may at first be procumbent and branched, soon giving rise to one or more erect filaments. Thus, either from the outset, or at an early stage, there is evidence of a polarised development, Fig. 10. This is also true of the developing zygote. While some brown algae are simple or branched filamentous structures, many show a greater degree of elaboration. Thus we recognise uni-axial, multi-axial and true parenchymatous types, some of the last reaching a comparatively high level of differentiation for aquatic organisms. The larger and more elaborate forms also begin as simple filaments, their ontogeny being characterised by a regular sequence of growth phases and by a distinctive segmentation pattern. Thus far, these phases have received comparatively little attention from the standpoint of morphogenesis. The inception of the large apical cell in the Sphacelariales and its regular growth and segmentation suggest problems which, in some respects at least, are comparable with those of the apical meristem in the pteridophytes. Again, in the corticated and multi-axial types, the parts and members are formed in an orderly and characteristic manner. These configurations, however, do not result from the segmentation of a coherent meristematic tissue, as in *Fucus* or a higher plant, but from the coordinated growth of more or less separate filaments, the development of which is apparently regulated in various ways by their mutual contiguity. This is an aspect of morphogenesis of which we have very little knowledge. It is important in the fungi and lichens just as it is in the complex filamentous algae.

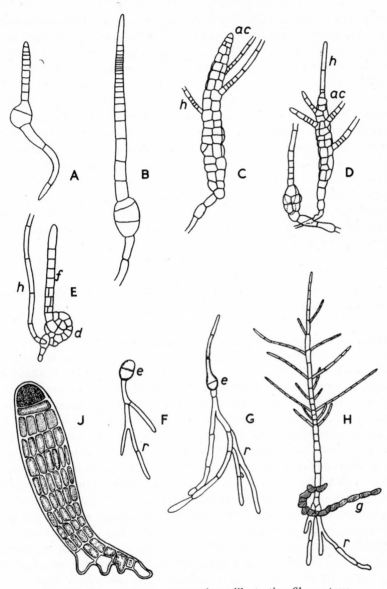

Fig. 10. Brown algae: young plants illustrating filamentous
and axial development

A, B, *Tilopteris mertensii.* Germlings from monospores (after Sauvageau). C, D,
Dictyosiphon foeniculaceus. Germlings from zoospores (after Sauvageau). E,
Cladostephus verticillatus; d, disc; *f,* filament of limited growth; *h,* hair (after
Sauvageau); F–H, *Desmarestia aculeata.* Embryos at different stages of develop-
ment; *e,* erect axis; *r,* rhizoid, *g,* gametophyte (after Schreiber); J, *Dictyota
dichotoma.* Young plant, with apical cell (after Cohn).

Various examples of early development in the brown algae are illustrated in Figs. 1c, d; 2b; 3d; 6e; 10; 11. In these, as in many others which might equally have been selected, polarity is apparently determined as soon as the germination of the settled swarmer or zygote begins. The growing filament soon shows a distinction of apex and base, the latter usually developing as a colourless rhizoidal structure of limited growth, while the former constitutes the actively growing and photosynthetic region of the plant. In some species, growth results in the formation of an entirely procumbent soma, and in several, perhaps many, brown algae, a cushion or a procumbent system is first formed from which one or more erect filaments grow out, e.g. *Cladostephus*, Fig. 10e. In this connection Fritsch (1939) has pointed to the importance of the heterotrichous soma, comprising procumbent and erect filaments, which is characteristic of all filamentous and larger algae. Thus far, the factors determining the two kinds of development remain almost completely unexplored. So, too, are those which determine whether growth will become localised in a distal apical cell or in some intercalary position. Böcher (1951) has discussed some of the relevant problems from the morphological point of view.

Among the filamentous brown algae, those species in which a conspicuous and physiologically dominant apical cell gives rise to new parts by a regular system of segmentation are of special interest, Fig. 10, c, e. As in vascular plants, this aspect of organisation is evident at an early stage in the embryogeny. In these algae there is evidence of a regulated process of development, as in *Chara* among the green algae (Fig. 9h–k), the subapical cells giving rise to lateral branches in a characteristic and orderly manner.

In a limited fashion, the brown algae as a class, though growing in an aquatic environment, show many of the organisational features found in land plants, a point which was duly emphasised by Church (1919). These several points gain in importance when we survey the embryonic developments in the large parenchymatous algae, i.e. the Laminariales and Fucales.

In *Laminaria*, Figs. 1c; 11a–c, the ellipsoidal ovum is extruded from the oogonium but remains attached to it. After fertilisation, the zygote elongates, divides by a transverse wall and thereafter forms a multicellular filament, usually lying in the axis of the oogonium. This raises the question, as yet unanswered, as to whether the polarity of the germling is already established in the egg, i.e. under the influence of gradients or other factors in the oogonial environment, or whether polarity is essentially a post-fertilisation development. The embryo of *Laminaria*, *Costaria*, and related organisms, at first filamentous, enlarges into a cylindrical, club-shaped, or flattened body and undergoes cell divisions in the longitudinal planes, Fig. 11B–E, the segmentation pattern being not unlike that found in some archegoniate and seed plants. After some time growth is continued by means of an intercalary meristem.

THE FUCALES

The Fucales have provided classical materials for studies of the embryogeny of seaweeds. Indeed, more is known about the ova and young embryos of these plants than of any other group. Accordingly, the main points in the development of *Fucus* and related genera will here be considered in some detail (Figs. 3, 4, 11).

The Ovum at, and after, Fertilisation. The eggs of *Fucus* and related genera have afforded botanists materials which are comparable in many respects with the eggs of various amphibians extensively used in zoological studies. The spherical egg of *Fucus*, with an average diameter of 75μ in *F. furcatus*, and a nucleus which usually occupies a central position, is similar in size to a number of sea urchin and other marine invertebrate eggs. The eggs contain brownish green photosynthetic plastids and are naked before fertilisation; but immediately after there is a secretion of mucilage which hardens to form a close-fitting, cellulose-like wall.

Levring (1947, 1949, 1952) has advanced our knowledge of the submicroscopical structure of the eggs of the Fucaceae by using the phase-contrast, polarising and centrifuge microscopes and various special techniques. He has shown that the surface of a mature, unfertilised egg consists of the following layers: (i) a gelatinous outer coat, stratified tangentially, which seems to be partly dissolved by water; (ii) a very thin egg membrane, which is of primary importance in the subsequent formation of the *fertilisation membrane*; (iii) a lipo-protein *plasma membrane*; and (iv) an innermost *cortical layer*, which produces the materials for wall-formation after fertilisation. Levring agrees with other observers that the eggs of *Fucus*, both before fertilisation and in their post-fertilisation behaviour (*see* p. 20), are remarkably like those of the sea urchin. Both before and after fertilisation, the egg is in a state of active metabolism.

The penetration of the spermatozoid into the ovum and the rapid nuclear fusion which follows—a matter of minutes according to Farmer and Williams (1898)—set in motion a sequence of biochemical changes. Within a few minutes a fertilised egg secretes a surrounding membrane, whereas an unfertilised one does not. If fertilised and unfertilised eggs are placed in fresh water, the former burst at one point, the contents being extruded through the hole, whereas the latter do not burst but simply swell up and become altered in appearance.

Various observations recorded by Farmer and Williams suggest that rapid and probably complex metabolic changes are associated with, or induced during, the period when the spermatozoids are being attached to the ova and the subsequent fertilisation and post-fertilisation phases. The evident repulsion of spermatozoids from the ovum as soon as fertilisation has taken place is probably a biochemical phenomenon. Levring (1952) has suggested that a substance acting like dupunol is released from the egg at the moment of penetration by a spermatozoid. This causes the spermatozoids in proximity to lose their mobility. Oospheres passing out from the conceptacles may become fragmented, and these fragments, which are of variable size and mostly enucleate, become rounded-off, attract spermatozoids like normal ova, and form an enveloping wall. Their further development and segmentation have not, however, been observed. Farmer and Williams have called attention to the fact that whereas the unfertilised ovum has a microscopically indeterminate, somewhat frothy homogeneous protoplasm, the zygote has a distinctly alveolar cytoplasm with spindle-shaped aggregates of chromatophores, or striations, disposed in a radiate pattern in relation to the nucleus.

Levring has shown that the wall which is formed soon after fertilisation consists of two layers: (i) the outermost is the remnant of the egg membrane covered with the gelatinous coat; (ii) the innermost is strongly birefringent and comprises rod-shaped molecules tangentially arranged on the surface of the egg. This layer contains cellulose and polysaccharide sulphates (fucoidin). The cortical layer also contains fucoidin. Various enzyme systems are involved in these surface and sub-surface reactions. It appears that, at fertilisation, cell wall material is released from the periphery of the egg, mainly in the cortical layer, from whence it is forced through the plasma membrane. It reacts with the egg membrane, the new wall being formed on its inner side. As wall formation begins before the spermatozoid has fused with the egg nucleus, it is not determined by the diploid nucleus.

In the eggs of *Fucus*, as in the meristematic tissues of vascular plants, auxin (indole-3-acetic acid) is closely associated with growth and morphogenesis. Olson and DuBuy prepared extracts of growth-regulating substances from (1) egg cells, (2) spermatozoids, (3) fertile branch tips and (4) thallus of *Fucus vesiculosus*, and showed, by using the *Avena* test, that high concentrations are present in (1) and (2) and lower concentrations in (3) and (4). This work, which was undertaken to explore a possible relationship between the presence of a growth-regulating substance and polarity, was taken a stage further by these investigators when they were able to demonstrate, by using the neat experimental technique illustrated in Fig. 3c, that the polarity of the fertilised egg can be regulated by a local application of auxin. When an egg was placed at the end of a very fine capillary containing the growth-substance in solution, the rhizoid originated towards the capillary, and the first dividing wall was at right angles to it: in the untreated controls, the rhizoid grew out at random. This and other evidence indicates that auxin is both present in the fertilised egg and is a factor determining polarity. The accumulation of auxin at some particular locus in the egg is, of course, another problem.

That metabolism is very active in the pre- and post-fertilisation egg of *Fucus* is clearly shown by the data of respiration studies (Whitaker, 1931). Unfertilised eggs of *Fucus vesiculosus* in the dark consume about 5·2 cu. mm. of oxygen per hour per 1000 eggs at 18°C, a high rate as compared with that of marine invertebrate eggs. With an illumination of 100,000 foot candles, *Fucus* eggs liberate in photosynthesis more than twice as much oxygen as they consume. There is a sharp increase in the consumption of oxygen immediately after fertilisation (to 190 per cent of the pre-fertilisation rate). This rate is maintained uniformly for about 13–14 hours after which there is a slight increase until 24 hours. At 18°C about 50 per cent of the eggs had undergone their first cleavage after 13–18 hours—average 15 hours. These data suggest that, in certain respects, the phenomenon of fertilisation is essentially similar in marine plants and animals.

Information on the constitution of the fertilised egg in *Fucus* is afforded by experiments in which eggs were subjected to unilateral irradiation with monochromatic ultraviolet light and then placed in a hypertonic sea-water-sucrose solution: 95–97 per cent of the eggs showed a polarised plasmolysis, the non-irradiated half which would normally have given rise to the rhizoid being affected. Reed and Whitaker (1944) have suggested that when water is withdrawn the non-irradiated half of the egg shrinks, the other half having been stiffened, strengthened and rendered more viscous by the treatment. These plasmolytic effects can be demonstrated considerably earlier than the first appearance of the rhizoid, i.e. metabolic changes precede the visible morphological development. The responsiveness of eggs to irradiation and plasmolysis increases gradually after fertilisation reaching a maximum after about 7 hours and remaining at that level for about 3 hours.

When fertilised eggs of *Fucus furcatus f. luxurians* were placed in sea water in a salinity range of 60–150 per cent of the normal concentration, practically all formed normal rhizoids and continued to develop. In salinities greater or less than 90–100 per cent normal, 4-day embryos showed a reduction in their growth rate (elongation). Below 60 and above 150 per cent salinity there is a rapid decline in rhizoid formation. At 10–20 per cent salinity the eggs burst and cytolyse and in concentrated sea water development is inhibited but this may be reversible (Whitaker and Clancy, 1937).

After fertilisation there is a relatively long delay—12–24 hours, average 18 hours—before rhizoid-formation begins in eggs kept in darkness at 15°C. The first cell wall, separating the rhizoid from the spherical body of the zygote, is visible after about 25 hours. In considering how various experimental treatments affect the egg of *Fucus*, Whitaker (1940) points out that the physiological and morphogenetic analyses require consideration of both the metabolic and biophysical aspects, which are, in fact, inseparable.

Indications of metabolic and biophysical changes in the *Fucus* zygote are afforded by its response to light. In fertilised eggs reared in the dark at 15°C, the susceptibility to light (as indicated by the induction of rhizoids on the non-illuminated side) begins 3–4 hours after fertilisation and ends at about 16–18 hours, the maximum response being at 8 hours. But this period of maximum susceptibility to light precedes the rhizoidal outgrowth by several hours: 8–10 hours elapse before 50 per cent of a population in the dark develop protuberances. (Whitaker and Lowrance, 1936). From such data it may be inferred that only when various metabolic and other changes have taken place is the zygote competent to react to certain morphogenetic stimuli.

The effect of centrifuging the eggs of *Fucus* and other algae has already been mentioned (p. 19). Whitaker (1940) has shown that when fertilised eggs of *Fucus furcatus* are stratified by ultra-centrifuging, most of the eggs remain spherical and the stratifications usually persist during rhizoid formation and until the first transverse wall appears. In normal sea water, with a pH of 7·8–8·1, in the dark, the rhizoid grows out at the centrifugal pole; but if the sea water is acidified to a pH of 6·0, the developmental response is reversed, the rhizoid being formed in the centripetal half (Fig. 4). If the pH is between 6·0 and 8·0 the response of a population of eggs is intermediary, the rhizoids arising at random with respect to the stratification. To explain these experimental data Whitaker points out that the rhizoid typically forms at the more acid end where there is an associated accumulation of auxin, and he has suggested tentatively that the centripetal or lipoid pole (at which there is an accumulation described as an oil cap) has less buffer capacity than the centrifugal pole, and that its pH is therefore more affected by the pH of the medium. An internal pH gradient would result unless the pH of the medium and the protoplasm were identical, and its direction would be reversed in a medium at pH 8·0 as compared with pH 6·0. In these experiments Whitaker also observed that 'a group effect' i.e. the effect of diffusates from adjacent eggs, may be superimposed on the stratification effect when eggs develop in close proximity at pH 6·0 and that auxin (indole-3-acetic acid) in the medium at pH 6·3 and 8·0 tends to promote rhizoid formation at the centripetal pole.

Whitaker has also explored the effect of mechanical factors on the growing *Fucus* egg. When fertilised eggs of *F. furcatus* were sucked into a small pipette while the cell wall was still hardening, the elongated shape which they assumed was retained when they were released into sea water. In normal sea water, at pH 7·8–8·2, the rhizoids grew out at or near one end of the long axis, and cell division took place at right-angles to this axis. The shape imposed on the zygote thus determined its polarity. But when similar zygotes were released into sea water acidified to pH 6·0, rhizoids were typically formed towards the base of the dish, i.e. where the concentration of diffusates from the eggs would be greatest. A biochemical effect is thus able to overcome the mechanically-imposed shape effect in the determination of polarity (Fig. 4).

Not only are there well marked differences in the oogenesis of different genera, but this also holds for the size of the ova, the time required for fertilisation (e.g. 15–16 minutes in *Halidrys* as compared with a few minutes for *Fucus*), and their reactions during and after fertilisation. These differences are indicative of differences in the respective genetical constitutions. Some of these may be of a far-reaching kind. For example, in *Fucus* the egg is naked and free-floating, whereas in *Pelvetia* and several other genera it remains enclosed within the oogonial wall, and actually undergoes its early embryonic development therein (Thuret, 1854; Fritsch, 1945, p. 372–374). In *Sargassum* and *Bifurcaria* the extruded oogonia remain for several days attached to the inside of the conceptacle by means of long gelatinous stalks (*see* p. 54).

Early Embryonic Developments. In *Fucus*, *Ascophyllum* and *Pelvetia* the division of the zygote nucleus is followed by the formation of the first transverse wall. In *Himanthalia* it is otherwise, several nuclear divisions taking place before segmentation begins (*see* Figs 1D; 2B; 3D; 6E; 11F–L).

The unfertilised (or newly fertilised) ovum either has no definite polarity or a very labile and readily alterable one. As we had seen in Chapter III, polarity may be determined by such factors as the entry of the spermatozoid or other random disturbances, by unilateral illumination, gradients of electrical potential, temperature, pH, auxin or other substances diffusing from the zygotes, and by the redistribution of materials effected by centrifuging. It may be assumed that the materials in the zygote are initially symmetrically distributed about the central nucleus. In relation to one or more of the factors indicated above, a redistribution of materials takes place within the zygote: a superficial pellicle is soon formed, while later a pale or colourless rhizoid grows out at a particular locus, affording evidence that the materials of the zygote have now a heterogeneous and polarised distribution. The establishment of polarity is, in fact, accompanied if not caused by a characteristic and persistent distribution of the substances essential to growth and morphogenesis. Whether there is also some attendant arrangement or orientation of the 'fine structure' of the protoplasm, i.e. of the long-chain protein molecules, is not known. Since the rhizoid grows out from the least illuminated side, and also from the side which is exposed to the highest concentration of diffusate from other zygotes, its downward growth towards the substrate follows naturally. In different natural circumstances, i.e. in the several habitats and environments in which the species of the Fucales grow, some diversity in the early ontogenetic development is to be expected, and this may be accentuated by genetical differences. As a fact, different segmentation patterns are found in different genera and species. Thus, in *Sargassum linifolium*, Fig. 11K, L, the rhizoidal cell is initially small and inconspicuous, while, at an early stage, a median longitudinal wall divides both the upper and lower regions of the pear-shaped zygote.

When the zygote of *Fucus* divides, the first transverse wall separates the rhizoid from the spherical region, Fig. 2B. As the rhizoid continues to elongate, a second cross-wall is laid down; simultaneously a transverse wall also divides the spherical region into an upper (or distal) and a lower (or proximal) segment, Fig. 3D, the former being normally somewhat larger than the latter. The embryo now consists of a row of four cells. A longitudinal wall next divides the upper segment, and a second longitudinal wall at right-angles soon follows, the distal region of the embryo now consisting of four quadrants, Figs 1D, 11F. At this stage the segmentation pattern closely resembles that of certain archegoniate and seed plant embryos. A phase of rapid growth now follows. Further transverse and some longitudinal divisions take place in the rhizoidal portion while the distal segment divides by a transverse wall, so that two quadrant tiers are now present. Periclinal walls are now laid down, Fig. 11G, the outer or peripheral cells becoming photosynthetic and histologically distinguishable from these of the central region. Meanwhile the rhizoid has elongated considerably, divided by walls which may be oblique and, in response to tactile stimuli, has become attached to the substratum. The primary rhizoid is later supplemented by secondary ones, a compact holdfast system being formed. All these basal cells, however, have the same physiological character, and differ from those which constitute the body of the young plant above.

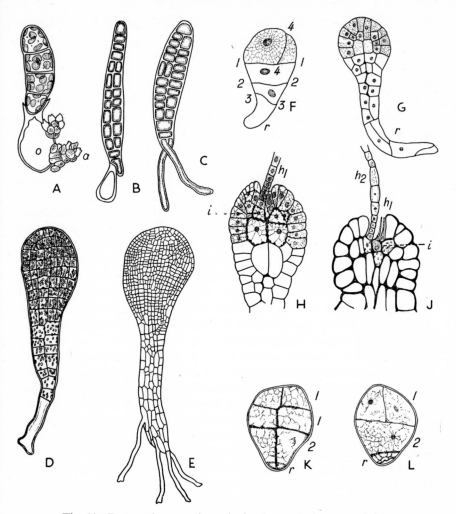

Fig. 11. Brown algae: embryonic developments in some of the
larger forms

A, B, C, *Laminaria*. A, *L. saccharina*. Young sporophyte seated on oogonium; *a*,
antheridia (after Kukuck); B, C, *L. digitata*. Young sporophytes becoming parenchymatous (after Kylin). D, E, *Costaria turneri*. Germlings (after Yendo). F–J,
Fucus vesiculosus. F, Young embryo showing the first four walls 1–1–4–4; *r*, rhizoid.
G, Older embryo, showing regular segmentation pattern. H, J, Older stages, showing the origin of the apical cell of the thallus at the base of the first terminal mucila-
ginous hair, h_1; h_2, second hair; *i*, initial cell (after Nienburg). K, L, *Sargassum
linifolium*. Segmentation of the zygote; 1, 2, the two primary cells; *r*, rhizoid
(after Nienburg).

The further growth of the embryo is characterised by abundant anticlinal divisions and occasional periclinal ones in the peripheral layer; the inner cells, on the other hand, tend to enlarge with fewer divisions. An incipient differentiation of tissues thus takes place. The embryo as a whole is now elongating and widening distally, i.e. it shows obconical development.

Naylor (1953) has followed the development in culture of embryos of *Marginariella urvilliana*, a submerged, endemic New Zealand member of the Fucales. The early development of zygotes took place while they were still attached to the receptacle; the germlings subsequently dropped off and became attached to the bottom of the culture dish. The oospore is enveloped in a firm wall. The formation of the rhizoidal protuberance is attended by the aggregation of denser cytoplasm in that locus. The first partition wall is now formed in an approximately transverse or median position, but obliquely disposed walls were also observed. The rhizoid, which typically bursts through the oospore wall, is separated off from the body of the embryo by a transverse wall. The further development of the embryo is in general like that of *Fucus*.

As noted above, the early development in *Sargassum* is somewhat different. Blomquist (1944) has given a general account of the embryogeny of the Sargassaceae. The discharged oval oogonium is anchored on a stalk and lies outside the conceptacle and the developing embryo usually remains attached in this position for 2–3 days until it has developed into a several-celled structure. The zygote is first divided across the shorter diameter into two approximately equal cells, if the egg is ellipsoidal. At the second division, a small lenticular cell is cut off at one end. *Sargassum linifolium* (*see* above, and Fig. 11K, L) may be an exception in this respect. The embryo proper develops by a regular quadrate method of cell division until it has become manycelled and an apical cell is established. There is considerable variation among the different genera, and even among the species of one genus (*Sargassum*), in the number of rhizoids and their mode of formation.

At an early stage important developments begin to take place in the most distal region of the embryo. The details for *Fucus* are as follows. Of the distal group of superficial cells, one—the *initial cell*—develops a conspicuous nucleus and grows out as a hair. As it lengthens, what has been described as a *meristem* (*see* Fritsch, 1945; and the authors cited by him) appears above the initial cell (Fig. 11H). The hair, in fact, undergoes a kind of intercalary or trichothallic growth. The initial cell, however, remains unchanged during this and the subsequent course of events. As the hair develops, the adjacent cells grow rapidly, separate from the hair and form a rapidly-widening funnel-shaped depression round it. Cells adjacent to the initial cell also grow out as hairs, so that the embryo is characterised by an apical tuft of hairs. The first hair soon becomes disorganised and shrivelled but its initial (i.e. basal) cell persists, and it is this cell which thereafter constitutes the apical cell proper of the embryo. As Fritsch (1945) points out, the origin of the apical cell below a trichothallic meristem recalls the condition met with in certain Ectocarpales. It is not at present known whether the apical cell originates in a similar manner in other Fucaceae. In *Pelvetia* and *Ascophyllum*, the young embryos do not show the characteristic distal tuft of hairs seen in *Fucus*.

All young embryos in the Fucales thus far investigated have a 'three-sided' apical cell lying in a distal depression. Actually the cell is like the basal portion of a truncated three-sided pyramid, the base being directed inwards: in longitudinal section it appears to be biconvex. This cell cuts off lateral segments which, on dividing by periclinal walls, give rise to the peripheral and inner tissues of the thallus.

At an early stage in the embryogeny of *Fucus*, the distal region of the thallus begins to flatten and, as growth proceeds, the strap-like soma is seen to have a midrib, while the apex occupies a slit-like depression extended in the plane of flattening. At this stage, probably in relation to the inception of bilateral symmetry, the three-sided apical cell is transformed into a four-sided one, i.e. it is now like the basal portion of a four-sided pyramid. It is thought that this definitive apical cell arises from the three-sided one by longitudinal division. In *Fucus*, the four-sided apical cell gives rise successively to basal segments, which form the central medulla, to segments from the narrower faces, and then to a segment from one, sometimes both, of the broader lateral faces. This last segment is often as big as the apical cell and, in fact, it affords a histological basis for the bifurcation of the thallus, i.e. the lateral segment becomes an apical cell. As each of the two apical cells cuts off a considerable number of segments, they become separated and give rise to the two limbs of the dichotomy. The lateral segments collectively give rise to the inner and outer peripheral tissues.

Lastly, in considering how the characteristic organisation of the plant becomes manifest during the ontogeny, it should be noted that in the Fucales it is not enough to study the apical cell and its characteristic divisions: in these algae, as in the ferns, a well developed superficial *apical meristem*, with distinctive component cells, becomes organised during the ontogenetic development, the formation of the lateral members, and the orderly development of the plant as a whole, being referable to this meristem. There is, in fact, a quite remarkable

3

parallelism between the apical meristems of the Fucales and the ferns (and also some other pteridophytes, e.g. *Selaginella*). The dichotomous branching of the thallus in *Fucus, Pelvetia* and *Ascophyllum* is strongly reminiscent of the dichotomy of the shoot or rhizome seen in ferns and species of *Selaginella*. But in *Ascophyllum* there is also monopodial branching, and this affords a close parallel with the monopodial branching in leptosporangiate ferns such as *Matteuccia, Onoclea, Dryopteris* and *Athyrium*. In these ferns the lateral branches normally arise later in the development from quiescent bud rudiments, or detached meristems, these having initially constituted part of the apical meristem. (Wardlaw, 1943, etc.). Now, in *Ascophyllum, Seirococcus* and *Halidrys*, the rudiments of the lateral branches also have their inception in the apical meristem. A longitudinal section parallel to the strap surface of the thallus in *Ascophyllum* or *Seirococcus*, or through the apex of *Halidrys*, shows the characteristic apical meristem. Among the meristematic cells are some with conspicuously dense protoplasmic contents. As growth is more rapid in the intervening cells, these dense but somewhat inactive meristematic cells come to occupy depressions in the thallus and are left behind as the apex grows on—a process in many respects closely comparable with the isolation of detached meristems in ferns. Subsequently these meristematic cells may become active and give rise to a lateral branch or branches. In the brown seaweeds, as in the ferns, these lateral apices, and the branches to which they give rise, do not occur at random: they occupy definite and regular positions and hence the adult plant is characterised by a harmonious and distinctive configuration. *Halidrys*, for example, has alternating branches, while *Sargassum* has regularly disposed lateral branch systems of some complexity.

The embryogeny and subsequent development of the Fucales are thus in many respects closely parallel to, and commensurate with, those of vascular plants; in particular, the ferns. The problem of homology of organisation is thus raised in a particularly acute and interesting form, in that it relates to organisms which can have only the most remote taxonomic relationship, if, indeed, it can be held that there is any affinity at all.

Anomalous Developments. Various anomalous developments have been observed. In some fertilised eggs the nucleus divides first and the rhizoid rudiment develops subsequently; in others, the zygote divides repeatedly but remains spherical, with no evidence of rhizoid formation even in cultures a month old (Farmer and Williams, 1898). The reasons for these developments are not known. As we have seen, this type of development is normal in *Himanthalia*. Some of the *Fucales* e.g. *Halidrys*, are characterised by a delay in the production of rhizoids and then several develop at a common point. When such a delay occurs in *Fucus* or *Ascophyllum* there may also be a development of several rhizoids, or the single rhizoid may branch profusely (Farmer and Williams, 1898). Kniep (1907) has described various anomalies in the formation of rhizoids and in the initial segmentation of the zygote in experimental and other materials.

Parthenogenesis. Overton (1913) has reviewed the evidence relating to parthenogenesis in the brown algae and has expressed agreement with some earlier workers that this phenomenon is probably of rare occurrence in *Fucus*. He has shown that some embryonic development can be induced in unfertilised eggs by the experimental treatment used by zoologists for eggs of various invertebrates. Batches of eggs of *Fucus vesiculosus*, in which great care had been taken to exclude and eliminate any contamination by spermatozoids, were placed for 1·5–2 minutes in 50 c.c. of water to which 3 c.c. of 0·1 *m* of acetic, butyric or other fatty acid had been added. In the course of 10 minutes many of the eggs treated with acetic and butyric acids formed a membrane or wall comparable with that of a fertilised egg. Most of the eggs continued to develop, became pear-shaped, formed a rhizoid, and underwent segmentation within 24 hours, this being followed by other cell divisions of the usual kind. In cultures which were kept properly aerated, plantlings developed which were indistinguishable from those resulting from normal zygotes. Overton has called attention to the close parallelism between these developments in *Fucus* eggs and those observed in the eggs of various marine animals.

The cytology of the induced embryos was not investigated by Overton, but he points to the interest that would attach to the rearing of such plants to sexual maturity—unless, of course, a doubling of the chromosome number takes place at some point during the vegetative development.

RED ALGAE

Although the red algae probably constitute a taxonomically coherent group, the several subdivisions show considerable morphological diversity and specialisation. Thus there are procumbent and erect filamentous types, heterotrichous types, and uniaxial and multiaxial types. In many species the young plants, whether originating from carpospores, tetraspores or monospores, are characterised by a polarised filamentous development, Figs. 1E, F; 2C; 6A–D; 12. These organisms have a further interest in that closely comparable, if not identical, somata are formed from the diploid carpospore and the haploid tetraspore. The developmental data for the more bulky uniaxial and multiaxial forms raise special problems on which we have thus far

little information. In them the germinating spore divides, with a greater
or less degree of regularity, to form a basal cushion or attachment disc,
the centre of which grows out to form the thallus, Fig. 12u–w. The
data, which have been surveyed in some detail by Fritsch (1945),
indicate that the red algae do not all conform to one pattern in their
embryonic development. Accordingly, the group is one which is likely
to repay a closer examination.

Oltmanns (1904) has described three types of development in the
group. Kylin (1917) has also described three types, including and
extending the Oltmanns types, as follows: (i) the *germ-tube* type,
found in the Nemalionales and some Cryptonemiales; (ii) the attachment-disc type, as in Gigartinales, Rhodymeniales and many Cryptonemiales; (iii) the *erect type*, as in the Ceramiales. Chemin (1937), on
the basis of an extensive investigation, considers that it would be more
appropriate to recognise five types of young plantling. He would
retain the polarised or erect *Ceramium*-type as a well-defined configuration. Contrary to the view of Kylin, he would retain the *hemispherical*
type of Oltmanns which Kylin had included in the attachment-disc
type; because of its similarity to the morula in animal embryogeny,
he suggests that it might be referred to as the *morula* type (type
moruléen) but he suggests the designation *Dumontia*-type. As to
Kylin's germ-tube or filamentous type, Chemin considers that this in
reality comprises three types: (i) the *Nemalion*-type, in which the
spore-contents move entirely into the germ-tube; (ii) the *Gelidium*-type,
which is more accurately designated as an attachment-disc type; and
(iii) the *Naccaria*-type, in which the spore is not emptied of its contents.
Chemin notes, however, that while these five types show well marked
differences, they are in no sense absolute, intermediate types being also
known. He also observes that the adult form is seldon realised from
the outset: almost invariably it is preceded by a more or less characteristic embryonic form—like the protonema in the development of a
moss. Without necessarily adhering closely to the so-called types,
some features in the embryogeny of various red algae may now be
briefly noted.

In *Nemalion multifidum*, Fig. 12a–d, the essential features of
the germ-tube type of development are well seen. The carpospore
germinates to form a tube or filament into which all the spore-contents
pass, and a transverse wall is formed. The distal cell now elongates and
undergoes further divisions, and soon, or after some time, the lowermost cell gives rise to a rhizoid. Similar developmental features are to
be seen in *Batrachospermum* and *Lemanea* among the Nemalionales,
in *Grateloupia*, *Halymenia*, *Dudresnaya* and *Cryptonemia* among
Cryptonemiales, and in *Gelidium* among the Gelidiales, (Killian, 1914;

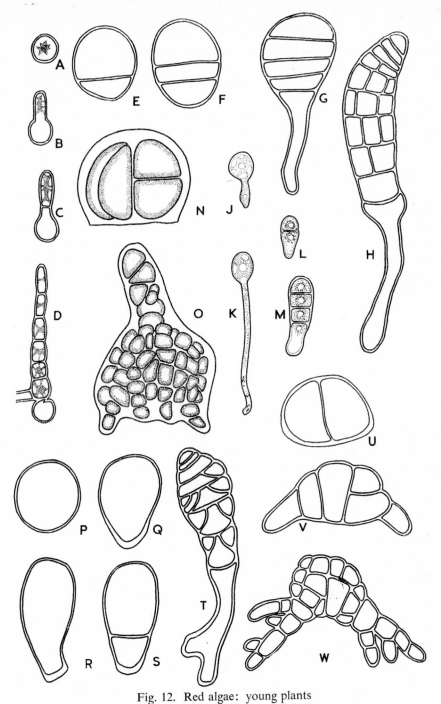

Fig. 12. Red algae: young plants

A–D, *Nemalion multifidum.* Germlings from carpospores (× 390). E–H, *Poly-siphonia nigrescens* (× 280). J–M, *Bangia fuscopurpurea.* Germination of spores of two kinds. N, O, *Cystoclonium purpurascens* (× 520). P–T, *Ceramium rubrum* (× 280). U–W, *Bonnemaisonia asparagoides.* (U, V, × 380; W, × 300); (J–M, after Drew, all others after Kylin).

Kylin, 1917; Fritsch, 1945). The plantlings obtained from monospores of *Bangia fuscopurpurea*, Fig. 12J–M, may be either of the germ-tube type (the *Naccaria*-type of Chemin) or of the erect type, the reason for the different kinds of growth not being understood. Thus, when Drew (1952) cultured spores of this species, she found that at first the spores gave rise to a creeping horizontally-growing filament, whereas later germinations from the same material showed a gradual transition to the upright type.

The ontogeny of *Nemalion* has the added interest that, from the simple beginnings illustrated in Fig. 12A–D, a multiaxial, cylindrical, dichotomising and sometimes branching thallus is built up. Fritsch regards the development of *Nemalion* as being essentially heterotrichous, a basal system of short rounded cells giving rise to well-branched erect filaments. In these developments, as also in the inception of differentiation as between the central and cortical filaments of the cylindrical thallus, there is scope for the investigation of the related morphogenetic factors.

The attachment-disc and hemispherical types of development are well seen in such genera as *Chylocladia*, *Cystoclonium*, Fig. 12N, O, *Dumontia*, *Bonnemaisonia*, Fig. 12U–W, and *Chondrus*. The spore, surrounded by its gelatinous coat, becomes attached to the substratum and, without increase in size, divides by a vertical wall and then by a second vertical wall at right-angles to the first, Fig. 12N, U. Divisions by horizontal walls and further vertical divisions follow. A centrally placed cell on the upper side of the hemispherical embryo now becomes a locus of growth and grows out to form the thallus, while cells along the base develop as rhizoidal attachment structures, Fig. 12O, V, W. Contemplation of the high degree of regularity in the segmentation pattern, and in the sequence of the developmental phases usual in these organisms, leaves little doubt that we are here concerned with a true embryogeny, comparable with that found in the brown algae and in higher plants, and also, in some respects, with features found in the development of some marine animals. Here it is appropriate to note that the type of embryogeny described above may precede and give rise to both uniaxial and multiaxial types of construction: *Cystoclonium*, Fig. 12N, O, *Rhodophyllis* and *Plocamium*, for example, are specialised uniaxial forms, while *Chondrus*, *Gigartina*, *Chylocladia*, *Rhodymenia* and *Lomentaria* exemplify multiaxial construction.

In the erect type of embryogeny, the spore elongates and divides by successive transverse walls, the distal cell becoming the apical cell, while the proximal cell develops as a rhizoid. Typical examples are seen in the Ceramiales, e.g. *Antithamnion*, Fig. 6A–D, *Ceramium*, Fig. 1E, F; 12P–T, *Polysiphonia*, Figs. 2C; 12E–H, and *Delesseria*, Fig. 7A.

After the first few transverse divisions of the elongating embryos have taken place, longitudinal divisions follow, these being distinctive for different genera. This is at once evident in a comparison of the segmentation patterns in *Ceramium, Polysiphonia, Delesseria* and other forms. The close similarity between these embryos and those of the Fucales and archegoniate plants is evident: polarity is determined at an early stage, the distal cell becomes the seat of growth, and the whole embryonic development is characterised by great regularity in the cellular pattern. Further evidence of the existence of important homologies of organisation in the early stages of development is thus afforded by this brief survey of the red algae.

Like the green and brown algae, many of the red algae show evidence of polarity as soon as spore germination begins. This is particularly conspicuous in the erect type of embryo, seen in the Ceramiales; it is also seen in the germ-tube type. In the hemispherical and attachment-disc types of germling there is also presumably an early establishment of polarity, though in these organisms polarised or axial development may not be evident for some time; and it is accompanied, or preceded, by quite a different type of segmentation pattern from that seen in filamentous and erect types. Nevertheless, in organisms such as *Cystoclonium* or *Bonnemaisonia* it could be argued, on the morphological evidence, that polarity is established as soon as the spore becomes attached to the substratum. If so, then in these organisms there is a departure from the fairly general rule that the first dividing wall is at right-angles to the axis of the embryo. Experiments relating to the effect on polarity of centrifuging have been briefly noted in Chapter II.

Since the spores are pigmented and photosynthetic bodies, light has an important effect on their development. The food reserves within the spores are apparently relatively small in amount and hence, as Chemin has pointed out, the rapidly growing germs soon show modified and arrested development if kept in the dark. The spores are also readily disorganised by excessive illumination, especially by exposure to ultra-violet radiation. Direct sunlight and temperatures above 35°C also cause disorganisation.

SUMMARY

Although at the outset the existence of true embryogenesis in the algae was only tentatively postulated as a working basis, the data which have been set out in this Chapter undoubtedly justify the position which has been adopted: the algae have an embryogeny just as have the higher plants and, indeed, afford many close parallelisms with them. It is true that in some of the algae, especially the green and the simpler brown and red algae, there is little in the initial development that is strictly comparable with the embryogeny of land plants. But in all the larger, more advanced and elaborate forms, especially among the brown and red algae, the details of the early development are closely comparable with what we find in archegoniate plants. The early determination of polarity, the axial development, the early inception of a self-determining, distal growing point, the regularity of the segmentation pattern, in short, all the developments by which embryos are usually characterised and described, are found in the algae. These parallelisms are the more remarkable in that in the algae the development takes place in a purely aquatic environment and independently of parental nutrition.

Chapter V

EMBRYOGENESIS IN THE BRYOPHYTA

THIS subdivision includes the simplest and most primitive members of the *Embryophyta*, i.e. land plants in which an embryonic phase follows the fertilisation of an enclosed ovum. Bryophytes and pteridophytes have been treated by some botanists as subdivisions of one great and related group—the Archegoniatae; but others have held that the presence of an archegonium in the two groups is merely evidence of parallel evolution from algal ancestors. In bryophytes the conspicuous phase of the life cycle is the gametophyte, the plant consisting of a flattened thallus in liverworts such as *Marchantia* or *Pellia*, or of a leafy or foliose axis in the leafy liverworts and mosses. Although some of these gametophytes are at a relatively low level of organisation, their development can be referred to an apical growing point: hence it may be of interest to consider the development both of the free haploid spore and of the enclosed zygote.

The embryonic development, which follows the fertilisation of the ovum, takes place within the enlarging venter of the archegonium. Indeed, in many bryophytes, the sporophyte remains within an enveloping calyptra—an organ of gametophyte origin—until its dissolution at spore dispersal. The whole sporophytic development in bryophytes is of a very limited kind—a brief embryogeny on which a sporogenous phase quickly supervenes. The initial embryonic phase, in fact, passes almost directly into the sporogenous, reproductive phase, whereas, in other classes of Embryophyta, the embryonic and reproductive phases are separated by a very considerable period of vegetative development.

In the liverworts the sporophyte remains dependent on the gametophyte for most of its nutrition and for protection until the time of spore dispersal (*see* pp. 82, 83). In the mosses, with some exceptions, the sporophyte attains to a greater somatic differentiation and development, and contributes to its nutrition by means of a photosynthetic system. The several aspects of vegetative development in the bryophytes were held by Bower (1908, 1935) to exemplify the advance of the sporophyte, but others, e.g. Wettstein (1903–1908), Goebel, (1930), Evans (1939) and Bold (1948), have given reasons for the view that the Hepaticae would more truly be interpreted as exemplifying a reduction series (*see* p. 83). In phanerogams the embryo in the mature seed constitutes a well-defined 'stage' in the development of the sporophyte: in bryophytes, no such definitive embryonic stage can be indicated. The growth of the sporophyte is continuous and uninterrupted and the embryonic and adult phases are, as it were, telescoped together so that it is virtually impossible to say where one ends and the other begins.

EARLY DEVELOPMENT OF THE GAMETOPHYTE

The haploid spore on germination gives rise to a germ-tube or filament, sometimes described as a protonema. From the outset, as in *Riccia*, there is an evident movement of the granular cytoplasmic materials from the spore to the distal end of the germ-tube, a densely protoplasmic growing region being thus established. This filamentous development is generally comparable with that seen in the algae and with the initial embryonic development in vascular plants. The distal region of the filament next becomes separated off from the remainder by a transverse wall. As growth continues, further transverse and then longitudinal walls are laid down. The distal cell retains its identity as a recognisable apical cell, the eventual multicellular thallus being formed by its continued meristematic activity. In different species characteristic and regular segmentation patterns can be recognised both in the initial developments and at the apical meristem, Figs. 6H–L; 15M; 17L. In some bryophytes, e.g. *Pellia*, Fig. 15M, and *Sphagnum*, the spore contents may undergo a number of regular divisions, a cellular pattern being thereby constituted before the germling emerges from the exospore. The moss spore on germination yields a branching filamentous structure—the protonema—which grows by the division of a distal cell. This initial development closely resembles that of filamentous green algae. Thus, although we are here dealing with gametophytic material, i.e. with the growth of a spore which is not encased in surrounding tissue, nevertheless the early stages of development are not unlike some of those encountered in the development of the sporophyte. In particular, we may note that although the liverwort thallus, e.g. that of *Riccia* or *Marchantia*, is a non-vascular structure, it nevertheless attains to a certain level of organisation; and this can be referred to the early establishment and subsequent activity of an apical growing point. In some Jungermanniales, and in the mosses, the gametophyte is an axial structure consisting of an axis and lateral foliar members. Moreover, in large species such as *Polytrichum*, a primitive or incipient central conducting system is differentiated. All these features, both external and internal, are due to the activity of an apical cell. Here, then, we have gametophytic developments which are in some important respects comparable with the sporophytic developments found in the pteridophytes and seed plants.

Bünning and Wettstein (1953) have shown that the polarised development of the germinating spore in *Funaria* can be suppressed by various chemical treatments.

THE DEVELOPMENT OF THE EMBRYO: GENERAL ACCOUNT

In most bryophytes, the Anthocerotae being an exception, the archegonium is typically free and seated on a short stalk, i.e. it is not

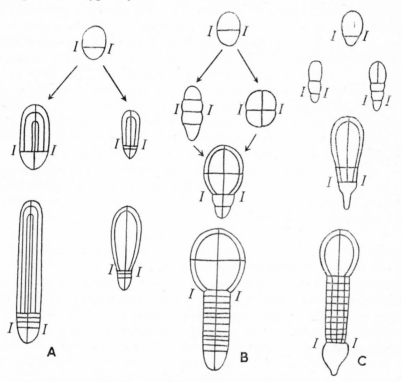

Fig. 13. Liverworts: segmentation of the zygote and development of the sporophyte in the three principal groups

A, Anthocerotales. B, Marchantiales. C, Jungermanniales. I–I₁, the first partition wall of the zygote. In the Marchantiales, Meyer distinguishes filamentous and quadrant types, the latter being held to be derivative. (After Müller).

embedded in the tissue of the gametophyte. The fertilised egg is therefore unlikely to be affected by compression due to the contiguity of prothallial tissue, (though it might be by the stout venter wall), while effects of gradients, other than those of gaseous concentration, must be exercised by way of the stalk. That metabolic gradients determine or affect the position and formation of the archegonia as well as embryogenesis seems probable, but the relevant facts have still to be obtained.

The bryophyte ovum is a spherical, ellipsoidal or pear-shaped body which is free within the venter, i.e. it does not fill the whole of the venter cavity. The indications are that the protoplasm of the ovum is probably not homogeneous. Thus Cavers (1904) has depicted the egg in *Conocephalum conicum* as being ovoid with a clear receptive spot at the upper end, while Meyer (1929) has described and illustrated it as an inverted pear-shaped structure with dense protoplasm at the base and more vacuolated protoplasm above. Very soon after fertilisation, if not before, the polarity of the embryo is established. All bryophytes have an exoscopic embryogeny, the first partition wall of the zygote being typically, though not invariably (*see* the Anthocerotae), at right angles to the archegonial axis, Figs. 5A, 13. As conspicuous differences in the growth of the upper (epibasal) and lower (hypobasal) segments soon become evident, it could be argued that regional metabolic differences were already present in the egg at the time of fertilisation. Factors determining this heterogeneous, polarised distribution of metabolites might include physiological gradients in the gametophyte tissue, an oxygen gradient having its source at the open neck of the archegonium, or disturbances caused by the entry of the spermatozoid into the distal region of the ovum. In *Anthoceros*, the first partition wall is parallel to the axis of the archegonium as in leptosporangiate ferns, but the embryogeny is nevertheless typically exoscopic.

PARTHENOGENESIS AND APOGAMY

According to Steil (1939) parthenogenesis is unknown in bryophytes but apospory has been described by a number of observers (cited by Steil). Apogamy has been recorded for one moss, *Phascum cuspidatum* by Springer (1935); the apogamous sporophytes originated from aposporously produced diploid gametophytes.

THE HEPATICAE—MARCHANTIALES

The initial embryonic developments are closely comparable in all liverworts but some diversity is characteristic of the ensuing phases in the different groups, Fig. 13. After fertilisation, the ovum in *Marchantia* and related forms enlarges until it fills the venter, when it secretes an enveloping wall. The zygote, now an ellipsoidal or pear-shaped body extended in the axis of the archegonium, is divided by a transverse wall, Fig. 14. In its further development, the embryo may show considerable differences in different genera: in some, the second wall is at right-angles to the first and a *quadrant stage* results; in others, the next partition walls are parallel to the first and a short *filamentous stage* results. But in some species, e.g. *Conocephalum conicum*, both the quadrant and filamentous types of development have been recorded (Cavers, 1904; Meyer, 1929).

The Quadrant Type. In some species such as *Targionia hypophylla,* Fig. 14F, and *Conocephalum conicum,* as described by Meyer (1929), the zygote is unequally divided into a large epibasal and a small hypobasal cell: on further development the former will give rise to the capsule and seta, the latter to the foot or to the basal region of the seta and the foot. In quadrant types, the embryo is next divided by longitudinal walls at right-angles to the first wall and to each other, so that it now consists of an octant of approximately equivalent cells. Although we know very little about these cells, their subsequent developments suggest that even at this early stage they are not all alike physiologically. The cells of the hypobasal region function as the absorbing system of the embryo from the outset, the individual cells tending towards a parenchymatous type of development. The epibasal cells, on the other hand, remain meristematic and constitute the region of active growth and differentiation. After the octant stage the embryo begins to elongate, the next divisions in both epibasal and hypobasal regions being similar, and the segmentation pattern developed being of considerable regularity. The divisions in the two regions do not, however, proceed at the same rate, nor are they duplicates of each other. The new walls are typically laid down at right-angles to the curved outer wall and adjoin the internal walls as shown in Fig. 14c, G. Other transverse walls are also laid down. Then, at a characteristic stage of development, periclinal walls are formed and these divide the upper region of the embryo into the amphithecium and endothecium, the former giving rise to the capsule wall, the latter to the archesporium. It is about this stage of development that we might perhaps regard the embryogeny proper as coming to an end; for on further growth and development the sporophyte becomes differentiated as a distal spore-containing capsule with a short seta and a basal haustorial foot. In these organisms there is, in fact, no sustained, adult vegetative phase, antecedent to the spore-producing phase, as in pteridophytes.

The sporophyte in the Marchantiales, then, is characterised by a very regular initial embryonic development which soon merges, or is transformed, into the mature spore-bearing capsule. As in the development of certain animal embryos, the fates of particular regions of the developing germ are determined from an early stage. In that no steady state of vegetative development is established, but rather that there is an early transition from the embryonic to the sporogenous phase, we may assume either that the quantity and quality of the nutrients being received by the embryo from the parent gametophyte vary in a characteristic manner during development, due perhaps to ageing, to photoperiodic effects, or other causes, or that particular genes, in a consistent and orderly sequence, determine the highly regulated development of these organisms. Alternatively, the regulated development may be due to factors of some other kind, as yet unknown. To attempt to describe the observed developments in terms either of metabolism or of genic action, both of which are undoubtedly involved, is merely to indicate how very little is known about these phenomena.

In several genera, e.g. *Grimaldia, Plagiochasma,* and in *Conocephalum conicum* Fig. 14, the zygote, after filling the venter and dividing transversely, continues to elongate and divides by several transverse walls. The short, thick filament thus formed, consisting of 3 or 4 cells, is also a very characteristic feature of the embryogeny of the Sphaerocarpales, Fig. 14k. After some further transverse divisions, longitudinal divisions appear towards the middle of the embryo. Oblique divisions of the distal cell result in the establishment of a two-sided apical cell, Fig. 14.

Meyer (1931; *see also* Müller, 1951) considers that the filamentous and quadrant types (as in *Marchantia*) are quite distinctive, the former being the more primitive and the latter derivative. On this basis he recognises two types of embryo in the Marchantiales, each including both relatively simple and primitive forms and more highly differentiated ones, Fig. 13. Among the filamentous types are *Plagiochasma, Conocephalum, Grimaldia, Reboulia,* and *Fimbriaria* and probably also *Cryptomitrium* and *Cyathodium,* while the quadrant type is exemplified by *Marchantia, Conocephalum, Preissia* and by members of the Astroporae, Ricciaceae and Corsiniaceae. *Conocephalum conicum* may show either the quadrant or filamentous type of development.

The analysis of the problem of segmentation pattern can be taken a stage further. There is support for the view that, at any particular stage in development, the segmentation pattern is determined by the shape of the organism, or organ, and by the internal distribution of

---

Fig. 14. Embryogeny in Marchantiales and Sphaerocarpales

A–D, *Conocephalum conicum (Fegatella conica)* (after Cavers). A, Embryo at octant stage, showing the first and second partition walls. B, Similar embryo as seen in transverse section. C, D, Older embryos, showing the regular segmentation pattern ($\times$ 360). E–G, *Targionia hypophylla.* E, Venter of mature archegonium with ovum. F, The first division of the zygote. G, Regular segmentation pattern (E, $\times$ 500; F, G, $\times$ 500). H, J, *Riccia glauca.* H, First division of the zygote, as seen in longitudinal section. J, Older embryo ($\times$ 260). K, *Sphaerocarpus* sp. Young embryo in l.s.; the fertilised egg elongates and divides transversely, and further transverse walls are formed before any longitudinal ones appear ($\times$ 260) (E–K after Campbell). L–Q, *Conocephalum conicum* (after Meyer). L, Unfertilised egg ($\times$ 900). M, Two-celled embryo ($\times$ 133). N, Second division of the zygote ($\times$ 200). O, Four-celled embryo ($\times$ 200). P, Anomalous division in four-celled embryo ($\times$ 200). Q, Older embryo with apical cell ($\times$ 133).

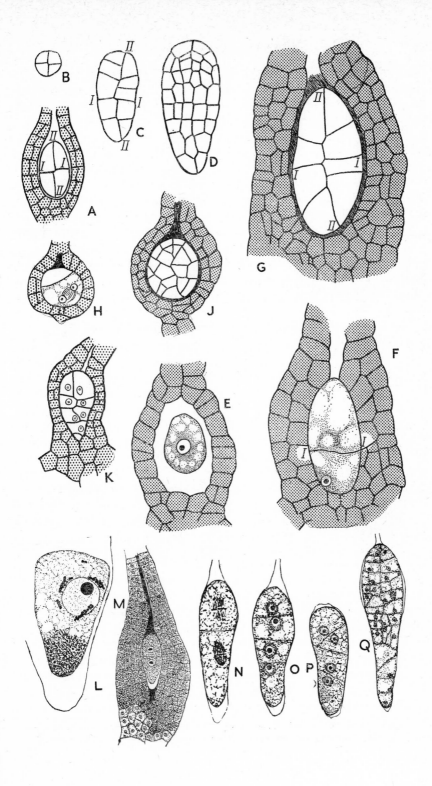

metabolites. In some genera, the axial growth of the embryo considerably exceeds its transverse growth, whereas in others such differential growth is considerably less evident. In the former the young embryo will almost certainly divide by a sequence of transverse walls; in the latter it is likely to divide into quadrants; both being in conformity with Errera's law. Since differential growth is probably gene-controlled, (though it may also be affected by environment factors), it follows that the initial embryonic segmentation pattern may have phylogenetic significance. But in that relatively small genetical differences may apparently have quite considerable effects on the distribution of growth, as in *Conocephalum conicum*, it would appear that the extent of differentiation and of specialised development, rather than the nature of the initial segmentation, are the criteria which should be used as evidence of evolutionary status.

In the Marchantiales, the more elaborate members, e.g. *Marchantia*, have an adult sporophyte which consists of a foot, a seta and a spore-containing capsule, whereas in the simpler members, e.g. *Riccia*, Fig. 14H, J, the adult sporophyte consists of a mass of spores, with a surrounding wall, one cell thick. Nevertheless, the early stages in the embryogeny of *Riccia* are closely comparable with those in *Marchantia*, i.e. there is an octant pattern of cell division. The division of the octant cells by curved walls is also common to both genera but thereafter the close resemblance between them ceases. In *Riccia* the next cell divisions are periclinal, an outer capsule wall and an inner archesporial tissue being thus formed, i.e. the early embryogeny is followed immediately by the sporogenous phase. The extremes of development thus exemplified by *Marchantia* and *Riccia* are of special phylogenetic interest, a number of intermediate conditions being also known, e.g. in *Dumortiera* the sporophyte consists of a large sporogenous region, a very short seta and a parenchymatous basal foot region.

From the evidence presented above, the *Marchantiales* seem likely to afford a fruitful field for further studies of embryogenesis. Already we have seen that, within a single species, e.g. *Conocephalum conicum*, the early embryogeny may show considerable variability, under the impact of either genetical or environmental factors. A somewhat similar conclusion emerges from comparative studies of the embryogeny in different species of *Marchantia*. In *M. polymorpha*, the embryo passes through a characteristic quadrant stage (Durand, 1908). In *M. domingensis* Anderson (1929) has shown that the spherical embryo does not invariably divide by a transverse wall or pass through a typical quadrant stage: other segmentation patterns are possible, e.g. the epibasal cell may divide by oblique walls, yielding a two-sided apical cell. In *M. chenopoda* the first dividing wall of the zygote is obliquely transverse, and sometimes very markedly so (McNaught, 1929). A typical quadrant stage was not observed in this species. Two primary transverse walls yield a short filamentous embryo of three cells, which develop respectively into the foot, seta and capsule. In *Marchantia* sp. from Peru, Heberlein (1929) observed the first division of the zygote to be transverse or somewhat oblique. After a typical quadrant stage the embryo broadens out, i.e. enlarges at right-angles to its axis. According to the shape of the embryo, the next walls may be formed in somewhat different positions, the successive divisions resulting in a spherical mass of small cells. At this stage the cells are all much alike, but later those in the distal half become more densely protoplasmic, i.e. in preparation for the formation of the capsule. That species of the same genus do not necessarily show the same type of early development is demonstrated by the foregoing observations. Again, in two species of *Cyathodium*, *C. cavernarum* has a filamentous type of embryo (Lang, 1905) while *C. foetidissimum* has an octant type.

Lastly, it may be noted that, following the fertilisation of the ovum, the venter wall and the tissues round the base of the archegonium are stimulated to a considerable growth development, the results being seen in the formation of the enveloping calyptra and the pseudoperianth. These developments are indicative of the active outward diffusion of growth-regulating substances from the zygote and developing embryo (*see also* p. 73, Fig. 16).

(*see also* p. 73, Fig. 16).

HEPATICAE—SPHAEROCARPALES

In the Sphaerocarpales the zygote is divided by a transverse wall into two approximately equal parts. Each of these cells is again divided by a transverse wall (or walls) before any vertical walls appear. The young embryo thus consists of a simple row of cells as in some Marchantiales, the first wall defining the epibasal and hypobasal regions. In the hypobasal region, however, growth is considerably less vigorous, the result being a pear-shaped embryo with a narrow base, Fig. 14K. On further development the hypobasal region forms a short, narrow seta and a somewhat distended parenchymatous foot. Thus, although the early embryogeny in *Sphaerocarpus* is typically filamentous, a not untypical hepatic sporophyte is eventually formed. It is apparent that the growth rate at different points along the axis is very different and it seems unlikely that this can be explained in terms of metabolic gradients having their source in the gametophyte tissue, though these are no doubt involved. The morphological development is a distinctive and regulated one and, in order to explain it, it is necessary to account for the differential distribution of metabolites in the basal, median and distal regions. Genetical factors are, no doubt, of primary importance, but the actual working of the system is still very obscure.

The filamentous type of embryonic development is also well seen in *Geothallus* and *Riella*. The presence of chloroplasts in the sporophytes of some of these Hepaticae indicates that they have some capacity for self-nutrition. Studhalter (1938) has shown that when young sporophytes of *Sphaerocarpus texanus* and *Riella americana* were excised and cultured in water, they continued their normal development and reached maturity through their own photosynthetic activity.

HEPATICAE—JUNGERMANNIALES

In the Jungermanniales the embryogeny is typically filamentous in its early stages, e.g. *Aneura, Fossombronia*, and many others, Fig. 15. The zygote typically enlarges, elongates and becomes divided by several

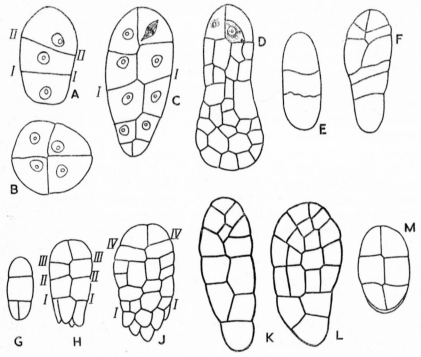

Fig. 15. Embryogeny in Jungermanniales

A–D, *Fossombronia longiseta*. A, Young embryo in l.s. showing the first and second walls, I–I, II,II. B, C, Transverse and longitudinal sections of an older embryo. D, An older embryo, showing the beginning of the archesporial differentiation (× 525; after Campbell). E, F, *Porella bolanderi*. Embryos in longitudinal section (× 525; after Campbell). G–J, *Frullania dilatata*. Embryos in longitudinal section (× 300). K, *Symphyogyna*, Embryo. L, *Blasia*, Embryo. M, *Pellia calycina*. Young gametophyte plant from spore, showing characteristic segmentation pattern (× 420). (G–M after Leitgeb).

transverse walls. Median longitudinal walls are then formed, especially in the epibasal region, Fig. 15F. Thereafter, the divisions in the epibasal region are periclinal, an amphithecium, or capsule wall, and an archesporial endothecium being differentiated. As in the Marchantiales, the epibasal segment of the first zygotic division gives rise to the capsule and seta, while the hypobasal segment forms the foot. The genus *Porella*, Fig. 15E, F, exemplifies the filamentous type of embryo in which the subsequent divisions are of a somewhat irregular nature.

POST-FERTILISATION DEVELOPMENTS IN THE GAMETOPHYTE

In the bryophytes, the dependence of the sporophyte on the gametophyte is usually, and rightly, stressed. The movement of metabolic substances, however, is not all in the acropetal direction: the developing embryo may have important effects on the adjacent gametophyte tissue. Indeed, in some species, conspicuous and biologically important structural changes are induced in the gametophyte. The renewed growth of the ventral region of the archegonium after fertilisation is general in bryophytes, a protective calyptra being thus formed. The adjacent tissues of the thallus may also be stimulated to grow. In *Corsinia* and *Boschia*, Fig. 16A, B, a protective shield-like investment grows up from the thallus and covers the developing sporogonium. In the Jungermanniales, e.g. *Pallavicinia*, the embryro is first of all protected by a considerably enlarged and elongated perianth: this is a gametophyte structure which has undergone further growth as a result of the stimulus of the embryonic development. Examples of remarkable post-fertilisation gametophytic developments are found in those Jungermanniales in which a 'pouch' or marsupium is present, Figs. 16C–G. As the illustrations show, the ensuing morphological changes are of a far-reaching kind, in which the embryo becomes protected in a characteristic pouch more or less deeply embedded in gametophyte tissue. Among the mosses, *Sphagnum* and *Andreaea* show an interesting post-fertilisation gametophyte reaction in the development of a pseudopodium, a stalk-like structure which elevates the maturing capsule above the level of the foliage, in very much the same way as does the sporophyte seta in the mosses. In the absence of fertilisation and zygotic development, these several gametophyte developments in liverworts and mosses do not take place.

ANTHOCEROTAE

This group is sometimes included as an order of the Hepaticae, but it has also been treated as a class commensurable with that group and with the Musci. The sporophytic development of *Anthoceros* is of special interest: it is held by some authors that *Anthoceros* is the bryophyte of which the sporophyte most closely resembles primitive pteridophytes such as *Rhynia*; i.e. if we assume a common origin for bryophytes and pteridophytes, *Anthoceros* may resemble the ancestral type from which the pteridophytes have arisen.

When the spore germinates, a filament is formed. This divides by transverse walls. An apical cell is established and a thallus is formed as a result of its regular segmentation, Fig. 17L.

The archegonia in *Anthoceros* are formed behind the growing tip of the thallus, Fig. 17A, and are completely embedded in it. In contrast to other liverworts, the ovum is thus liable to be affected by biochemical factors present in the surrounding tissue. At maturity the spherical, or approximately spherical, ovum lies at the base of the venter, filling only part of the space. On being fertilised, the ovum swells up; its uniform, granular cytoplasm becomes highly vacuolated and fills the cavity of the venter; and it secretes an outer wall, Fig. 17B. The nucleus also increases in size. Thereafter, some interesting differences have been observed in the development of different genera. In *Anthoceros fusiformis* and *A. pearsoni*, Campbell shows the somewhat egg-shaped zygote as dividing by a longitudinal wall into two equal parts, each of these being divided transversely but unequally into a small basal cell and a larger distal one, Fig. 17C, D. In each of the quadrant cells a vertical wall is laid down and the octant stage is reached, the upper cells being considerably larger than the lower ones. The upper cells are next divided by transverse walls so that the embryo now consists of three tiers each of four cells. On the further division and development of the lower tier, which is considerably less regular, the characteristic haustorial foot is formed, the constituent cells being typically enlarged and parenchymatous, Fig. 17R. In these several developments in *Anthoceros* it is evident that polarity is established from the outset— though the first partition wall is *not* at right-angles to the axis—and that the embryonic development is marked by a differential distribution

---

Fig. 16. Reaction of gametophyte to embryonic development in
Marchantiales and Jungermanniales

A, B, *Corsinia marchantioides.* Longitudinal section of thallus. A, Shows outgrowth of thallus in midst of group of archegonia. B, Considerable development of this outgrowth, associated with the development of the embryo (from Cavers, after Leitgeb). C–E, Diagrammatic longitudinal sections of various Acrogynae, showing the archegonial group and the sporogonium with the structures developed round it. C, Perianth and involucre free, as in *Lophocolea, Plagiochila, Frullania.* D, Perianth and involucre fused; the formation of an incipient marsupium is indicated by the bulbous swelling of the stem below the foot of the sporogonium, as in *Nardia geoscypha.* E, Development of 'coelocauly,' i.e. the complete embedding of the sporogonium in the stem tissue, as in *Gottschea* and *Trichocolea.* (C, D, after Cavers; E, after Goebel). F, G, *Kantia trichomanis.* Stages in the development of the hollow marsupium. (F, after Goebel; G, after Cavers); *per* perianth; *inv,* involucre; *c,* capsule; *s,* seta; *f,* foot; gametophyte tissue stippled.

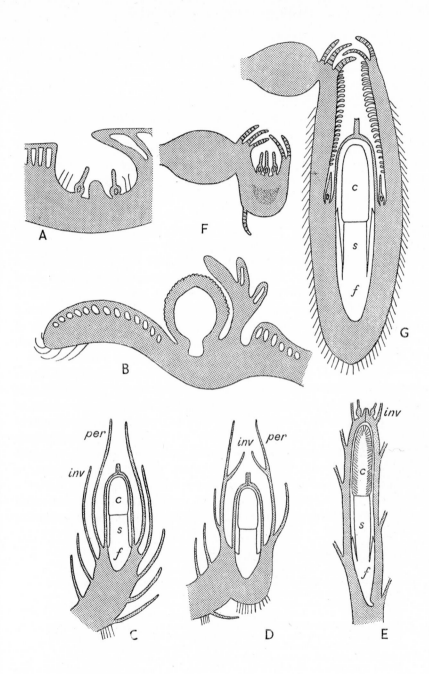

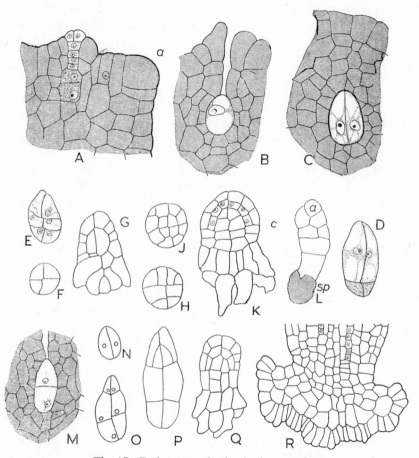

Fig. 17. Embryogeny in the Anthocerotales

A–D, *Anthoceros fusiformis*. A, Development of sunken archegonium behind the apex of the thallus. B, The undivided zygote. C, The first, vertical wall. D, The first transverse wall. E–K, *Anthoceros pearsoni*. E, Young embryo in l.s. F, Segmentation pattern as seen in cross-section. G, Older embryo in l.s., showing foot development. H, J, Two stages in the development of the segmentation pattern, in cross-section. K, Older embryo in l.s. showing differentiation of archesporium and development of haustorial foot. L, *A. fusiformis*. Germinating spore showing growth of thallus by an apical cell and characteristic segmentation pattern. M, *Notothylas orbicularis*. Four-celled embryo. N–Q, *Notothylas breutelii*. Stages in the development of the sporophyte as seen in l.s. R, *Notothylas orbicularis*. L.s. through base of sporophyte, showing the enlarged cells of the foot. (A–M, R, after Campbell; N–Q, after Lang.) (A–D, × 400; E–K, × 200; L, × 170; M, × 300; N–P, × 350; Q, × 250; R, × 200.)

of growth along the axis. As is well known, a characteristic intercalary meristem is established at a later stage. In *Notothylas orbicularis*, as described by Campbell (1918), the first division of the zygote may be at right-angles to the neck of the archegonium, Fig. 17M—the earliest stage observed showed four quadrants of equal size; but in a species described by Lang (1907) the first wall is as in *Anthoceros*, Fig. 17H–Q.

MUSCI

The Musci, comprising the Sphagnales, Andreaeales and Bryales, yield points of interest in the development both of their gametophytes and sporophytes.

The spore of *Sphagnum* on germination gives rise to a short filament of three to four cells. Growth is most active in the distal cell. In fact, according to Ruhland (1924), it functions briefly as an apical cell with two cutting faces, a flat thalloid protenema, one cell thick, being formed. On further growth, the apical cell becomes less active, and a protonema of somewhat irregular contour arises by the division of the marginal cells. New protonemal filaments may arise from these marginal meristematic cells and in turn give rise to flat protonemata at their extremity. Later, as a result of active growth and division of a marginal cell, a bud with a three-sided apical cell is initiated and this gives rise to the erect leafy stem.

The archegonia in *Sphagnum* are formed at the apex of short branches at the summit of the plant; they are shortly stalked and quite free like those observed in other mosses. The first division of the elongated zygote is by a transverse wall: the polarity is thus determined early, the upper cell becoming the apical cell of the embryo. On further growth the embryo becomes a transversely divided filament, Fig. 18A. The basal cell meanwhile divides by a somewhat oblique longitudinal wall; this is followed by other divisions and a parenchymatous foot with somewhat irregular cellular pattern results. In the epibasal region the apical cell continues to divide by transverse walls and the subjacent cells by longitudinal ones, the resulting cellular pattern affording an almost classic example of Errera's law, Fig. 18B, C. When the embryo is of a cylindrical-conical shape, periclinal divisions take place in the cells of the epibasal region, the amphithecium and endothecium being thereby defined, Fig. 18C, D, F. This may be taken as marking the transition from the embryonic to the sporogenous phase, the further developments consisting in the formation of the capsule and seta from the epibasal segment and of the large distended foot from the hypobasal segment, Fig. 18E. *Sphagnum* shows an interesting post-fertilisation development in the gametophyte, the distal region enlarging into a stalk-like pseudopodium (*see* p. 73).

In *Andreaea* the spore contents divide in a regular and characteristic manner and form a cellular tissue whilst still enclosed within the intact outer wall. This wall is then ruptured and the young multicellular gametophyte emerges. In the inception of the gametophyte we have thus what is virtually an enclosed embryogeny. A filamentous development ensues and in due course buds give rise to erect stems as in other mosses.

As the zygote enlarges, the first division is by an approximately median transverse wall. The developments of the two segments are somewhat different from those in *Sphagnum*. The first division of the epibasal cell is by a curved oblique wall, as shown in Fig. 18G, the distal portion being considerably larger than the other. If the two cells are in equilibrium, we must suppose that the distribution of metabolites in the epibasal cell before division was far from homogeneous. With the formation of a second curved oblique wall, an apical cell is constituted. Similar divisions also take place in the hypobasal cell, with the result that the embryo becomes an elongated spindle-like structure, with an apical cell at either end. In the epibasal region, periclinal walls are next laid down and define the amphithecium and endothecium. On further growth and development, the capsule and seta are differentiated, while the hypobasal region becomes specialised as a haustorial foot, Fig. 18K.

Here we may note that whereas in *Sphagnum* the archesporium is derived from the inner layer of the amphithecium, the endothecium giving rise to the columella only, in *Andreaea*, as in the Bryales, the archesporium is formed from the outer layer of the endothecium. While this is not a matter which strictly pertains to the embryology, it provides further evidence that in the precisely regulated development of the bryophyte sporophyte, certain genetical factors apparently become active at particular stages in the ontogeny.

In a moss such as *Funaria*, the spore germinates to form simple filaments which emerge from opposite sides (*see* also p. 64). These filaments divide by transverse walls and branch freely: those which are exposed on the soil surface become photosynthetic and have transverse septa, whereas those which penetrate the soil are colourless, or have brown walls, and typically oblique septa.

The moss archegonium is typically a distal and free structure, seated on a short or long pedicel through which the embryo is supplied with nutrients from the gametophyte. Acropetal gradients are thus involved in the embryonic development. In the Bryales, the mature ovum is spherical or ovoid with a colourless region on the side towards the neck of the archegonium. The zygote divides by a transverse wall as in *Sphagnum* and *Andreaea*. The next developments are closely

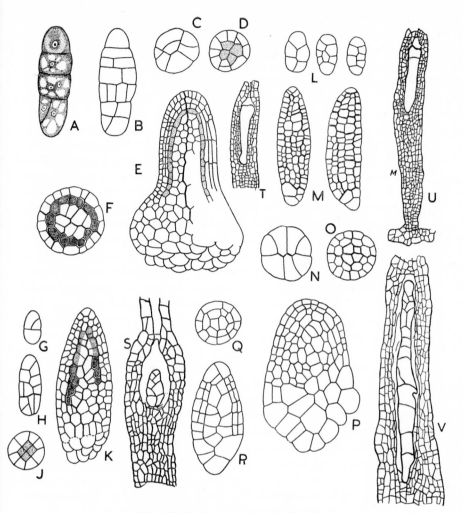

Fig. 18. Embryogeny in the Musci

A–E, *Sphagnum acutifolium.* A, The initial filamentous embryo in longitudinal section. B, Longitudinal walls are being formed. C, D, The young embryo in transverse section, showing the regular pattern of segmentation and the beginning of differentiation. E, Older embryo in l.s. showing the beginning of differentiation in the distal region and the marked enlargement of the foot cells. F, Archesporial region in transverse section (A–D, × 240; E, × 100; after Waldner). G–K, *Andreaea.* G, *A. crassinervia.* H, K, *A. petrophila.* Stages in the embryonic development as seen in l.s.; in K, the differentiation of tissues is taking place in the distal region. J, Cross-section of a young embryo (G, × 220; H–K, × 165; after Waldner). L–O, *Phascum cuspidatum.* L, M, Stages in the embryonic development as seen in l.s. N, O, Segmentation pattern as seen in transverse section (after Kienitz-Gerloff). P–R, *Archidium phascoides.* P, R, Embryos in l.s. Q, Embryo in t.s. (L–R after Leitgeb.) S, *Tortula muralis.* Longitudinal section of archegonium with young embryo (× 160). T, V, *Mnium hornum.* T, Elongated zygote (× 100). V, Filamentous embryo with a two-sided apical cell (× 160). U, *Catharinea undulata.* Two-celled embryo (× 100); (S–V, after Bishop).

comparable with those described for *Andreaea*. The formation of oblique walls in both the epibasal and hypobasal cells results in the establishment of two-sided apical cells, on the further growth and division of which a spindle-like embryo is formed, Fig. 18L, M. In some mosses, e.g. *Tortula*, Fig. 18s, the hypobasal region undergoes little development. When periclinal walls are laid down in the epibasal region, the amphithecium and endothecium are defined. Even in the simpler Bryales, e.g. in cleistocarpic genera such as *Archidium* and *Ephemerum*, Fig. 18P–R, the early stages in the embryogeny are as described above.

Bishop (1929) has recorded the occurrence of well marked filamentous embryos in various Bryales, Fig. 18s–v. Early workers, e.g. Hofmeister (1851, 1862), had shown that in mosses such as *Fissidens*, *Phascum* and *Funaria*, the sporophyte is derived almost entirely from the epibasal segment of the two-celled embryo, the hypobasal cell undergoing a few divisions of a somewhat irregular nature. Hofmeister, however, noted that in some species, e.g. *Bryum argenteum*, the zygote may elongate and the epibasal cell divide by several transverse walls, before the apical cell is established, i.e. the young embryo is essentially filamentous. Bishop has shown that a filament of at least three cells, and usually more, is typically formed before the two-sided apical cell becomes functional in *Mnium hornum*, Fig. 18T, V, *M. punctatum* and *Bryum capillare*. A filament of nine cells was observed in *M. hornum*, this being the result of the formation of transverse walls acropetally in the epibasal segment. A seven-celled filamentous embryo was found to be typical of *Catharinea undulata*, Fig. 18U, and it may well be that filamentous stages will be found in many species. Bishop has also illustrated a remarkable elongation of the fertilised egg in these three genera and calls attention to the long, narrow archegonial pedicel or stalk in them, Figs. 18U, V. The occurrence of these elongated filamentous embryos, and their characteristic mode of division, lend strong support to the view that acropetal gradients are important factors in the embryogenic development.

DISCUSSION

The bryophyte sporophyte is small and limited in its organographic development, the sporogenous phase almost immediately supervening upon the brief and simple embryogeny. Each species, however, is characterised by the distinctive size, highly regular development and organisation of its sporophyte.

If we regard the embryonic development as ending with the periclinal divisions that lead to the initiation of archesporial tissue, then the task of the embryologist is to attempt to explain such phenomena as the characteristic polarity, the different developments of the epibasal and hypobasal regions, the development of a characteristic histological pattern including the establishment of a growing apex, and the brevity of the vegetative phase in the sporophytic development.

In the bryophytes the archegonium is typically a stalked organ, otherwise free of tissue on all sides. The zygote typically divides by a transverse wall, except in the Anthocerotae where it usually is a longitudinal one, and the embryogeny is invariably exoscopic. In *Anthoceros*, with its embedded archegonium, the constitution and metabolism of the ovum and zygote are evidently considerably different from those of other bryophytes. Also, contrary to Bower's generalisation, the first partition wall is not at right-angles to the polar axis. In the absence of experimental data, the polarity and exoscopic embryogeny of the bryophytes (other than the Anthocerotae) may be provisionally attributed to metabolic gradients, which have their source in the gametophyte, acting on the ovum or zygote. If we regard the unfertilised egg as an initially homogeneous reaction system (*see* Chapter III), then the stimulus of fertilisation and the impact of acropetal gradients might well explain the transition to a heterogeneous system, the metabolic complex at the apex of the zygote being different from that at its base. The hypobasal region of the embryo, which lies closest to the source of nutrients, typically undergoes limited growth and a parenchymatous development, whereas the distal region remains embryonic and capable of further growth and formative activity. In these organographic developments and relationships, the bryophytes resemble pteridophytes such as *Psilotum* and *Equisetum* (*see* Chapter VI) and, indeed, vascular plants in general.

The characteristic segmentation pattern in the several orders is the result of a sequence of regular cell divisions. These take place in general conformity with Errera's law. There are, of course, cell divisions which do not appear to conform with this principle. But here the reader should be reminded that, as the embryonic development proceeds, the distribution of metabolites becomes progressively more heterogeneous, new factors become incident and new forces come into play, and these are all liable to have an effect on the nature of cell growth and division. As each genus has a characteristic protoplasmic constitution and metabolism, differences in the cellular pattern are to be expected; but, as we are concerned with a group of related organisms, these differences will not be of a major kind. These views are in keeping with those of the older anatomists who held that the mode of segmentation in the embryogeny had taxonomic significance, but here the part played by physical factors is given greater prominence.

Contemplation of the embryonic and sporogenous development of bryophytes suggests that the process can be envisaged as a sequence of biochemical phases of increasing complexity, the later phases being characterised either by a greater variety of metabolites, or more highly elaborated ones, or both. The embryo is dependent on the parent gametophyte for all the substances—minerals, carbohydrates, nitrogen-containing and possibly growth-regulating substances—necessary for its growth. The fertilised ovum as an active centre of metabolism may itself be a source of growth-regulating substances. These and other substances may diffuse basipetally and induce effects in the gameto-phyte. Now, if the substances supplied to the embryo from the gameto-phyte remained unchanged both quantitatively and qualitatively, it would be reasonable to expect that the embryo would continue its vegetative growth indefinitely and give rise to an elongated cylinder, or axial structure. If the substances increased in amount, an obconical axis would result. But, in fact, after a brief embryonic or vegetative phase, the growth and segmentation of the distal apex cease, and, by a succession of what appear to be closely regulated developments, the sporogenous capsule becomes differentiated. Accordingly, as a working hypothesis, it is now suggested that the sequence of distinctive histolo-gical developments is determined by a sequence of changes in the underlying reaction system. For any bryophyte species, the fidelity with which these developments take place is a very remarkable thing. On the hypothesis proposed above, how, in fact, can we account for the regulation of the underlying biochemical processes?

In terms of contemporary genetical theory, the explanation might take the form that different genes, or sets of genes, are successively evoked during the ontogenetic development of the sporophyte. At any particular stage, as a result of the biochemical action of particular genes (or gene groups) on the cytoplasm of the embryonic cells, characteristic growth and histological developments will ensue. In relation to the new situation thus produced, the action of other genes will be evoked; and so on, each phase preparing the way for the succeeding one, the whole development being characterised by an orderly and distinctive sequence of physiological events; or, in other words, by the orderly sequence of metabolic activities in a gene-determined reaction system. These become manifest in the successive morphological and histological developments which characterise the ontogeny of the species. While this kind of general statement may approximate to the truth, it tells us little of the processes that are involved; for our ultimate aim in the study of embryogenesis is to explain, in physiological terms and in as much detail as possible, how the orderly morphological and histological developments are brought about. The basic assumption that is made here is that genes are the primary factors determining the inception and the specific character of the biochemical phases that underlie the morphological development. At any particular stage, the state of the organismal reaction system regulates the entry of particular genes, or their products, into the system. The state of the system at any moment is determined or regulated, by its antecedent state, by the contemporary supply of reacting substances to it, and by environmental conditions. The parent gametophyte, as the sole source of nutrients for the young bryophyte embryo, is evidently very important. (In this connection the experimental investigation of gametophyte-sporophyte relationships, using modern surgical, tissue culture and biochemical techniques, may be indicated as affording real scope for advancing our knowledge of embryogenesis.) Important as gametophytic and environmental factors may be, however, the embryo, from a very early stage, is in many respects a self-determining entity. The cumulative effect of the points indicated above is to show that, for any species, the regularity and specific character of the embryonic development are to be attributed to a whole nexus of physical and biological factors and relationships, each of which requires individual investigation.

The importance of genetical factors is also seen in the early transition from the embryonic to the sporogenous phase and in the limited growth and differentiation of the sporophyte as a whole.

Phylogeny. In considering the problems of phylogeny, the Ricciaceae are of special interest because their sporophytes are structurally the simplest in all the bryophytes. A basic question is whether this simplicity is of a primitive or derivative character. Bower (1908, 1935) and Campbell (1940) favoured the former view, and saw in the small and relatively undifferentiated sporogonium of *Riccia*, which is apparently almost completely dependent on the gametophyte for its nutrition during development, an early stage in the upgrade development of an antithetic or intercalated sporophytic generation. Goebel (1930), Evans (1939) and Bold (1948), on the other hand, see in the Ricciaceae the culmination of a reduction series which can be traced throughout the Marchantiales. Evans has pointed out that it is erroneous to describe the simpler sporophytes in the Jungermanniales and Marchantiales as being devoid of chlorophyll and therefore entirely dependent on the gametophyte for organic nutrients, as well as for inorganic salts and water. Bold (1938, 1948) has emphasised that chloroplasts have long been known in the sporophytes of some genera and he has shown that some chlorophyll is present even in the small and feebly differentiated sporogonia of *Riccia*, *Ricciocarpus* and other genera. As these sporophytes are not entirely dependent, or 'parasitic,' on the gametophytes which bear them, he considers that the evidence lends support to the view that the Ricciaceae are derivatively simple organisms, and that their feebly developed chlorophyll is a remnant of that which is present in forms with more elaborate sporophytes. Furthermore, he has argued that since self-nutrition by photosynthesis 'was apparently a primary attribute of all sporophytes both in the algae and land plants,' his observations are in accord with a homologous theory of alternation of generations as the basis for the evolution of land plants, rather than with the antithetic theory as advocated by Bower. Bold (1940) has also suggested that the scarcity and inactivity of the chlorophyll in the sporophytes of bryophytes may be a result of the retention of the sporophyte within the gametophyte: and, similarly the intrasporic development of the gametophytes in many heterosporous pteridophytes and seed plants may have been a factor in their loss of chlorophyll. Support for his views may perhaps be seen in the experimental investigations of Studhalter (1938) in which he showed that young excised sporophytes of *Sphaerocarpus* and *Riella*, cultivated in water, reached full maturity through their own photosynthetic activity. However, it is evident that during the early embryogeny of all bryophytes, the sporophyte is completely dependent on the gametophyte for its nutrition.

Evans (1939) considers that the Anthocerotales also exemplify a phylogenetically descending series, the relatively simple sporophyte of *Notothylas*, as compared with the considerably more complex one of *Anthoceros*, being due to reduction; i.e. *Notothylas* is the most advanced genus in this group.

Chapter VI

EMBRYOGENESIS IN THE PSILOTALES AND EQUISETALES

PSILOTALES

PSILOTUM and *Tmesipteris*, the only two genera in this pteridophyte order, illustrate the embryonic development in the most primitive of living vascular plants. Both genera are rootless and *Psilotum* is also leafless. Their closest affinity is with the ancient Palaeozoic fossil group, the Psilophytales, which includes such leafless and rootless genera as *Psilophyton, Rhynia* and *Horneophyton*. Nothing is known of embryonic development in the fossil forms.

In both *Psilotum* and *Tmesipteris*, Figs. 19, 20, the prothalli are branching, irregularly cylindrical, mycorrhizic bodies, devoid of chlorophyll and completely saprophytic. The short-necked archegonium is immersed in, and in cellular continuity with, the prothallial tissue. The early embryogeny is similar in the two genera. After fertilisation, the ellipsoidal zygote enlarges, fills the venter and divides by a transverse wall. The polarity of the embryo is now defined. The embryogeny is exoscopic and in due course the epibasal segment gives rise to the shoot apex and shoot, and the hypobasal segment to a parenchymatous haustorial foot. The first divisions of both the epibasal and hypobasal cells are by walls lying in the axis of the archegonium. On further growth, transverse walls are laid down. Thereafter the histological development of the foot is somewhat irregular; it becomes roughly cylindrical in shape and grows down into the gametophyte tissue from which it withdraws the nutrition required by the embryo by means of short haustorial cells. In this connection, comparisons with the haustorial foot in *Anthoceros*, Fig. 17, have been made. After the quadrant stage the divisions in the epibasal segment tend to be somewhat irregular, but soon a single initial or apical cell can be distinguished, usually in an approximately median position. The further growth of the shoot is due to the activity of this cell. In some quite young embryos, two separate apical initials are established on opposite sides of the rounded distal region, their further development resulting in the formation of a vasculated, dichotomously branched embryo, Fig. 19D, G. As these developments are accompanied by growth of the adjacent gametophyte tissue, the embryo becomes overarched by a calyptra-like structure. On emerging from the calyptra, the embryo becomes infected by the mycorrhizic fungus and develops

85

as a cylindrical and somewhat irregularly bifurcating rhizome. Subsequently, on exposure to light, some of its branches become erect and photosynthetic (Holloway, 1917, 1921, 1939; Lawson, 1917).

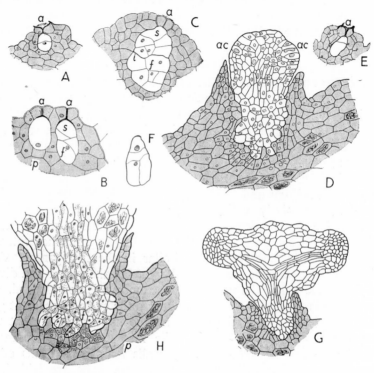

Fig. 19. *Tmesipteris tannensis*

A, Transverse section of prothallus, showing archegonium (*a*) and young embryo in longitudinal section; the zygote has divided by a median wall; the epibasal segment will give rise to the shoot (*s*) and the hypobasal segment to the foot (*f*). B, An undivided egg and a zygote showing somewhat irregular divisions. C, An older embryo in l.s., showing the segmentation pattern in the shoot and foot segments. D, An older, leafless, rootless embryo which is about to dichotomise; two apical cells (*ac*) can be distinguished. E, A zygote unequally divided by the first wall. F, A zygote showing anomalous segmentation. G, An embryo showing the characteristic bifurcation. H, The foot region (*f*) of an older embryo; note the haustorial outgrowths and the starch grains in the cells of the gemetophyte and foot. (A–E, H, × 50; F, × 90; G, × 27; after Holloway).

In both *Psilotum* and *Tmesipteris* the young sporophyte is rootless and leafless and Bower (1935) has pointed out that the whole character of the early embryonic development 'suggests an imperfect differentiation of parts, which in consideration of the adult structure may be held to be a relatively primitive rather than a reduced state of organisation.' As we have seen, true leaves are never formed in *Psilotum* but small scale-like emergences of the shoot may be observed. In *Tmesipteris* the young sporophyte is initially leafless, but as it enlarges small scale-like leaves begin to appear and normal leaves are subsequently formed. There is thus an ontogenetic delay in the formation of the first leaves, this possibly affording an example of what Haldane (1932) has described as neoteny or paedogenesis. Because of their similarity

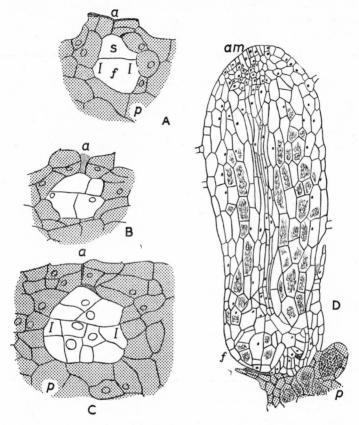

Fig. 20. *Psilotum triquetrum*

A–D, Stages in the embryonic development as seen in longitudinal section; I–I, first partition wall; *a*, neck of archegonium; *s*, shoot segment; *f*, foot segment; *am*, apical meristem. (A–C, × 137; D, × 50; after Holloway).

to the Psilophytales, e.g. the rootless, leafless fossils, *Rhynia* and *Psilophyton*, it has been generally accepted that the living Psilotales, of which no immediate or direct fossil ancestors are known, are simple and primitive plant organisations which have remained relatively unchanged over vast periods of time; i.e. *Psilotum* is rootless and leafless because in its ancestors these organs never had been evolved. As noted above, however, *Psilotum* does possess small scale leaves,

4

sometimes with a vascular strand, while *Tmesipteris* has first of all similar scale leaves and later normal vasculated photosynthetic ones. The possibility that the ancestors of the Psilotales were root-bearing, leafy plants cannot therefore be completely ruled out. Manton (1950) has shown that both *Psilotum* and *Tmesipteris* have high chromosome numbers and considers that these genera may be 'the end-products of very ancient polyploid series.'

Holloway has shown that considerable irregularities may be found in the early segmentation pattern, Fig. 19B, F. These show considerable departures from Errera's law. It may be that these embryos are degenerating or abortive and have an abnormal distribution of metabolites. Whether the anomalous histological condition is due to environmental factors, to the simultaneous development of several embryos on the same prothallus, to the nature of the nutrients supplied by the prothallus, or to genetical factors, cannot be decided on the evidence thus far available. Comparable irregularities are known in other groups, e.g. the Equisetales.

The normal embryogeny of the Psilotales would appear to afford a model of what the development of a simple vascular plant might be expected to be like: i.e. exoscopic embryogeny, the foot region in contact with the source of nutrition, the organisation of a distal formative region, and the growth and differentiation of a leafless and rootless vasculated axis. It may be that the embryogeny of *Rhynia*, *Psilophyton*, etc., was not unlike that of *Psilotum*, but information is lacking. According to general phylogenetic theory, all classes of vascular plants may have sprung from plants of psilophytean affinity, or have passed through a psilophytean stage. It will, therefore, be of interest to see to what extent the embryonic developments in other classes of pteridophytes and seed plants correspond to the *Psilotum* type of embryogeny. As we have seen in Chapter V, the bryophytes have points in common with the Psilotales in respect of their early embryogeny.

In the *Psilotales* there is no suspensor—an organ found in the embryogeny of some other pteridophytes considered to be primitive. Lang (1915) pointed out that embryos without suspensors were probably derived from forms with suspensors. This raises the interesting question as to whether the Psilotales have lost their suspensor in the course of descent or whether that organ never was present in their embryogeny.

EQUISETALES

In *Equisetum* the germinating spore divides by a curved wall into a large and a small cell, the latter growing out as a rhizoid. Polarity is

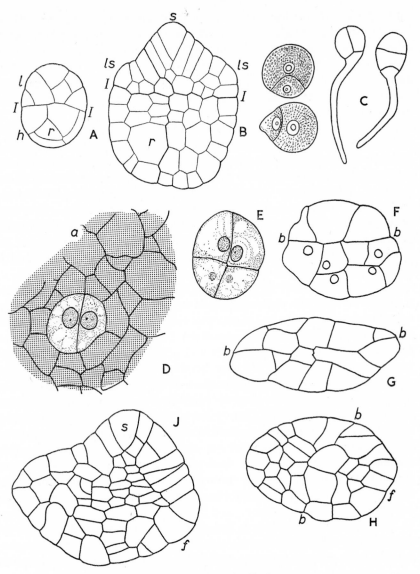

Fig. 21. Embryogeny in *Equisetum*

A, B, *E. arvense*. Young and older embryo, in longitudinal section (after Sadebeck); I–I, first wall of zygote, at right-angles to archegonial neck. C, *E. maximum*.
Germinating spores. D–J, *E. debile*. Development of embryo; the first or basal
wall, *b-b*, may vary in position from horizontal to vertical and the embryo, which may
pass through an almost perfect octant stage, tends to become flattened; the shoot
apex, and perhaps the first root are of epibasal origin, the hypobasal cell giving rise
to the very large foot; *s*, shoot apex; *r*, root; *ls*, first whorl of leaves; *f*, foot; *a*,
archegonial neck. (D, × 240; E–J, × 270). (C–J, after Campbell).

thus established during the initial development of the gametophyte. The larger, distal cell, which contains most of the protoplasmic contents of the spore, now divides either by a transverse or a longitudinal wall, Fig. 21c; other divisions of a somewhat irregular character follow and an apical cell is sometimes distinguishable. The mature gameto-phyte is a lobed thalloid structure. The venter of the archegonium is surrounded by gametophyte tissue.

Although a considerable amount of variation has been observed in the position of the first dividing wall of the zygote in the same and in different species, the embryo is invariably exoscopic. The first wall may be typically transverse, as in *E. arvense* and other species, Fig. 21A; but in *E. debile* it may in some instances be vertical, i.e. aligned in the axis of the archegonium, Fig. 21D (Campbell, 1928). The next two walls are at right-angles to each other and to the first or basal wall, the embryo thus attaining to the octant stage. These octant cells are not invariably of equal size. In *E. maximum* the largest quadrant of the epibasal hemisphere at once becomes the apical cell of the shoot. According to Sadebeck (1878, 1900), the epibasal cell in *E. arvense* and *E. maximum* is so divided by three intersecting walls that a tetrahedral apical cell is formed, Fig. 21A, together with three peripheral cells which give rise to (or correspond to) the three fused leaves of the primary leaf sheath. In the hypobasal segment, comparable divisions give rise to the foot and the first root, the latter with a conspicuous apical cell and an incipient root cap. In other words, Sadebeck relates the primary organogenic developments to an exact system of cellular segmentation. Bower (1935), however, has emphasised that the hypothesis of an exact correspondence between segmentation pattern and organogenesis should not be too closely pressed and suggests that Sadebeck rather tended to interpret embryonic development 'in accordance with the custom of his time,' i.e. his interpretation was based on the assumption of a regular relation between organ formation and the embryonic cleavages; and (to quote Bower) 'as a consequence he drove a direct comparison between the results of his own observa-tions on *E. arvense* and *E. palustre* and the embryology of the leptospor-angiate ferns which was already known.' In Bower's view it should not be assumed, either in *Equisetum* or in other pteridophytes, that the embryology 'will accord consistently with any set segmental scheme.' This, indeed, emerges from Campbell's study of *E. debile*; for although a highly regular octant stage has been observed in this species, Fig. 21E, there is considerable variability in the position of the first wall. The root, moreover, is formed from the epibasal segment, the whole of the hypobasal region becoming an enlarged foot, Fig. 21F–J. At this stage the embryo has a somewhat flattened form. In *E. hiemale*, also, the root arises from the epibasal segment (Jeffrey, 1899). In *E. variegatum* Buchtien (1887) found a flattened embryo like that of *E. debile*. This type of embryonic development is considered to be primitive.

Kasyap (1914) and Campbell (1928) have noted that a gametophyte of *E. debile* may have a large number of developing embryos, some of which become abortive. Now, in *Equisetum*, as in other archegoniate plants, the gametophyte tissue is probably affected by growth substances diffusing from the developing embryo. It may be that those embryos, in which the first and subsequent walls are formed in what may be regarded as anomalous positions, have been affected by secretions from earlier-formed embryos; i.e. the anomalous developments are indicative of changes induced in the zygotic reaction system. With new and refined techniques, the experimental testing of this hypothesis need not be regarded as impossible.

A well defined tetrahedral apical cell becomes functional at an early stage in the embryogeny and, together with its segments, it constitutes the highly regular, conical meristem characteristic of the adult *Equisetum* shoot. At an early embryonic stage also, cells lateral to the apical cell grow out and form the sheath of small scale-like leaves. Usually there are three leaves in this first whorl, but there may be two or four, affording evidence of the absence of an invariable and exact correspondence between cellular segmentation and organ inception. On the growth of the apex, other fused leaf-whorls arise at regular intervals, and the articulate, or jointed, character of the equisetoid stem begins to be apparent. The genetical and other factors which determine the whorled phyllotaxis and the articulated stem character in *Equisetum* are therefore active at an early stage in the ontogenetic development.

The embryological data for *Equisetum* are of particular interest, because not only is it the sole surviving genus of the Articulatae, i.e. the Articulate Pteridophyta or Sphenopsida, but it can be traced back, almost unchanged, to Palaeozoic times, through fossil forms known as *Equisetites* (Hirmer, 1927). In fact, *Equisetum* may be regarded as the living correlative of the smaller and simpler members of a great Palaeozoic group, the Equisetales. That being so, it is worthy of note that the supposedly primitive embryonic organ, the suspensor, is completely absent from *Equisetum*, and that at an early stage in the embryogeny all the characteristic features of land plants can be observed, viz. an axis with leaves and a root.

The major features of the embryogeny in *Equisetum* occur with a considerable degree of regularity and constancy, the differences being of the kind that we might expect to find in related species. Thus, in *E. debile*, the whole of the hypobasal region develops into an enlarged, parenchymatous foot, and the differentiation of the organs of the young sporophyte takes place somewhat later than in *E. arvense*. Such differences may be referred to genetical factors. Comparable differences have been found among the species of *Lycopodium* and *Selaginella* (Chapter VII).

EMBRYOGENESIS IN THE LYCOPODINEAE: LYCOPODIUM AND PHYLLOGLOSSUM

GENERAL ACCOUNT

THE initial stages in the embryogeny of all species of *Lycopodium* and of *Phylloglossum* are closely comparable. The venter of the archegonium is in cellular continuity with the prothallial tissue. At the first division of the zygote a transverse wall is formed and the polarity of the embryo is determined. The cell next the archegonium neck remains undivided, or divides only occasionally, and is known as the *suspensor*; the inner or *embryonic cell* gives rise to the embryo proper. The embryogeny is thus typically endoscopic. The embryonic cell then divides by transverse and longitudinal walls to form two quadrants of cells. The *hypobasal* quadrant, contiguous with the suspensor, gives rise to a parenchymatous foot; the *epibasal* quadrant forms the distal meristem and first root. As the embryo grows it becomes deeply embedded in the tissue of the prothallus. In different species, as the embryogeny progresses, characteristic differences become evident. This is largely due to the fact that different regions of the embryo may undergo a considerable relative enlargement: in some, a conspicuous foot is formed; in others, a modified tuberous shoot known as a 'protocorm' develops; while, in yet others, localised swellings do not occur (Treub, 1884, 1886, 1890; Bruchmann, 1910).

LYCOPODIUM SELAGO AND L. PHLEGMARIA

The prothallus of *L. selago* may be subterranean or superficial and varies from an elongated, cylindrical structure in firm soil to a more compressed and flattened one at or near the soil surface. Its nutrition is mainly mycorrhizic, though some green pigment develops in prothalli exposed to the light. The prothallus of *L. phlegmaria* is an attenuated and repeatedly branched structure and is entirely subterranean and saprophytic.

In these, as in other species, the polarity of the embryo is apparently determined by internal factors and not by gravity or factors in the external environment. In *Lycopodium selago*, Fig. 22A–D, the embryonic cell divides by two vertical walls at right-angles to each other, the ensuing transverse division thus yielding an eight-celled embryo. The further longitudinal, transverse and periclinal divisions take place with considerable regularity as the embryo enlarges, Fig. 22B. With these developments the embryo becomes deeply immersed in the tissue of the prothallus, Fig. 22C. On its further enlargement a gradient of cell size from base to apex becomes apparent. The hypobasal tier forms the parenchymatous foot, while the epibasal tier becomes organised as a distal meristem. An older embryo is typically curved and elongated and eventually bursts through the prothallus in an upward direction, Fig. 22D. At its distal end there is an apical meristem where leaf primordia are formed in a spiral sequence. The cells of the suspensor and foot have now become conspicuously enlarged, presumably as a result of the entry of osmotically active substances from the prothallus. The first root becomes differentiated laterally above the foot, Fig. 22D. An incipient vascular strand of elongated cells now traverses the tissue between the shoot and root apices, but no strand is present in the large-celled foot.

In *L. phlegmaria*, Fig. 22H, the embryonic cell is divided unequally by a somewhat obliquely transverse wall. The larger distal, or epibasal, cell now divides by a vertical wall, and, a little later, so also does the hypobasal cell. The embryo now consists of four quadrants and an octant stage almost certainly follows. The lower tier gives rise to the foot, the upper to the first leaf and the apical meristem. Rather later, the first root is formed at the base of the leaf quadrant.

LYCOPODIUM CLAVATUM AND L. ANNOTINUM

The prothalli are subterranean, saprophytic and massive, and accumulate considerable quantities of storage materials. The initial stages in the embryogeny are as in *L. selago*, Fig. 22E–G, but soon the foot, which develops in close relation to the sources of nutrition in the prothallus, becomes conspicuously enlarged—a result both of cell division and cell distension, Fig. 27C. This development suggests that the path of nutrients from the prothallus is by way of the suspensor and foot to the apex of the embryo and that considerable quantities of

---

Fig. 22. Embryogeny in *Lycopodium*

A–D, *L. selago*. A, Young embryo in l.s. showing the first transverse wall, I–I, which divides the zygote into the shoot segment, s, and the suspensor segment, *su*, the embryo being endoscopic. B, An older embryo in l.s. showing the orderly segmentation pattern, the position of the first, second and fourth walls, the conspicuous suspensor, and the adjacent foot region, *f*. C, An older embryo, with the shoot apex directed inwards, lying within the tissue of the prothallus, *p*; the embryo has elongated and the foot is now evident. D, Well-developed embryo, with shoot apex, first leaf, incipient vascular strand and large foot. E–G, *L. clavatum*. Stages in the embryonic development as seen in l.s.; *e*, the embryonic or distal cell, directed away from the neck of the archegonium (*see also* Fig. 27C). (A, B, × 240; C, D, × 96; E–G, × 150; after Bruchmann). H, *L. phlegmaria*. Embryo in l.s., showing segmentation pattern (× 310, after Treub).

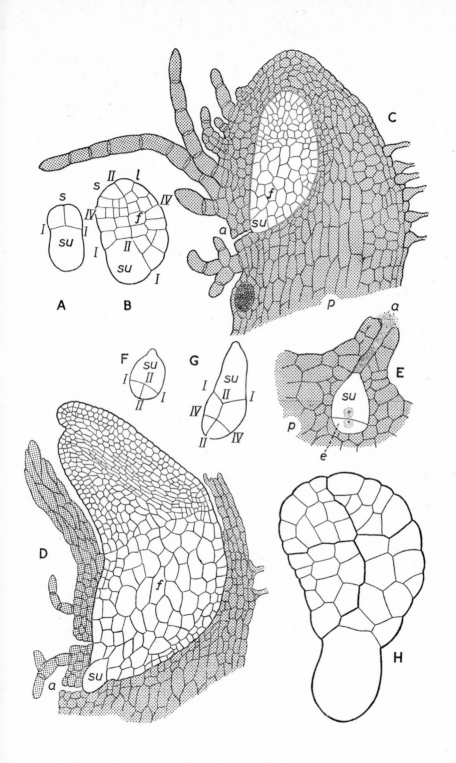

carbohydrate pass into the embryo from the prothallus. In these species, it should also be noted (i) that the growth of the apical region is very slow, (ii) that the first leaf primordia—two opposite leaves—are formed late as compared with *L. selago* and are only of the status of scale leaves, and (iii) that incipient vascular tissue, which is slow to appear behind the apical meristem, is completely absent from the parenchymatous foot. The relative inactivity of the shoot apex suggests that there is a deficiency in some essential nutrient, that it is being inhibited, or that environmental conditions are unfavourable.

LYCOPODIUM CERNUUM AND L. INUNDATUM

In these and related species the prothallus is a massive, cylindrical structure, the lower, obconical, mycorrhizal portion being sunk in the soil, while the upper exposed part bears numerous irregular, green, leaf-like lobes. The initial stages in the embryogeny are as in other lycopods. The cells of the lower or hypobasal tier become enlarged, but a distended foot is not formed. The upper or epibasal tier soon breaks through the prothallial tissue, emerges as a free-growing structure, and enlarges into an undifferentiated tuberous body, which Treub described as the 'protocorm,'[1] Figs. 23, 24. This organ is roughly spherical in form, is composed entirely of parenchyma, and is attached to the soil by rhizoidal hairs. A symbiotic fungus is present. On the upper surface of the protocorm, a conical outgrowth develops into a cylindrical green leaf, or protophyll; this may or may not have a vascular strand. Subsequently, other leaves of similar type are formed; these are described as being indefinite both in number and in position, Figs. 23, 24. Only at a relatively late stage can a shoot apex be definitely recognised: its position is close to the last-formed of the irregular sequence of protophylls. Thereafter, leaves arise round the apex in normal phyllotactic sequence, and a typical leafy shoot is formed.

If, now, we examine these data from the physiological point of view, some interesting points emerge. Treub's illustrations show that carbohydrates are abundantly present in the massive prothallus and he calls attention to the presence of 'grains d'amidon . . . en grande quantité' (Fig. 23D; also Fig. 7D). Again, the histological details indicate that metabolites from the prothallus reach the embryo apex by way of the suspensor and foot. The foot does not show any great amount of cell division but its cells enlarge considerably and starch is deposited in them. It may accordingly be inferred that sugars are passing into the embryo more rapidly than they can be used. When the embryo emerges from the prothallus it forms green protophylls and has therefore

---

[1] It has been suggested that the term should be discarded as being misleading: it is retained here as a handy descriptive term.

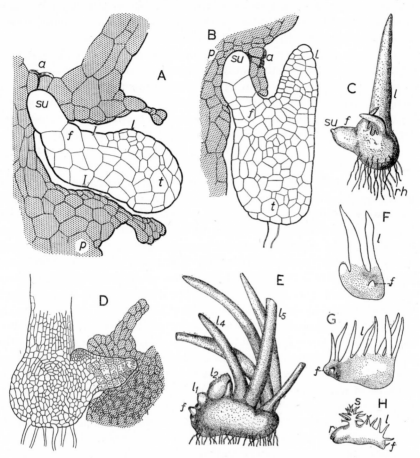

Fig. 23. *Lycopodium cernuum* and *L. laterale*

A–E, *L. cernuum*. A, Young embryo emerging from the prothallus, *p*; *a*, neck of archegonium; *su*, suspensor; *f*, foot; I–I, position of first partition wall; *l*, position of first leaf primordium; *t*, beginning of tuberous development. B, As before, the tuber is now becoming conspicuously developed. C, An older embryo showing the group of primary awl-shaped leaves, the tuber, with rhizoidal development, the suspensor and foot. D, An embryo in l.s. showing the enlarged cells of the foot, containing starch grains. E, An older embryo showing the remarkable tuberous development and the somewhat irregular sequence of leaves. (A, × 200; B, × 140; E, × 23; D, × 27; after Treub). F–H, *L. laterale*. Tuberous embryos, like those of *L. cernuum*, showing linear sequence of leaves (*l*) along the upper surface. H, An older embryo in which the normal leafy shoot has eventually been formed; *r*, first root. (F, × 11; G, × 8; H, × 3; after Holloway).

a second source of carbohydrates. From an early stage these will be passing downwards into the embryonic shoot, which, as we have seen, is also receiving carbohydrates from below. The constituent cells of the shoot region divide, enlarge, and become the repositories of abundant starch grains. In short, the swollen, tuberous structure, which we know as the protocorm, is formed. These developments are attended by a delay in the organisation of a recognisable and actively functioning shoot apex; or it may be that a small apex is present but is masked by the strong parenchymatous development in proximity. That a feeble or attenuated apical meristem, readily escaping observation, is present can scarcely be doubted. A further inference from these data is that, during the early embryogeny of *L. cernuum*, either the supplies of nitrogen-containing metabolites reaching the apex are limiting, or some essential growth factor is lacking. Seasonal factors which restrict apical growth but admit of the accumulation of carbohydrates may also be involved. Some of these are known to be important in promoting tuberous developments in lycopods and some other pteridophytes. The development of storage parenchyma in close proximity to the apical meristem may not only make the latter difficult to recognise: it may also lead to displacements of the protophylls.

That a modified shoot meristem is present throughout the embryogeny, giving rise to leaf primorida (protophylls) on its flanks, is a reasonable assumption. How, otherwise, are we to account for the inception of the protophylls, for the inception of the apex itself, and for the fact that, when a shoot apex at length becomes recognisable, the protophylls to which it gives rise are identical with those previously formed? As a fact, when the apex becomes readily visible, it is found to be in close proximity to the last-formed protophyll, Fig. 24. Inconspicuous, and seemingly inactive, apical meristems are also characteristic of the embryogeny of ferns such as *Angiopteris* (Campbell, 1921); and almost unrecognisable though still functional apical meristems, in contiguity with swollen storage parenchyma, are known in the vasculated prothalli of *Psilotum* (Holloway, 1939), and have been produced experimentally in the rhizome of *Onoclea* (Wardlaw, 1945).

While the shoot apex remains in the inconspicuous and relatively inactive phase, no vascular tissue is differentiated in the protocorm. In the protophylls, each of which is formed from a foliar apex that soon becomes attenuated and parenchymatous, a vascular strand may or may not be differentiated; such strands as are formed end blindly in the upper region of the protocorm. But later, when an actively growing shoot apex is established, an axial or cauline vascular system is differentiated, with which the vascular strands of the new leaves become conjoined peripherally. This close relationship between the activity of

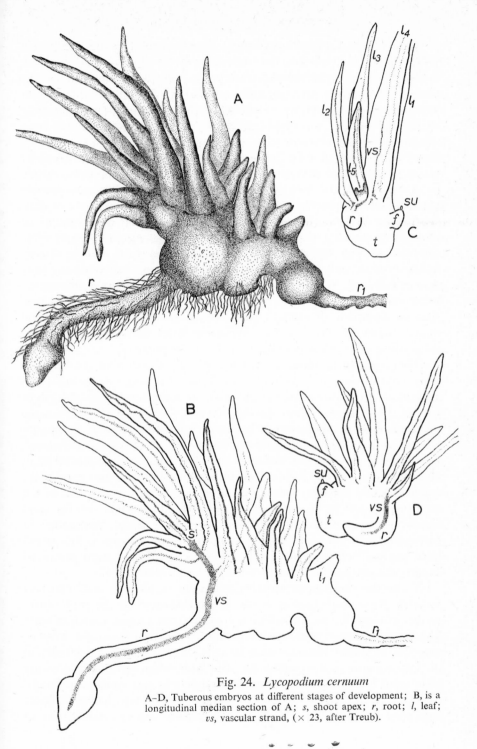

Fig. 24. *Lycopodium cernuum*

A–D, Tuberous embryos at different stages of development; B, is a longitudinal median section of A; *s*, shoot apex; *r*, root; *l*, leaf; *vs*, vascular strand, (× 23, after Treub).

the apex and the inception of vascular tissue is general in pteridophytes (Wardlaw, 1944).

The conclusion of early investigators that the protocorm of *L. cernuum* is a shoot that has been considerably modified during its embryonic phase is thus confirmed. Since the formation of a protocorm is a regular and characteristic feature of *L. cernuum* and other species, and since this development cannot be attributed solely to seasonal conditions, genetical factors must be involved. As to the precise nature of this genic action we have no information, but from other sources we know that protein synthesis is gene-controlled and that it may be delayed, impeded, or 'blocked' under environmental conditions that impede or delay the action of particular genes. If we apply these conceptions to what we know of the embryogeny of *L. cernuum*, it could be inferred that the genes which determine protein synthesis at the shoot apex are initially ineffective. But after the embryo has been growing for some time, and possibly in relation to the photosynthetic activity of its several protophylls, certain metabolites essential for apical growth, but hitherto limiting, become available and normal shoot growth ensues. In this interpretation, the protocorm is a morphological expression of factors in the hereditary constitution, but whether or not it should be regarded as a phyletically 'primitive' organ is debatable. It could, in fact, be argued that the protocorm is a 'derivative,' though a retrograde (but non-lethal), result of genic mutation or chromosome change. Whether or not the tuberous development is biologically advantageous, as in the older view, might well be the subject of further investigation. The view that these parenchymatous swellings in lycopod embryos are biological adaptations should, in the writer's view, be received with caution, though it may well be that further investigation will show that it is not without justification. In this connection, mention should be made of the fact that Wetmore and Morel (1951) have successfully grown the prothalli and young sporophytes of *L. cernuum* aseptically by the methods of tissue culture. This discovery should make possible a whole series of new and interesting experimental investigations.

Lycopodium laterale. The prothallus and embryogeny of *L. laterale* are of the *L. cernuum* type with the protocormous development greatly increased, Fig. 23. In the early stages, a starchy tuberous protocorm, surmounted by one or two protophylls, is formed, a conspicuous foot being also present (Holloway, 1909). According to Holloway (1915), the protocorm and protophylls (in which stomata occur) are of a vivid green colour. The third protophyll arises in a lateral position and, when fully grown, has a swollen base which is distinct from the original protocorm though it is conjoined with it. The fourth protophyll, which arises alongside the third and forms a pair with it, also develops a swollen base. Holloway noted that in no case 'was the prothallus found attached to a young plant which has more than two original protophylls.' From this observation it can be inferred (i) that the enlargement of the protocorm is the result of photosynthetic activity in the protophylls, and (ii) that, from an early stage, the sporophyte must depend for mineral and nitrogenous nutrients on its basal rhizoids. The 'protocormous rhizome' continues to elongate laterally in relation to the further development of protophylls which may be 8–12 in number, Fig. 23. The protophylls arise in pairs along the dorsal side of the rhizome, i.e. there is a certain regularity in the positions in which they are formed. This suggests that an apical meristem is present, even though it may be feeble and inconspicuous. Each protophyll has a vascular strand which ends blindly in the dorsal parenchyma of the protocorm. This organ, in fact, consists of parenchyma throughout. Eventually the shoot apex becomes an actively growing and readily distinguishable region. Its position and activity are indicated by (i) the aggregation of several protophylls, (ii) the differentiation of a cauline vascular strand immediately below it, (iii) the development of the first root on the distal (or growing) end of the protocorm, i.e. the side remote from the foot, and (iv) by the differentiation of vascular tissue between shoot and root. Soon after this stage has been reached, the embryo grows into a recognisable plantling of *L. laterale*, the elongating shoot axis bearing leaves which are 'in no wise different from the protophylls.' This statement gives further support to the view that the protophylls of the protocorm are formed in relation to a shoot apex.

The comparative inactivity of the shoot apex in the early embryogeny of *L. laterale*, as in *L. cernuum*, is associated with a phase of metabolism in which carbohydrate synthesis is predominant. The protophylls, however, yield evidence of some apical growth; they elongate into needle-like structures and each has a vascular strand. Why the apex of a leaf primordium should show active growth while the shoot apex remains relatively inactive is a phenomenon for which no adequate explanation has so far been advanced.

A comparison of *L. cernuum* with *L. laterale* shows that although the former typically develops a small group of protophylls on the top of the protocorm, some lateral development may also be observed. *L. ramulosum* resembles *L. laterale*, but, in addition, may develop swollen bulbils on the protocorm (Holloway, 1915).

In some other species of *Lycopodium* the foot may be partly penetrated by vascular tissue. *L. complanatum* (Wigglesworth, 1907) and *L. volubile* (Holloway, 1915) may show such developments. This may be due to a greater diffusion from the apical meristem of the substance (or substances) which determines the inception of vascular tissue. Holloway examined plantlings of different species in some detail and noted that the development of vascular tissue in the foot of the young plant varies in extent in different individuals of the same species. He thought that this is possibly related to the size of the parent prothallus.

PHYLLOGLOSSUM DRUMMONDII

The embryonic development in this species has been briefly described by Thomas (1901) and Sampson (1916). The prothallus and embryo are generally like those in *Lycopodium cernuum*. The embryo is attached laterally, the first organ to emerge being the first leaf which is green and photosynthetic. A tuberous swelling is soon formed below this leaf. The first root may or may not have developed at this stage. Bower (1935) has shown how, in its annual growth, the tuberous adult plant closely follows the embryonic development.

DISCUSSION

The Suspensor. Much importance has been attached to the presence of a suspensor in pteridophytes. It has been regarded as a primitive feature that has been 'retained' in some modern survivors. Jeffrey suggested that it is useful in pushing the developing embryo deeper down into the prothallial tissue (Campbell, 1911). Here we may note that the suspensor enlarges like the adjacent parenchymatous cells of the foot. The formation of a suspensor shows that the physiological conditions at the outer or neck end of the zygote are very different from those at its inner end. Whether the distinctive developments of the suspensor and the embryonic cell are due to a gene-controlled differentiation in the zygote, to metabolic gradients in the prothallus, to gradients of gaseous concentration, or to some residual effect of fertilisation, is not known. Certainly there would appear to be some quite fundamental difference between those pteridophytes with the embryonic cell adjacent to the neck of the archegonium, as in *Psilotum*, and those in which it is directed inwards, as in *Lycopodium*. But, as already mentioned (p. 25), it may be that a relatively small difference in the reaction system may determine whether the embryogeny is exoscopic or endoscopic (*see also* p. 328). (An endoscopic embryogeny is not always associated with the presence of a suspensor. In the Marattiaceae, where the archegonium points downwards, the embryogeny is endoscopic whether a suspensor is present or not: *see* Chapter IX.)

The Foot and the Protocorm. Treub regarded the protocorm as a primitive organ—an ancestral feature which has been retained in some contemporary species. He even held that it might have been of general occurrence in the ancestry of vascular plants. This view did not receive the general approval of Treub's contemporaries and is now little more than an interesting idea. To Bower (1907, 1935), the protocorm was not so much a primitive organ as an 'opportunist growth'; and even though it may be of ecological importance in establishing the young sporophyte of certain species, it should not be regarded as a phylogenetic feature in the Lycopodiaceae, still less in vascular plants as a whole. Browne (1913), impressed by the great stem development in Palaeozoic lycopods, suggested that the protocorm might be a modified and reduced stem. The adaptive value of the embryonic swellings in lycopods has been freely invoked.

Bower (1922, 1935) has pointed out that several species of *Lycopodium*, in different ways and in different degrees, tend to a 'parenchymatisation' during their embryonic development. *L. selago* has a comparatively small foot and an embryonic growth that might be described as exemplifying a 'normal' axial development; in *L. phlegmaria*, the parenchymatous foot is more conspicuous; in *L. clavatum* and *L. annotinum* there is a considerably enlarged parenchymatous foot; while in *L. cernuum* and *L. laterale* a parenchymatous foot and a greatly enlarged tuberous shoot or protocorm are formed.

Bower (1935) has related the differences between the *selago* and *clavatum* types of embryo to the prothalli which bear them. The prothallus of *L. selago* may develop at or near the surface, it may be partially green and autotrophic and partially mycorrhizic, and the nursing period of the embryo may be relatively brief. In *L. clavatum*, on the other hand, the prothallus is a large, cakelike, underground structure, depending entirely on mycorrhizal nutrition. The formation of a large swollen foot has been described by Bower as an 'intra-prothallial haustorium,' and as 'an opportunist growth.' These details are considered by him to accord with the view that 'the embryo is long dependent for nourishment entirely upon the large prothallus; hence its swollen haustorial foot, which is developed most strongly in the direction of the largest nutritive supply.'

Position and Nutrition of the Embryo. All lycopod embryos are initially nourished by the prothallus. In some species the embryo may be completely immersed in the prothallial tissue for a considerable time. Bower (1908, 1922, 1935) has given some attention to relevant nutritional aspects. In his view the endoscopic embryogeny of *Lycopodium*, with its consequential deep immersion of the embryo in the prothallial tissue, has 'doubtless an immediate advantage in point of nutrition of the embryo in its earliest stage. *But the ultimate end is the establishment of a young plant with an upward-growing shoot suitable for self-nutrition. The orientation of the archegonium will then be a*

factor affecting the further behaviour of the embryo.' (1935, p. 528). He further suggests that the suspensor, a primitive organ which has been 'retained' in this genus, as also in *Selaginella*, is a highly inconvenient feature except where the archegonium points downwards, and that its presence has necessitated marked curvatures in the embryo before an upright shoot can be established. 'It can hardly be assumed that such shifts as these should have been attained in the course of opportunist evolution, unless there be some initial disability. . . .'
. . . 'In more than one evolutionary line the simplified form of the embryo may be explained by its having broken loose from the tie of the suspensor.' As against these views, advanced chiefly in relation to the embryos of *Lycopodium* and *Selaginella*, it may be noted that in different Marattiaceae, all with endoscopic embryos, the suspensor, which may or may not be present, would appear to have very little effect on the embryogeny (*see* Chapter IX).

The quotations given above reflect a typical approach from the standpoint of the comparative morphologist. Here our chief interest is in the processes that may be involved in the nutrition of the young embryo. Where, as in *Psilotum*, *Tmesipteris* and *Equisetum*, the embryogeny is exoscopic, we appear to be on familiar ground—though it is, as a fact, practically unexplored. The hypobasal cell, which remains in contact with the prothallial tissue, behaves as perhaps might be expected: it becomes the absorbing region of the embryo, the nutrients taken up by it being passed on to the epibasal region which becomes the actively meristematic shoot apex, i.e. as in a fully organised shoot, the distal region of the embryo depends on nutrients passing up from below. We should not, indeed, expect the epibasal cell, which lies in contiguity with the archegonial neck and may soon emerge from the prothallus, to be the absorptive region of the young embryo. All this seems to be in conformity with our general knowledge of axial growth. Nevertheless, it is doubtful if such reasoning, based on a consideration of the anatomical data, goes to the root of the matter; for in endoscopic species, such as *Lycopodium*, the suspensor and the nutrient-absorbing foot are in contiguity with the archegonium neck and the growing embryo becomes deeply embedded in the fleshy tissue of the prothallus. In short, the uptake of nutrients by the embryo is not so simple and direct as it at first appears. Thus we may ask: Do these embedded endoscopic embryos absorb nutrients over their entire surface, or is the uptake confined to the foot? While the embryo is still very small, it may well be that nutrients are absorbed over the whole of the embryonic surface; but, as it enlarges, the indications are that the foot is the main absorptive region. Certainly, from an early stage, there is a marked difference in the development of the basal cells as compared with those at the apical or distal end. Thus the cells of the foot soon become considerably distended; they may extend what appear to be suctorial processes into the tissue of the prothallus; they may contain deposits of starch grains; and they show a gradient of size from the proximal to the distal region. Collectively, these observations suggest that, from a very early stage in the embryogeny, the relation of the distal to the basal region of the embryonic axis is essentially the same as that between the distal and proximal regions in a normal adult shoot, i.e. the former remains meristematic and draws upon the latter for its nutrients. A growing body of experimental evidence supports the view that the apex of a normal shoot is a self-determining, morphogenetic region; the data given above indicate that this relationship is probably established at a very early stage in the embryogeny.

On further growth the apex of the endoscopic embryo bursts out of the prothallus, but the embryo may continue for some considerable time to draw upon the prothallus for its nutrition. At this stage there is no longer any question of the nutrients being absorbed over the whole embryonic surface: they must be taken up by way of the foot region; and in this we probably see what is no more than the continuation of a system established at a much earlier stage.

In considering the growth of embryos in species of *Lycopodium* two conditions may be envisaged: (i) the embryo, under favourable environmental conditions, receives a normal, balanced nutrition; i.e. the supply of nutrients, including growth-regulating substances, and the $\frac{C}{N}$ ratio, are such as to permit of continuous meristematic activity at the shoot apex, and the further growth and differentiation of tissues and organis below the apex, so that an elongating leafy shoot is produced; (ii) the embryo does not receive a balanced nutrition and/or environmental conditions may be unfavourable. In the second case it is conceivable that a high $\frac{C}{N}$ ratio, an inadequate supply of some essential growth-regulating substance, or some unfavourable environmental condition, might modify the character of the growth in different regions of the embryo. The early distension of meristematic tissue in the foot and shoot regions of *L. clavatum* and *L. cernuum* respectively is indicative of abundant supplies of carbohydrate to the young embryo; and this, as we have seen, goes hand-in-hand with a delay in the organisation of a 'normal' apical meristem and the formation of an elongating leafy shoot.

These characteristic parenchymatous developments are exemplified by such subterranean species as *L. clavatum, L. volubile, L. scariosum,*

L. densum and *L. billardieri*, in which the foot is greatly distended, and by the protocormous species *L. cernuum*, *L. laterale*, and *L. ramulosum*, which develop at the soil surface, and which, as well as being supplied with carbohydrate from substantial prothalli, are themselves green and photosynthetically active from an early stage. That the carbohydrate supply in the latter three species far exceeds growth requirements is shown by the development of a conspicuous, starch-filled, tuberous protocorm. With this development goes a suppression or delay in the activity of the shoot apex. The relation of these developments to light and other factors would be an investigation of considerable interest and importance. These observations on carbohydrate metabolism in the embryogeny can be extended to characters seen in the adult plant. Thus, some species of *Lycopodium* have a large sappy cortex with abundant starch, whereas others have little starch but a conspicuous development of fibrous tissue. Both environmental and genetical factors are involved. On the evidence thus far available, those species with a protocorm are also conspicuous for starch deposition in the adult state.

Evolutionary Relationships. In the light of the data now presented, can it be said with any assurance that one type of embryogeny, e.g. that of *L. selago*, is more primitive than another, e.g. that of *L. clavatum* or *L. cernuum*? As we have seen, there are distinct differences and these can be ascribed to factors in the genetic constitution and in the environment. But as to the relative evolutionary status of one type as compared with another, it seems almost impossible to arrive at a definite conclusion. If, for the sake of argument, we assume that *L. selago* is a central, primitive type, then the condition which we see in *L. clavatum* or *L. cernuum* could be due to mutation or chromosomal change, possibly affecting protein metabolism. In this case, these species would be 'derivative' but not necessarily upgrade forms. In a cytological investigation of the five British species of *Lycopodium*, Manton (1950) has reached the conclusion that these are so very unlike cytologically that they have probably been taxonomically widely divergent for a very long period of time; and *L. selago*, so often considered to be a central and primitive type, is found, on the cytological evidence, to be a hybrid of very high chromosome number.

Chapter VIII

EMBRYOGENESIS IN THE LYCOPODINEAE: SELAGINELLA AND ISOETES

SELAGINELLA

SELAGINELLA is a large, coherent and widely distributed genus of ancient origin, having evident affinity with the fossil *Selaginellites*. The species, which number upwards of 600, show a considerable range in size, symmetry and morphology, e.g. from the small, radially symmetrical, temperate *S. spinulosa*, to the large, climbing, dorsiventral, tropical *S. Willdenovii*. Thus far there is little information on the interrelationships of the species as revealed by genetical or cytological studies. Manton (1950) has shown that the three European species, *S. spinulosa*, *S. helvetica* and *S. denticulata*, have low chromosome numbers, with $n=9$. In *Isoetes hystrix*, $n=10$. According to Manton: 'The pteridophytes seem almost certainly to have possessed in the past, and to have retained in these two genera, the simple nuclear state that the modern Flowering Plants still for the most part display.' These low numbers in plants of ancient stock are perhaps surprising, the more so in that these genera show what is generally accepted as the considerable advance to the heterosporous condition.

THE EMBRYONIC ENVIRONMENT

In *Selaginella* the embryo is nourished by the prothallus or gametophyte formed within the large megaspore while the latter is still inside the sporangium. In this respect, *Selaginella* resembles some of the primitive seed plants. There are indications that carbohydrates accumulate considerably more rapidly than proteins in the megaspore, and this may affect the subsequent embryonic development. In the young megaspore of *S. helvetica*, according to Fitting (1900), the megaspore walls outgrow the cytoplasm and the cytoplasmic film becomes rounded off as a spherical vesicle attached to the endospore wall. On further development this vesicle begins to increase in size, many free nuclear divisions take place, and the cytoplasm again makes contact with the endospore membrane. Many of the nuclei now move towards the apical end of the megaspore and active growth of the cytoplasmic layer ensues. Thereafter the synthesis of protoplasm takes place rapidly and the central vacuole of the spore disappears. Cell formation, i.e. the formation of gametophyte tissue, begins at the apical end and progresses towards the basal end. There is differential development as between the cells at the apex and base of the megaspore, the former being small and dense, whereas the latter are large and irregular. These large cells, which are described as being filled with oil and albuminous granules, provide the nutrients on which the young embryo will depend until it emerges from the prothallus and becomes a rooted, green, autotrophic plant.

The first archegonium, as in *S. kraussiana*, is formed from one of the small distal cells about the time the megaspore is shed; and others are formed later. The archegonial neck, of four cells in cross section, is characteristically short, with but two cell tiers and a single neck-canal cell. Numerous rhizoids, which develop at the apical region, may have a nutritive function (Campbell, 1940). The retention of the megaspore within the sporangium, the full development of the gametophyte therein, and even the fertilisation of the ovum prior to shedding, have been indicated by Lyon (1904) for *S. apus* and *S. rupestris*. These developments are of interest because of their analogy with seed plants.

THE OVUM AND YOUNG EMBRYO

The available illustrations do not disclose any asymmetry or protoplasmic differentiation in the ovum or zygote. Nevertheless, the embryogeny is invariably endoscopic and polarity is determined from the outset. As in *Lycopodium*, a suspensor is typically present. The very considerable differences in the size and protoplasmic contents of the embryonic cell and the suspensor indicate that the metabolism at the two poles is very different indeed, Figs. 25, 26, 28. The outermost segment of the two-celled embryo, i.e. the suspensor, may enlarge but usually undergoes little further development; the innermost or embryonic cell gives rise to the body of the embryo. The growing embryo becomes more or less deeply embedded in the prothallial tissue, but eventually it curves upwards and emerges as a leaf-bearing shoot. As the megaspore lies on its side, the young embryo actually grows in a horizontal position until it begins to respond to the stimulus of gravity. In some species it will be convenient to refer to the two-celled embryo as consisting of the embryonic cell and the basal cell.

SELAGINELLA SPINULOSA

In this temperate species, which is characterised by radial symmetry, a simple stele, and a '*Selago*-condition' in the distribution of its sporangia, botanists have recognised a phylogenetically primitive member of the genus. The *suspensor* and *embryonic cell* are determined by the first transverse division of the zygote which soon elongates in the axis of the archegonium, Fig. 25A–C. The suspensor undergoes vacuolation and further elongation, with only an occasional transverse

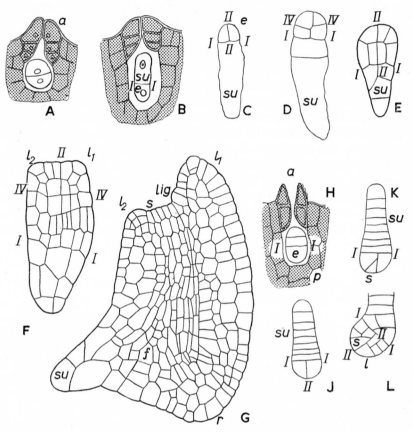

Fig. 25. Embryogeny in *Selaginella*

A–G, *Selaginella spinulosa*. A, Longitudinal section of archegonium, *a*, showing newly divided zygote. B, The same, slightly older: the embryo has lengthened; the outermost cell, *su*, will become the suspensor, the innermost or embryonic cell, *e*, will give rise to the rest of the embryo. C–F, Stages in the development of the embryo, showing the very considerable enlargement of the suspensor, the division of the embryonic cell into quadrants and octants, the positions of the successive walls being shown, I–I, II–II, etc. G, A well-developed embryo showing the shoot apex, *s*, the first leaf, l_1, and its ligule, *lig*, the second leaf, l_2, the first root or rhizophore, *r*, the incipient vascular strand, the foot, *f*, and the suspensor, *su*. H–L, *Selaginella denticulata*. The embryo undergoes considerable elongation and repeated divisions by transverse walls before the distal embryonic cell divides longitudinally. A shoot apical cell, *s*, results from an oblique cleavage of a distal cell. (All × 350; after Bruchmann.)

division, whereas the distal cell grows and divides to form the main body of the embryo (Bruchmann, 1897). The embryonic cell first divides by two vertical walls at right-angles to each other, and then by a transverse wall. A two-tiered quadrant stage is thus constituted, Fig. 25c, D. The more distal or epibasal tier on further development gives rise to the shoot apex and first leaves, and the lower or hypobasal tier to the hypocotyl and first root. Meanwhile, the suspensor may have divided by a second transverse wall and by an obliquely transverse wall. On further growth, the epibasal region is divided by periclinal walls, except for the most centrally placed, distal cells. It can already be seen that these are the nacent apical cells of the developing axis, Fig. 25F. Further cell divisions take place in all three planes in both the epibasal and hypobasal regions and the short embryo begins to curve upwards and to form its organs and differentiate its tissues. A distal group of superficial prism-shaped, embryonic cells constitutes an apical meristem, on the flank of which the first leaf, with its ligule, is formed. A second leaf is later formed approximately opposite to the first, Fig. 25G. Meanwhile the active growth in the hypobasal region has resulted in the elongation and curvature of the embryo which is now deeply embedded in the prothallial tissue. The central cells of the hypocotyl, from below the apical meristem down to a lateral and basal outgrowth which can be recognised as the first root (rhizophore), have become elongated and narrow and constitute the primary vascular strand or stele. Thus, from the outset, the stele is of axial and not of foliar origin.

According to Bruchmann, the first leaf may not be formed for some time: it may still be absent even when a considerable axis, curved relative to the suspensor, has already been formed. The formation of the second leaf may be still further delayed; in some specimens it only appears after the embryo has emerged from the prothallus. However, two nearly opposite but unequal leaves can eventually be seen at the shoot apex; these leaves which become green and of approximately equal size are sometimes described as cotyledons. The apical meristem of the young shoot consists of a number of equal cells, i.e. there is no single conspicuous apical initial. Bruchmann states that no large foot is formed in S. spinulosa, nor in S. apus, as in the well-known S. martensii. In those species in which a foot is present it usually occupies a position basal to the hypocotyl and in continuity with the narrow suspensor.

SELAGINELLA DENTICULATA; S. MARTENSII; AND OTHER SPECIES

In these species the zygote also elongates in the axis of the archegonium and divides by a transverse wall. The next conspicuous development consists in the considerable elongation of the suspensor which, in species such as S. denticulata, is divided by many transverse walls, Fig. 25H–L. Meanwhile the hemispherical embryonic cell has enlarged and undergone divisions, leading to the inception of the shoot apical cell and that of the first leaf. At this stage the young embryo is a filamentous structure which is being thrust into the nutritive prothallial tissue by the suspensor. In the ensuing development, the embryo

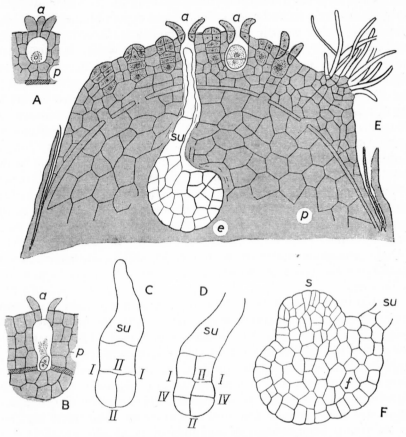

Fig. 26. Embryogeny in *Selaginella poulteri*

A, Archegonium, *a*, with ovum. B, Englarged venter with young embryo showing first transverse wall. C, D, The segmentation of the enlarging embryo. E, The elongated embryo, *e*, becomes deeply embedded in the gametophyte but begins to curve round. F, An early stage in the organisation of the embryo proper; *s*, the apical cell of the shoot; *f*, the greatly enlarged foot; *su*, suspensor; (all × 225; after Bruchmann).

becomes a short, massive, axial body, and begins to grow more rapidly on the lower side and therefore to curve within the prothallus. In due course this process results in the emergence of the embryo as an upwardly directed shoot. Meanwhile, the morphologically basal region of the convex side has enlarged into a large suctorial foot, the extent of this development varying from species to species (*see* below).

In *S. denticulata* (Bruchmann, 1912) the embryonic cell divides first by a vertical wall into two approximately equal cells. One of these cells now divides by an oblique wall, the single and persistent apical cell of the embryonic shoot being thus formed, Fig. 25H–L. This apical cell, in shape an inverted tetrahedron, undergoes segmentations which may be somewhat less regular than those observed in similar apical cells. The other segment of the embryonic cell gives rise to the first leaf; the second leaf is formed from the first segment of the shoot apical cell. Meanwhile, the suspensor shows some irregularity in its development. On the side opposite to the shoot apex it divides into several actively enlarging cells, with the result that the embryonic axis is tilted at right-angles to the suspensor, Fig. 25. Although the young plantling of *Selaginella* is sometimes described as being 'dicotyledonous', it will be realised that this is not quite exact, i.e. in the sense that the term is applied to flowering plants. These first leaves do not enlarge as a result of apical growth but rather from the activity of marginal initial cells. In *S. denticulata*, the large foot region is formed from the cells of the suspensor adjacent to the hypocotyl. In contiguity with the latter, and from the upper part of the foot, an outgrowth develops: this is the primary rhizophore from which the first roots are later formed. While these several organogenic activities are taking place, a central strand of elongated cells, having its inception below the shoot apex and traversing the hypocotyl to the primary rhizophore, is differentiated; this is the incipient vascular system, or stele, of the developing axis. In each of the leaves a small vascular strand is also differentiated and becomes conjoined with the axial stele. The embryonic development in *S. rubricaulis* is essentially similar.

The formation and differentiation of the embryonic parts in any particular species apparently takes place with a considerable degree of regularity. In *S. denticulata*, for example, the suspensor, foot and rhizophore originate from the basal segment of the two-celled embryo. But, in other species, there may be different relationships between the initial segmentation and the subsequent formation of organs. These differences between species are of the kind that might be expected if there is a specific genic control of the distribution of growth. They afford parallelisms with the precise embryonic segmentation patterns found in many flowering plants. Thus, in *S. martensii*, the basal cell of the two-celled embryo gives rise to the suspensor only, the large foot and all the other organs being formed from the distal embryonic cell, Fig. 27A; but in *S. galeottei* (*see* below), the shoot apex and first two leaves can be referred to the embryonic cell, while the hypocotyl, foot, rhizophore and suspensor all originate from the basal cell, Fig. 28E–K (*see* Bruchmann, 1909, 1912, 1913; Goebel, 1918; Campbell, 1940).

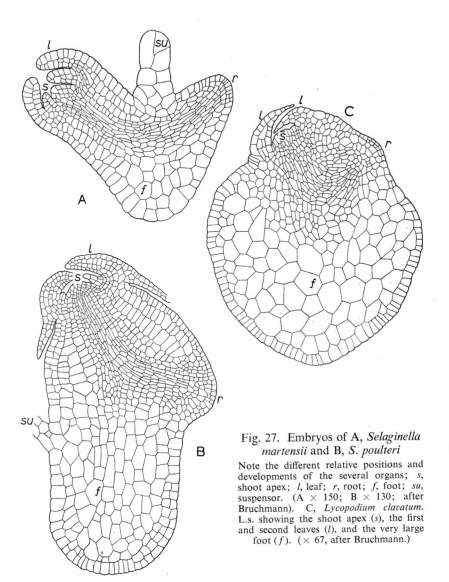

Fig. 27. Embryos of A, *Selaginella
martensii* and B, *S. poulteri*

Note the different relative positions and
developments of the several organs; *s*,
shoot apex; *l*, leaf; *r*, root; *f*, foot; *su*,
suspensor. (A × 150; B × 130; after
Bruchmann). C, *Lycopodium clavatum*.
L.s. showing the shoot apex (*s*), the first
and second leaves (*l*), and the very large
foot (*f*). (× 67, after Bruchmann.)

SELAGINELLA KRAUSSIANA, S. POULTERI, S. GALEOTTEI AND S. RUBRICAULIS

In these species, (Bruchmann, 1912, 1913) the embryogeny shows some curious and interesting developments which are rather different from those described above.

In *S. kraussiana*, Fig. 28A–D, the protoplast of the zygote contracts and a new wall is formed round it. It then divides by a transverse wall. Meanwhile the archegonial cavity grows rapidly and penetrates deeply into the prothallus as an elongated tube-like structure (*Embryoschlauch*), at the inner extremity of which lies the two-celled embryo, Fig. 28A, B. No evident suspensor is formed, its function, as it were, being taken over by the tubular development. In *S. galeottei*, Fig. 28E–K, there is a somewhat similar development, but in this species the archegonial tube not only penetrates deeply into the prothallial tissue, becoming sinuously curved by the resistance offered to its passage, but it brings about an active disintegration and digestion of the prothallial tissue, Fig. 28G. In this species a suspensor is formed, the pear-shaped zygote dividing by a longitudinal and then by a transverse wall, Fig. 28E–J. In *S. poulteri*, Fig. 26, the embryo is also thrust deeply into the prothallus, but this is due to a very elongated though infrequently septate suspensor, Fig. 26E. *S. rubricaulis* is generally like *S. galeottei*, the developing embryo showing some departure from exact symmetry in its several cell divisions, Fig. 28L. These several species may all develop a more or less considerable foot.

Bower (1935) has pointed to the variable development of the foot and to the different positions occupied by the first rhizophore in different species, Figs. 25G, 27A, B; 28L. The rhizophore may be formed below the suspensor but on the same side and opposite the foot as in *S. denticulata*; or opposite the suspensor and above the foot as in *S. poulteri*; or above the suspensor and foot as in *S. galeottei*. If we regard the suspensor as of transitory importance only, and the foot as a variable and 'opportunist' growth, the rhizophore is then seen to occupy a normal basal and lateral position relative to the shoot.

THE CONSTITUTION OF THE APICAL MERISTEM

Studies of the embryogeny in different species of *Selaginella*, together with morphological investigation of their development to the adult state, have been productive of interesting facts concerning the histological constitution of the apical meristem (Schuepp, 1926; Wardlaw, 1952). In some species the apical meristems of both shoot and rhizophore may have a definite apical cell, surrounded by its segments which consist of elongated prism-shaped cells; in other species a

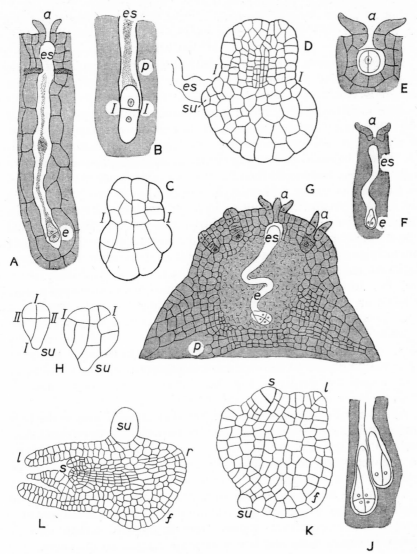

Fig. 28. Embryogeny in *Selaginella*

A–D, *S. kraussiana*. A, B, Archegonium, *a*, which has elongated into an embryo-tube (*Embryoschlauch*, *es*) containing the embryo, *e*, at its base; *I–I*, the first partition wall of the zygote. C, D, Older embryos in l.s. E–K, *S. galeottei*. The embryo develops deep within the gametophyte tissue at the base of an elongated embryo-tube. The suspensor, *su*, is greatly reduced in this species, e.g. as in K. E, The first wall is vertical. J, Two embryos side by side. L, *S. rubricaulis*. (A–D, × 225; E, × 370; H–K, × 230; G, F, L, × 150; after Bruchmann).

group of apical initials is present. During the embryonic development of *S. poulteri* the shoot apex has a three-sided (i.e. tetrahedral) apical cell; but as the apex enlarges a gradual transformation takes place so that several apical initials are present in older and stouter branches (Bruchmann, 1909). Bruchmann (1909, 1910) also found that the apical meristem in *S. lyallii* and *S. preissiana* consists of a group of similar meristematic cells, as in *Lycopodium*. In *S. wallichii*, Strasburger (1872) found that there were two conspicuous apical initial cells; similar observations have been recorded by Williams (1931) for *S. grandis*. Wand (1914) has stated that in different species apical growth may proceed from a three- or four-sided apical cell, from a divided apical cell, or from a group of similar initial cells. This last condition is characteristic of the primitive, radially symmetrical species *S. spinulosa* and is apparent at a very early stage in the embryogeny. In dorsiventral species on the other hand, a single apical cell is established as a distinctive feature at a very early stage in the embryogeny, e.g. *S. denticulata*, Fig. 25K.

The distinctive histological organisation of the shoot apex in any particular species is ultimately referable to its genetic constitution. While we are not yet able to explain how particular genes, or gene-groups, bring about this organisation, we may note that, as in certain other features of the embryogeny, the genic effect can be detected at a very early stage in the ontogenetic development.

ISOETES

At the outset it should be noted that this account of the embryogeny in *Isoetes*, is in two parts: in the first part use has been made of the descriptions given in standard works, e.g. those of Campbell and Bower; in the second the account by La Motte, based on experimental investigations, has been followed.

In *Isoetes* the megaspore is filled with a uniform prothallial tissue, the first archegonium being formed at the point of convergence of the apical fissures, i.e. it is closely comparable with *Selaginella*. The ovum is conspicuous and practically fills the venter, Fig. 29A. After fertilisation, the first partition wall is obliquely transverse to the axis of the archegonium, Fig. 29B; no suspensor is formed and the embryo-geny is exoscopic (*but see* below). The two segments of the divided zygote may be referred to as the epibasal and hypobasal cells. They have been likened to the two tiers seen in the embryogeny of some species of *Selaginella* (Bower, 1935). The next two divisions are at right angles to the first wall and to each other and yield an octant stage. These walls are somewhat irregular and not always clearly defined in *Isoetes*, Fig. 29C. On further growth and cell division the hypobasal tier gives rise to the foot only, while the epibasal tier forms the first leaf and root and, after some delay, the shoot apex, Fig. 29D. In the further development from the octant stage, the embryo consists of an ovoid mass of similar cells. It then widens out in the plane of the basal wall: one half of the epibasal region gives rise to the first leaf and the other, opposite half to the first root, Fig. 29D. A large cell at the base of the first leaf is recognised as the primordium of the ligule. The differentiation of the ligule is followed by the formation of a semi-circular ridge at the base of the root; this grows rapidly as a sheathing organ or velum and encloses the base of the leaf and its ligule. In the narrow cleft between the bases of the velum and first leaf there is an inconspicuous group of cells. These, in fact, are meristematic cells of the small and as yet unorganised shoot apex, of which, according to Campbell (1918), there is no indication at earlier stages in the embryogeny. Even for some time after, the shoot apex does not show any conspicuous organisation: there is general agreement among investigators (Hegelmaier, 1872, 1874: Farmer, 1891; Lang, 1915) that, as in *Lycopodium* and *Selaginella spinulosa*, no single initial cell can be observed at the apex. Campbell (1918) regards the first leaf ('cotyledon') with its ligule as the first organogenic development, this being followed by the inception of the first root opposite to it. Between these two organs, in a slight depression, is the locus of the shoot apex, which is still very small, feebly developed and quite unorganised. The second leaf is formed facing the first, with the inconspicuous shoot apex lying between. The subsequently formed leaves arise in a spiral sequence round the apex.

Campbell has noted that while the axes of the first leaf and first root may, or may not, coincide, their vascular strands are continuous. The foot is poorly developed in the young embryo, but becomes quite conspicuous later on, Fig. 29D, gradually filling the megaspore cavity. At this stage the prothallial tissue has virtually disappeared.

Many, probably most, investigators have regarded *Isoetes* as a ligulate lycopod, admittedly presenting many unusual features but, on the concensus of evidence, being such as to be included in the Lycopodineae and to be brought into a general, if not close, relationship with *Selaginella*. This, for example, is the view taken by Bower. But Campbell (1940), while agreeing that the ligulate leaf, the presence of microspores and megaspores, and the nature of the prothallus admit of fairly close comparisons being made between *Isoetes* and *Selaginella*, considers that *Isoetes* differs so much from other pteridophytes that its true affinity must remain a matter for conjecture. On balance, he considers that it may have a closer affinity with eusporangiate ferns, such as the Marattiales and Ophioglossales, than with *Selaginella*.

We may now consider how the facts of the embryogeny bear on these very different views.

Bower (1935) has pointed out that, at first sight, the embryogeny of *Isoetes* appears to be very different from that of *Selaginella*, although the parental prothalli are much alike. But (he argues) if it be assumed that *Isoetes* had once possessed a suspensor like *Selaginella*, and that this suspensor has been lost or eliminated in the course of descent, then the inversion of the embryo and a consequential exoscopic embryology might in due course follow. The variable obliquely transverse position of the first wall is regarded as being of some theoretical importance in this assumed inversion, i.e. it may be a residual condition associated with the inversion. Otherwise he considers that the two tiered octant stage in *Isoetes* may be compared with the two tiered embryonic region in *Selaginella*. The loss of the suspensor and the inversion of the embryo in *Isoetes*, if true, pose genetical and physiological questions of great interest and difficulty. Bower refers to the work of La Motte (1933) who showed that the embryo in *Isoetes* shifts its position as it grows, the axis constituted by the first leaf and first root lying approximately parallel to the surface of the gametophyte. It should be noted, however, that it is only the extensive growth in the transverse plane that brings about this disposition of the embryo, the direction of the very abbreviated shoot or axis being still that determined at the first division of the zygote.

As supporting his views on the affinity of *Isoetes*, Campbell sees in the organogenic development of the embryo (with its conspicuous, early leaf and root formation, delayed shoot formation, and the relationships of the vascular strands of leaf and root) arrangements like those found in the embryogeny of certain eusporangiate ferns, e.g. Marattiaceae and Ophioglossaceae. 'The embryo of *Botrychium virginianum* perhaps most nearly resembles that of *Isoetes*, but there are resemblances to the embryo of the Marattiaceae also.'

Fig. 29. Embryogeny in *Isoetes echinospora* and *I. lithophila*

A, The ovum at fertilisation; *a*, archegonium. B, First division of ovum by an approximately transverse wall. C, Older embryo, with fairly regular divisions; the first wall has been somewhat oblique to the archegonial axis. D, Median l.s. of an embryo, just before the cotyledon (*c*) breaks out of the prothallus; the foot, *f*, consists of enlarged cells; *lig*, ligule; *r*, root. The shoot apex originates in the depression at the base of the ligule. (A, B, × 330; C, × 300; D, × 200; after Campbell.) E, F, G, Diagrammatic representation of the embryonic development in variously orientated gametophytes of *Isoetes*; L, first leaf; R_1, first root; F, foot. H, J, K, L, M, Early stages in the embryonic development in *Isoetes lithophila*; 1–1, the first partition wall; 2–2, the second wall; I–IV, the quadrants; the position of the archegonial neck is indicated by the two short converging lines and the zenith by Z. N, O, P, *Isoetes lithophila*, showing the relation of the initial segmentation to the subsequent organogenic development; the finer shading represents the incipient vascular tissue; *s*, sheath of primary leaf; L_1, L_2, leaves; *st*, site of shoot apex; *lg*, ligule (all after La Motte).

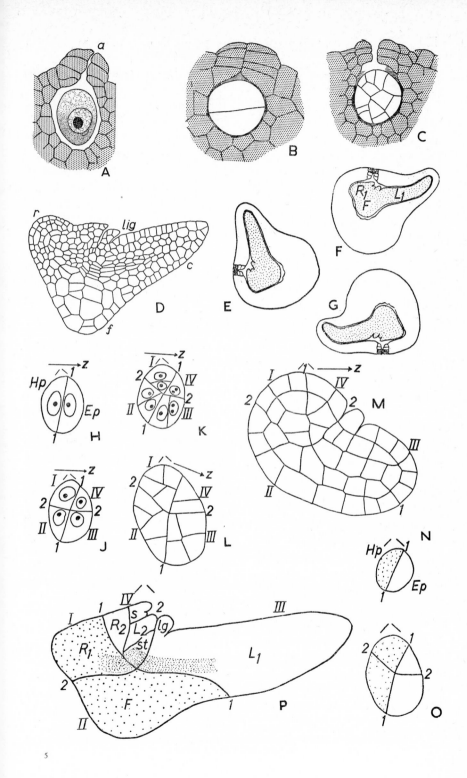

In the foregoing pages the writer has set out what may be regarded as the classical account of the embryogeny of *Isoetes* and the discussions associated with it. In a comprehensive experimental investigation of several species of *Isoetes*, La Motte (1937) has shown, by holding megaspores in agar in predetermined positions during fertilisation and the development of the embryo, that when the mature female gametophyte is fixed in a horizontal position, so that the neck of the archegonium is also horizontal, i.e. at right-angles to the direction of the force of gravity, the embryo emerges with the primary leaf pointing upward and the primary root downward, Fig. 29E. When the gametophyte is placed so that the archegonium neck is directed upward, i.e. in the line of gravity, the embryo emerges in a horizontal position, Fig. 29F, the leaf later curving in an upward direction and the root downward; and as the young sporophyte continues to grow it straightens itself out so that all trace of its original horizontal position is lost. Relative to the archegonial axis, however, the young embryos, both in position and shape, are closely comparable in the two experiments. When the prothallus is placed with the archegonial neck directed downward, the embryo is again horizontal but inverted, and stands in the same positional relationship to the archegonium as in the first two experiments, Fig. 29G. Lastly, when megaspores were constantly rotated in a horizontal klinostat, the position of the embryo relative to the archegonium was the same as before. Relative to gravity, however, the leaves of embryos in the rotated megaspores emerged at random. These experiments show clearly that factors in the prothallus or archegonium are of primary importance in determining the orientation and initital stages in the embryonic development. Because of the radial symmetry of the archegonium and prothallus, gravity also becomes effective and serves as a stimulus towards the vertical development of the leaf-root axis, the response to this stimulus being very pronounced. La Motte has ascertained that the period when the zygote can respond to the gravitational stimulus probably corresponds approximately to the period when it undergoes its first mitosis (between 24–36 hours after fertilisation).

The growth of the embryo is rapid: at 48 hours the embryo is spherical or ovoid and consists of about 12–20 cells; at 72–76 hours it is elongated, is more developed on one side than the other, and the ligule can be distinguished; during the fourth and fifth days the conformation of the foot, the first leaf, and the sunken ligule becomes evident; by the seventh day the leaf, in which chlorophyll has already been formed, is bursting out of the prothallus and the conformation of the root can be observed.

From his experiments La Motte had ample materials for histological study. When the zygote divides, the first partition wall is laid down in a vertical-oblique position relative to the archegonial axis (it is off-set at an angle of about 20°), and where the archegonium is horizontal, it is at right angles to the direction of gravity, Fig. 29H. Only rarely was this wall observed in a position at right-angles to the archegonial axis. Moreover, the tilt of this wall is such that a peripheral point nearest the archegonial neck is in the highest position (relative to the zenith) of the apex of the venter, Fig. 29H–K.

The innermost of the two cells is described by La Motte as the epibasal segment. A second wall divides both segments, somewhat unequally, the two quadrants next the archegonial neck being somewhat smaller than the other two. Of the latter, i.e. in the base of the venter, the cell nearest the zenith is the larger. An octant stage follows. The cell divisions now cease to be simultaneous, more rapid growth and division being characteristic of the cells in the base of the venter, Fig. 29L, M. La Motte's illustrations, Fig. 29N–Q, show the further development of the embryo, its several members being related to the early segmentation described above. It will also be seen that he considers the embryogeny to be endoscopic and not exoscopic as previous investigators had supposed. The innermost epibasal quadrant gives rise to the first leaf and the outermost one to the slowly-organised shoot apex; the innermost hypobasal quadrant becomes the foot and that next the archegonial neck the first root. This embryonic development is thus like that of a leptosporangiate fern, which the present writer would prefer to describe as being lateral. La Motte considers that, on various grounds, the Isoetales should be regarded as being coordinate with the Lycopodiales and therefore included in the division Lycopsida.

APOGAMY

The apogamous development of embryos in *Selaginella* has been reported in *S. rubricaulis* and *S. spinulosa* by Bruchmann (1912), and in *S. anocardia* by Goebel (1915). The details of development, in so far as they are known, appear to follow the normal pattern. If this is so, the biochemical differentiation which leads to the formation of an axial embryo must be present in the unfertilised ovum.

FOSSIL EVIDENCE

Although some rather good specimens of fossil megaspores with prothalli have been obtained, e.g. *Borthrodendron* from the Lower Coal Measures, nothing is known of the embryology of the arborescent fossil Lycopodineae.

DISCUSSION AND CONCLUSIONS

Any attempt at a causal analysis of the embryonic developments in *Selaginella* and *Isoetes* will necessarily be tentative and the conclusions reached are likely to be incomplete and they may be erroneous. Yet, if we are to advance in our knowledge of embryogenesis, it is essential that the morphological evidence should not simply be left as so much descriptive data and that explanations of the observed phenomena should be attempted. In this connection the discovery by Wetmore and Morel (1951) that the prothallus of *Selaginella pallescens* can be cultured aseptically *in vitro* should prepare the way for new experimental investigations.

Bower (1922, 1935) has pointed out that although the orientation of the embryo in *Selaginella* is usually related to the axis of the archegonium, attention must also be paid to the effect of gravity. As a convention, the archegonium in *Selaginella* is usually illustrated with the neck directed vertically upwards; but, in Nature, the oval spore is most likely to lie on its side, and therefore both the axis of the archegonium and of the young embryo are horizontal. The dispositions of the shoot and root in the young sporophyte bear out this view. The illustrations show that the effects of gravity become evident at an early stage in the embryogeny.

If the archegonial axis in *Selaginella* is horizontal, the elongation of the zygote and the first transverse wall seem likely to be determined by factors within the zygote or in the surrounding gametophyte tissue. The axis of the archegonium coincides with the direction of physiological gradients from the centre to the surface of the prothallus. Accordingly, either before or after fertilisation, the ovum may be affected by these gradients, and a differential distribution of its metabolic substances may result. The segmentation pattern in any species of *Selaginella* develops in a regular and characteristic manner, and this may be attributed partly to the distribution of gene-determined metabolites in the embryonic reaction system, and partly to physiological conditions in the surrounding gametophyte tissue.

As in *Lycopodium*, the distal pole of the *Selaginella* embryo is almost immediately established as the region of active protein synthesis, meristematic activity and organ formation, the basal pole being a region of accumulation of osmotically active substances, active cell enlargement and vacuolation. Thus, from an early stage, the embryo has an active apical meristem, and the organisation of a miniature shoot. As in procumbent shoots, the horizontal embryo may be characterised by a differential distribution of growth-regulating substances as between its upper and lower sides. In conjunction with other factors, this may account for the development of a more or less conspicuously swollen foot and for the upward curvature of the embryo. As auxin production at the shoot apex and the response of tissues to auxin are probably gene-controlled, the size of the foot may be expected to vary from species to species.

The swollen foot is generally held to be a suctorial or haustorial organ, i.e. takes up nutrients from the prothallus and passes them on to the growing apical region. To what extent, in the early embryonic development, the absorption of nutrients takes place over the whole embryo is not known, but from quite an early stage the embryo apex behaves very much like an adult shoot apex, i.e. as if it received all its nutrients from the tissues below.

The data for *Selaginella* support the view that the characteristic embryonic developments, i.e. the 'stages' illustrated in morphological studies, are fundamentally due to the patternised distribution of specific metabolites (*see* Chapter III). That biochemical and bio-physical conceptions have an essential place in interpretations of the embryogeny of *Selaginella* is evident from the anatomical data recorded by Bruchmann. In *S. poulteri*, for example, the slender suspensor does not simply thrust the embryo down into the dense tissue of the gameto-phyte; there is evidence of an active dissolution of the tissue by enzymes secreted by the distal region of the embryo, very much like the digestion of the endosperm by the embryos of flowering plants. Examples of this are seen in those species in which the archegonium elongates into a long tubular or sac-like structure which Bruchmann and Goebel have described as an *Embryoschlauch* (embryo-tube). In *S. kraussiana* this tube penetrates deeply into the prothallial tissue, just like a stout fungal hypha, with the small, two-celled embryo lying at the inner extremity; while in *S. galeottei* the long and sinuous tube, with a small four-celled embryo at its inner extremity, is surrounded by prothallial tissue in a state of dissolution or partial digestion. The characteristic size of the foot and the position of the first rhizophore in different species afford further evidence that a specific and orderly distribution of metabolites underlies the observed developments.

The suspensor in *Selaginella* is of interest on both phylogenetic and morphogenetic grounds. There can be little doubt that the factors which determine its presence are transmitted in heredity. But precisely how these factors, or genes, produce the observed effect, i.e. the differentiation of the zygote into two cells of different constitution and reaction, is not known. *Selaginella* also shows a trend in the direction of the loss of the suspensor: in various species the suspensor is replaced, as it were, by a deeply penetrating embryo-tube. In the genus as a whole, the suspensor may be more or less well developed and functionally important. In *S. denticulata*, for example, the foot, in whole or in part, is formed from the suspensor. In *Isoetes*, however, there is no suspensor, either because this organ was never present in the Isoetales or because it has been lost, or eliminated, in the course of descent. Although the embryo of *Isoetes* is not thrust into the prothallus as it is in *Selaginella*, its organogenic development is nevertheless broadly comparable: a basal foot makes intimate contact with the gametophyte tissue and transmits nutrients to the apical region. Bower has referred to the zygote of *Isoetes* as having become 'inverted' as a consequence of the loss, or absence, of a suspensor. This conception raises problems of some difficulty; for, as we have seen, there is support for the view that the development of the zygote is characterised by a heterogeneous distribution of metabolites at the two poles. Now, where a suspensor is eliminated in the course of descent, presumably as a result of mutation, the morphological modification will be referable to a change in the previous biochemical differentiation at the two poles. The suspensor segment of a zygote, as we have seen, has limited potentiality for growth but is a locus for the accumulation of osmotically active substances. Even where the suspensor is small or absent, the basal cells of the foot have these same characteristics. In some species the suspensor may have little functional importance and in general it is an organ of limited growth. Whether the genetical change determining the elimination of the suspensor is of a major or minor character is not known (*see* Chapters IX, XVI). If the ancestors of *Isoetes* possessed a suspensor, it is difficult to explain how the biochemical differentiation at the poles of the two-celled embryo could have become completely reversed. Considerations such as these suggest that the taxonomic relationship of the two genera cannot be a close one.

Bower (1935) has remarked that it is perhaps surprising that the embryonic developments in *Lycopodium* and *Selaginella* are so much alike, considering how very different are their respective prothalli: *L. selago* and *S. spinulosa*, for example, are closely comparable in a number of features. We do not, of course, know the magnitude of the genetical difference that separates the heterosporous and the homosporous conditions: it may perhaps be considerably less than is usually supposed by morphologists. Certainly, it would appear that the main factors determining the embryogenic development in the two genera were already present in the common ancestor and that subsequently the two lines of descent have afforded some remarkable examples of parallel evolution.

Lastly, it may be noted that the early embryogeny of *Selaginella* is not at all unlike that of some flowering plants, in which the proembryo consists of a multicellular suspensor with an approximately spherical embryonic region, the latter giving rise to the shoot, leaves and roots.

Chapter IX

EMBRYOGENESIS IN EUSPORANGIATE FERNS

GENERAL INTRODUCTION

THE living ferns constitute a large and coherent class descended from early Palaeozoic ancestors. Two subdivisions, the *Eusporangiatae* and the *Leptosporangiatae*, are recognised, the former being the more ancient and primitive, the latter the more modern and derivative (Bower, 1923 etc.). There is, however, no absolute separation of the two subdivisions: a gradual emergence of the leptosporangiate from the eusporangiate condition can be traced along several phyletic lines. Bower has argued that the ferns can be arranged in a phylogenetic scheme on the basis of twelve criteria of comparison, including external morphology and symmetry, the initial constitution of the plant body as indicated by segmentation, the nature of the vascular system, the inception and character of the sporangium, the morphology of the prothallus and the embryology of the sporophyte. If these criteria are applied to the whole class of living ferns, a rough division can be made into those, at one end of the series, in which the general plan of construction is on a robust or massive basis (the Eusporangiatae) and those at the other end, in which the general plan of construction is on a less massive but structurally more exact basis (the Leptosporangiatae) (Goebel, 1880). Between these extremes various intermediate conditions have been found. Campbell (1890) concluded that the massive eusporangiate ferns are primitive and the more delicate leptosporangiate ferns derivative. This conclusion is supported by the fossil evidence.

In Bower's comparative treatment, the young sporophytes of eusporangiate and leptosporangiate ferns afford materials for comparison. The two main features in the embryogeny which he regards as possibly having a phylogenetic bearing are (i) the relative complexity of the initial segmentation, and (ii) the presence or absence of a suspensor.

In the older classifications, the ferns constituted one of the six related classes of the Pteridophyta, or Vascular Cryptogams. But in more recent classifications (*see* Chapter XVI), their affinity is with the Gymnospermae and Angiospermae. As these problems of taxonomy have by no means been solved, it will be of interest to consider if the facts of embryology throw any light on the various relationships that have been suggested.

Although the prothalli of many ferns are very much alike, i.e. consisting of a thin strap-like or heart-shaped sheet of photosynthetic tissue, there is, nevertheless, some diversity in the morphology of the prothallus. Thus, some are underground and mycorrhizic and entirely saprophytic in their nutrition. As the embryo and young sporophyte are initially dependent on the prothallus, there is a question as to what extent, and in what way, the embryonic development is determined, or modified, by nutritional factors.

The types of zygotic segmentation in the ferns are illustrated in Fig. 30.

OPHIOGLOSSACEAE

The Ophioglossaceae, including the living genera *Ophioglossum*, *Botrychium* and *Helminthostachys*, are probably the most primitive of living ferns and may well be regarded as modern survivors of ancient Palaeozoic stocks. Actually no fossil progenitors are known. The Ophioglossaceae afford very typical examples of eusporangiate ferns (Bower, 1926, 1935; Campbell, 1911, 1918, 1940).

In all the Ophioglossaceae the gametophyte is a tuberous, mycorrhizic, saprophytic, underground body. The prothalli of *Ophioglossum* and *Helminthostachys* are typically elongated, cylindrical structures, sometimes branching, with a distal apical growing point; that of *Botrychium* is a dorsiventral, somewhat flattened structure, but growth is also by means of a meristematic apex. The prothalli thus afford evidence of features which we normally associate with the embryo.

OPHIOGLOSSUM VULGATUM

As only some of the early stages in the embryogeny of *O. vulgatum* have been ascertained, the relation of the organs to the initial divisions of the zygote still await clarification, Bruchmann's valuable paper (1904) does, however, give a substantial amount of information. The archegonia are situated at the surface of the cylindrical prothallus. The first division of the zygote is by a transverse wall, Fig. 31A. No suspensor is formed and the embryogeny is exoscopic. The segment next to the archegonial neck may be recognised as the epibasal segment and the other as the hypobasal segment. The quadrant and octant stages, though not yet observed, probably exist, for Bruchmann's next illustration is of a median section of an ellipsoidal embryo, in which the octant walls and those subsequently formed are indicated, Fig. 31B. In one hypobasal quadrant the inception of an endogenous root is indicated; the other hypobasal quadrant becomes the foot; but, for some considerable time, the whole of the epibasal region remains in the initial undifferentiated condition, all the cells being meristematic and

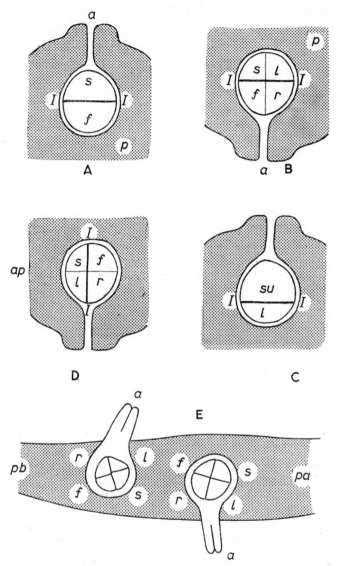

Fig. 30. Types of segmentation in the zygotes of ferns

A, Exoscopic embryogeny, as in *Ophioglossum vulgatum* and *Botrychium lunaria*, the first partition wall defining the shoot (*s*) and foot (*f*) regions; *a*, neck of archegonium; *p*, prothallus. B, The first wall is again at right angles to the archegonium, but the embryogeny is endoscopic, as in *Angiopteris*; *s*, shoot; *l*, first leaf; *f*, foot; *r*, root. C, Typical endoscopic embryogeny, as in some Marattiales, the suspensor (*su*) being next the neck of the archegonium. D, Lateral embryogenic development, as in leptosporangiate ferns, the first wall being in the axis of the archegonium. E, Diagrammatic representation (after Heinricher) of the disposition of embryos induced on both the upper and lower sides of the cordate prothallus of a leptosporangiate fern; *pa* and *pb* indicate the directions of the apex and base respectively of the prothallus. In both archegonia (*a*), the embryos have the same orientation towards the archegonial neck and the apical region of the prothallus.

of approximately the same size. The next development consists in the rapid growth of the root which bursts out from the tissue of the prothallus, Fig. 31C; its vascular strand can be traced from the apex backwards to the region of the root's inception close to the foot. The foot meanwhile has not undergone any conspicuous enlargement and the epibasal segment is still quite undifferentiated histologically. Development to this stage is said to occupy several seasons. The embryo is filled with nutritive substances but contains no endophytic fungus. In the next phase of development the shoot apex, the first leaf (which is situated on the side of the axis above the first root), and a surrounding leaf sheath, have their inception in a superficial, approximately median position in the epibasal segment. A column of elongated cells, actually incipient vascular tissue, is now differentiated in the tissue between the first leaf and the root stele, and the apex of the second root is now organised, Text-fig. 31D. This first leaf undergoes some further growth. The second leaf is formed at the apex in a normal manner, its vascular strand becoming joined with the root stele. No vascular tissue is differentiated below the apical meristem of the shoot. The first and second leaves have sheathing bases like the leaves in the adult shoot. The first leaf may be only slightly larger than the second, and the latter is not enclosed in the leaf-base of the former, Fig. 31E. In fact, the first leaf soon stops growing, but the second leaf grows on

---

Fig. 31. Embryogeny in Ophioglossaceae

A–E, *Ophioglossum vulgatum*. A, Archegonium in l.s. showing the first division of the zygote. B, An embryo in the post-octant phase, showing a regularly segmented but undifferentiated ovoid tissue mass, consisting of the epibasal (*ep*) and hypobasal (*hy*) regions; the latter gives rise to the first root (*r*) of which an endogenous initial can perhaps be recognised, and the foot, *f*; I–I, first or basal wall. C, An older embryo in l.s. showing the well-developed first root (*r*), the undifferentiated epibasal region (*ep*), which will later give rise to the shoot apex and first leaf, and the foot (*f*) in contact with the prothallus (*p*). D, Embryo in l.s. showing the shoot apex (*s*), the first leaf (*l*), and its encasing sheath (*ls*), the first root (*r*) with its vascular strand (*vs*), and the initial of the second root (*r₂*). E, An older embryo in l.s., showing the points indicated above, but here it can be seen that the first leaf (*l₁*) has remained small, while the second leaf (*l₂*) is becoming conspicuous; each is enclosed in a leaf sheath (after Bruchmann). F, *Botrychium lunaria*. First division of zygote, as seen in l.s. of archegonium. The embryogeny, as in *O. vulgatum*, is exoscopic (after Bruchmann). G, H, *B. obliquum*. Archegonium with zygote as seen in l.s.; the zygote elongates and penetrates the tissue of the prothallus. At the first division a transverse wall divides this cell into a suspensor and an embryonic cell and the embryogeny is endoscopic; *a*, archegonium (after Lyon). J–O, *Helminthostachys zeylanica*. J, Young arrested endoscopic embryo, consisting of first and second suspensor tier cells (*s₁* and *s₂*), and the embryonic cell (*e*); *ar*, archegonial neck. K, Mature embryo, seen from suspensor side, showing the suspensor (*s₂*), the foot (*f*), the shoot apex (*a*), the root (*r*), and the first leaf (*l*). L, Basal region of young plant showing the apical bud (*a*), the first leaf (*l*), the first and second roots (*r₁, r₂*), the hypocotyl (*h*), and the foot (*f*); *s*, suspensor. M, N, Two small embryos, showing the suspensor, the swollen embryo proper and the position of its apex (*a*). O, Prothallus and embryo in approximately longitudinal section, showing the several embryonic regions; lettering as above (after Lang). (A, × 150; B, × 225; C–E, × 23; F, × 100; J, × 130; K–N, × 20.)

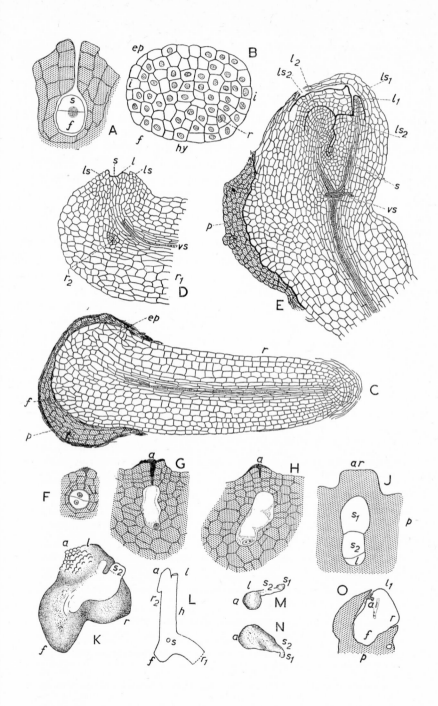

and emerges above ground as the first green leaf, this process being said to require some eight to ten years. This leaf is of small size and bears no fertile spike. The third leaf, which appears above-ground the following year, may, in some instances, be fertile. The further developments are as in the mature plant. Young sporophyte plants, both free in the soil or still attached to the prothallus, may have one to four well developed, horizontally disposed roots, while the shoot apex is still a very minute bud. In one specimen figured by Bruchmann, a secondary adventitious bud is present on a long root, the bud being at some distance away from the primary apex. Like the parent prothalli, all these plantlings occur several centimetres below ground and are holosaprophytic.

In terms of growth the following points emerge from a consideration of the embryological data given above: (i) the growth of the embryo takes place very slowly until a green leaf has appeared above-ground, i.e. mycorrhizic nutrition alone apparently admits of very slow growth only; (ii) the cells of the prothallus and young embryo are densely packed with starch grains; (iii) the nutrition of the embryo from the prothallus may at first be by way of the foot and root but subsequently, when the root has burst out of the prothallus, the foot must be the principal organ of uptake; (iv) root inception and development take place in advance of the organisation of the shoot apex and the formation of the first leaf; (v) as judged by the inception of vascular tissue, the shoot apex is relatively inert, the vascular tissue being largely, if not completely, foliar in origin.

Although the *times of development* of the different parts of the young embryo (shoot, leaf, root and foot) in the eusporangiate fern *O. vulgatum* are different from those in leptosporangiate ferns such as *Dryopteris* or *Adiantum*, the eventual patterns of embryonic development are closely comparable in the two types. Thus the embryo in *Adiantum*, Fig. 35, shows a characteristic spherical quadrant stage, after which the foot and root are formed from the two hypobasal quadrants and the shoot and first leaf from the epibasal quadrants; also the leaf and root quadrants are contiguous. This is just the relationship that has been described above for *Ophioglossum vulgatum*. It is, therefore, a reasonable assumption that the same general factors are at work in both ferns, and that constitutionally they have much in common.

Although in *Ophioglossum vulgatum* the embryonic development, and especially the organisation of a shoot apex, take place very slowly, it seems probable that the essential and primary differentiation of the several embryonic regions is a biochemical one, i.e. it is due to the inception of a patternised distribution of particular morphogenetic substances. The polarity of the embryo, as in other embryogenies, is determined at a very early stage, and the foot and first root, as also the first root and first leaf, are invariably contiguous. The first leaf, like the second and all subsequently formed leaves, is a dorsiventral structure, and arises in the normal foliar orientation to the radially-symmetrical shoot apex. It has been shown experimentally that not only do the leaves of ferns and flowering plants always originate in the shoot apical meristem, but that their characteristic dorsiventrality is probably due to biochemical effects proceeding from the shoot apical-cell-group. (Wardlaw, 1952; Sussex, 1951, 1952). All this is as much as to say that in *O. vulgatum*, no matter how sluggish and seemingly anomalous the embryonic development may be, a characteristic bio-chemical organisation, or pattern, not unlike that of other ferns, is present from an early stage and is maintained and elaborated during the subsequent development. (For further discussion of this aspect *see* p. 165.)

As a working hypothesis we may suppose that, for the 'normal' development of a fern embryo, each quadrant requires particular meta-bolites in certain characteristic concentrations and proportions. Or, alternatively, we might say that each quadrant develops as it does because it is 'normally' supplied with certain metabolites in charac-teristic concentrations and proportions. Now whereas the 'normal' embryo, as seen in *Dryopteris*, *Adiantum* or *Osmunda*, derives its nutrition from a green, photosynthetic prothallus, the embryo of *O. vulgatum* is nourished by a saprophytic, mycorrhizic underground prothallus. The *Dryopteris* type of embryo (*see below*, p. 142) is characterised by rapid growth, by the early and approximately simul-taneous formation of the apices of shoot, leaf and root, and by a balanced embryonic development. By contrast, the embryo of *O. vulgatum* is characterised by very slow growth, by heavy depositions of starch in the embryonic cells, by relatively precocious root formation and very belated shoot and leaf formation. However, once a photo-synthetically active leaf has appeared above-ground, the organogenic development becomes 'normal' and 'balanced' and, indeed, in all its general features, is closely comparable with that of *Dryopteris*. The delayed organisation of the shoot apex in *O. vulgatum* has a close parallel in those species of *Lycopodium* where the young embryo also derives the whole of its nutrition from a mycorrhizic, underground prothallus (*see* Chapter VII). A reasonable inference from the facts is that whereas the mycorrhizic fungus provides the prothallus (and, indirectly, the young embryo) with an abundance of carbohydrate, the supply of nitrogen-containing substances, and possibly of certain growth-regulating substances, is small and limiting: hence the delay in the formation of the protein-synthesising shoot apical meristem.

The precocious inception and development of the root in the embryo of *O. vulgatum* may provisionally be referred to (*a*) its position in proximity to the foot and to the prothallial sources of nutriment, (*b*) the presence of auxin in concentrations that admit of the inception of a root apex and of root growth. Whether or not a specific 'root-forming substance' is involved must remain an open question. For some considerable time after its inception, the root uses most of the nutrients drawn in from the prothallus. As the root grows, a vascular strand is differentiated behind its apex, the base of this strand being in the approximately central position in the ellipsoidal embryonic tissue mass at which the root apex originated.

The delay in the organisation of the shoot apical meristem and the first leaf may be provisionally attributed (*a*) to the deflection of the main supply of nutrients into the precociously developing first root, (*b*) to inadequate supplies of nitrogen-containing substances from the saprophytic prothallus, and possibly (*c*) to a delay in the building up of an effective concentration of some essential 'shoot-forming' substance in the epibasal hemisphere. This substance would be a metabolite other than auxin, for, as Bruchmann has shown, some embryos have already formed three or even four roots before the shoot apex has become at all conspicuous. In one specimen, the first root, which had attained a length of 6 cm, bore an adventitious root-bud about 0·7 cm behind its apex. Such observations may support the view of Went (1938) that a 'shoot-forming substance,' or caulocaline, is formed in the root; Goebel (1902) also considered that a bud-forming substance is normally formed in the roots of *O. vulgatum*, and hence root-buds can be formed both in attached and detached roots (Wardlaw, 1953). All such conceptions of the origin and action of single morphogenetic substances are probably a vast over-simplification of the processes actually involved. That some specific growth-regulating substance, or some nitrogen-containing metabolite, is limiting in the embryonic development of *O. vulgatum* seems to be fairly clear; for, as the evidence shows, the first leaf is not only very slow-growing but it remains rudimentary. It may here be noted, that, up to this time, the embryo, as in Fig. 31E, is still attached to the prothallus, and is still free from the endophytic fungus. After this stage, many of the embryos become detached from the prothallus. Whether or not the greater growth and morphogenetic activity of the shoot apex are associated with this detachment from the prothallus, and, for some time at least, dissociation from mycorrhizic nutrition, are questions that deserve fuller consideration than they have been given. The functioning of the root in direct contact with the soil and its uptake of water and salts also seem likely to have important effects on growth relationships in the embryo.

It is now well known that when a piece of plant tissue containing a shoot apex is placed in a culture medium, the growth and morphogenetic activity of the apex are greatly enhanced once a root has grown down into the medium.

From the foregoing analysis it appears that the early embryogeny of *O. vulgatum*, although seemingly very anomalous, is, in fact, comparable with that of other ferns, including leptosporangiate ferns, the morphogenetic anomalies being probably referable to nutritional factors. This view is supported by data relating to the inception and organisation of buds on this species (Wardlaw, 1953).

Organogenesis in Induced Buds. The earliest stages in the formation of buds in roots and shoots afford interesting materials for comparison with the embryogeny. When a bud is formed at the root tip, according to Rostowzew (1891), a cell of the root apical meristem divides several times, its segments forming the apex of the new bud and the first leaf. Root formation takes place some time later, and there may be considerable evidence of leaf growth before the first root emerges from the parent-root tissue. When a bud is induced at some point in the mature region of a root, the first stage consists in the development of an ellipsoidal or spherical mass of meristematic tissue in the middle or inner cortex. Within this mass a shoot apical meristem becomes organised (Wardlaw, 1953), and soon thereafter the first leaf is formed. The first root may then have its inception, or this may be delayed a little. A considerable amount of leaf growth may take place in the course of a few months. Once a root-tip has been differentiated, root growth may be rapid, so that a thick root, considerably larger than the first leaf, may be formed in 4–6 months. When an endogenous bud is formed in the pith of a decapitated shoot its development is closely comparable with that just described: a shoot apex is first formed; the first leaf is formed almost simultaneously and shows evidence of very rapid growth; the root apex is always the last to be differentiated, but subsequently root growth may be more or less vigorous in different instances. In buds formed laterally on the shoot, a shoot apical meristem is first organised; leaf formation follows and some time later a root apex appears. In these induced buds the relation of roots to the leaf-bases cannot be precisely specified (Wardlaw, 1954).

These induced buds are characterised by the very active formation of densely protoplasmic meristematic cells, as compared with the starch-filled cells of the embryo. The buds are also characterised by the early differentiation of a shoot apical meristem, with subsequent or simultaneous leaf formation, and the later inception of roots, whereas, in the embryo, root formation comes first. These differences in organogenic activities as between embryos and buds can almost certainly be referred to metabolic factors and relationships. In particular they appear to be largely, if not entirely, related to the nutritional resources which can be mobilised from a purely saprophytic prothallial system on the one hand, as compared with a photosynthetic leaf and mycorrhizic root system on the other. This finding may have a more general application. The 'normal' embryonic development of any species takes place as it does because the embryo is developing in a closely regulated and specific metabolic system. If, however, the nutrition available to the embryo is modified in certain ways, the embryonic development may be more or less considerably modified, but it will, nevertheless, take place within the general embryogenic pattern for the species. Extreme changes in the embryonic development of *Datura stramonium* have been made by van Overbeek, Conklin and Blakeslee (1941, 1942) and van Overbeek (1942) by culturing excised young embryos in a medium with added coconut milk (*see also* Chapter XV).

EMBRYONIC DEVELOPMENT IN OTHER SPECIES OF OPHIOGLOSSUM

Campbell (1911, 1940) has recognised three types of embryogeny in the genus *Ophioglossum*, namely, (i) the *O. vulgatum* type as described above; (ii) the *O. moluccanum* type as described by Mettenius (1856) and Campbell (1911, 1921, 1940); and (iii) the *O. pendulum* type as described by Lang (1902) and Campbell (1911, 1921, 1940).

In *O. moluccanum*, according to Campbell, the epibasal segment of the young embryo gives rise to the cotyledon, or first leaf, (*leaf* 1), the whole of the hypobasal region being occupied by the large foot. The primary root (*root* 1), which originates endogenously in the central region of the embryo, grows rapidly downwards through the foot and fastens the young sporophyte to the soil. The first leaf also elongates rapidly, breaks through the prothallial tissue, and appears above ground as a delicate lanceolate and presumably green leaf. At this stage, the foot consists of a zone of large cells in the equatorial region of the bipolar embryo which, according to Campbell, now consists of the cotyledon and root only. The first leaf is initially a conical object with an apical cell but later it becomes narrowly laminate and petiolate. The leaf stalk merges with the root, their tissue systems being continuous. The shoot apex, which originates as an endogenous bud close to the stele in the primary root, consists initially of a small mass of active meristematic cells. Campbell states that the second leaf originates independently of the shoot apex but is closely associated with it. Its vascular strand becomes conjoined directly with the stele of the primary root. No vascular strand can be discerned below the rudimentary shoot apical meristem; the latter is enclosed within the sheathing base of the second leaf, but root parenchyma may also contribute to this structure. The second root does not emerge until the second leaf is nearly complete: its stele joins the leaf stele near its conjunction with the first root. Thereafter, in Campbell's account, the development of the sporophyte is attributed to the activity of the shoot apex.

Considerable difficulties have to be overcome in any attempt to explain these developments in *O. moluccanum*. Campbell's data are admitted by him to be somewhat incomplete. As the hypobasal segment soon becomes enlarged and parenchymatous, it is perhaps not surprising that the primary root has its inception in some of the more deeply seated tissue which has remained meristematic. Again, although the whole of the epibasal segment seemingly gives rise to the cotyledon or first leaf, this leaf is not an organ of completely radial symmetry. It first appears as a conical structure but its inherent dorsiventrality becomes apparent on further growth. From this the present writer would conclude, on the basis of a biochemical theory of embryogenesis, that, as in *O. vulgatum*, the epibasal segment has two growth centres: one of these early becomes active as the first leaf, whereas the other remains relatively inactive as far as the development of structural organisation is concerned. But, later, this inconspicuous but persistent growth centre develops and becomes organised as the shoot apex. Because the vascular strand of the second leaf becomes conjoined with the root stele, it does not necessarily follow that this leaf is independent of the shoot apex. Since the third and all subsequent leaves are formed at the shoot apical meristem, it would be somewhat exceptional if the second leaf had its inception in a completely different organogenic relationship. Are we to suppose that there is some abrupt change in the developmental harmony and pattern as between *leaf* 1 and *leaf* 2, and again between *leaf* 2 and *leaf* 3, whereas the development from *leaf* 3 onwards is in conformity with a single pattern? If we consider the embryonic development in terms of an underlying biochemical pattern, and not simply in terms of the visible morphological results, many of the difficulties raised by these curious features in the embryogeny of *O. moluccanum* disappear. In this view, there is developmental harmony from the outset, as is common in embryos at large, and not a series of somewhat unrelated developments as Campbell's interpretation would appear to suggest. In the embryogeny of *O. moluccanum*, as in *O. vulgatum*, the root is precocious, presumably in relation to the nutrition drawn from the prothallus. Subsequently, possibly in relation to the photosynthetic activity of the first leaf and uptake of nutrients by the root, a more balanced metabolism supervenes and normal morphogenetic activity at the shoot apex is thereafter maintained.

In *O. pendulum* the young sporophyte is characterised by the formation of a very large foot from the hypobasal segment, while the epibasal segment may form a large and massive root, or a primary root may be formed from one side and a second root from the opposite side. These developments are evidently related to the nutrients taken up from the prothallus by the massive foot. The embryo grows to a large size before it emerges from the prothallus, and the primary root may attain to a length exceeding 2 cm before there is any evidence of the organisation of the shoot apex and the formation of the first leaf. The apical bud is probably formed endogenously in the primary root as in *O. moluccanum*. As the prothallus of *O. pendulum* is long-lived, it is considered that the young sporophyte may continue its underground saprophytic existence for an indefinite period.

From the fact that the shoot apex originates near the base of the primary root, i.e. near the centre of the embryo, it could be argued that it is not necessarily organised from a later-formed growth centre but that it is the original distal pole of the embryo which has been delayed and become displaced by the extensive development of the primary root. In short, the embryonic development in *O. pendulum* is in essentials like that of *O. vulgatum*, the differences being of degree rather than of kind. The same underlying biochemical pattern is present in both, and is never obliterated, however much the initial organogenic development may be modified by nutritional factors. Because the shoot apex exists for some time in a histologically rudimentary condition it is not necessarily completely non-functional. In the several species of *Ophioglossum*, the first leaf is always a dorsiventral structure, with a collateral vascular strand in which the xylem is on the adaxial, i.e. the apical, side.

BOTRYCHIUM LUNARIA AND OTHER SPECIES

In external morphology and internal structure *Botrychium* closely resembles *Ophioglossum* and from this it may be inferred that it has a similar underlying developmental pattern. In the smaller species of *Botrychium*, e.g. *B. simplex* and *B. lunaria*, which closely resemble *O. vulgatum* in size and organisation, the embryogeny is exoscopic, the first, basal wall is transverse, and the subsequent divisions yield a typical octant stage, Figs. 30, 31F. No suspensor is present. At the octant stage the embryo is subspherical or ellipsoidal. On further development and cell division the exact boundaries between the epibasal and hypobasal regions are not clearly defined and the subsequent organogenic developments cannot readily be related to the initial segmentation. However, in *B. simplex*, it seems probable that the foot and root are of hypobasal origin and the leaf and shoot apex of epibasal origin (Campbell, 1940). If so, the embryogeny in this species would be generally comparable with that of many other ferns. The young embryo, nourished by a saprophytic underground prothallus, consists of a massive foot and a primary root. In *B. lunaria* the first leaf is insignificant and non-vasculated, and several similar rudimentary leaves are formed before the first green leaf appears above ground. This requires several years. In both *B. simplex* and *B. lunaria* the shoot apex develops slowly as compared with the root system, but in the former species the first leaf is better developed and the second leaf appears above ground (Bruchmann, 1906).

Campbell (1911) has given some important comparative data relating to the early development in different species. In *B. virginianum*, there is a considerable enlargement and some elongation of the zygote before the first partition wall is formed; in *B. lunaria* this elongation is considerably less marked; while in *B. obliquum* the zygote becomes much elongated before the first division, Fig. 31G, H. Whether directly or indirectly, these differences reflect differences in the genetical systems of the three species. The basal wall in *B. virginianum* divides the elongated zygote unequally into a larger epibasal and a smaller hypobasal segment. Indeed, at a first glance, it appears as if a suspensor might be present (Campbell, 1911). However, Campbell (1940) states that this species has no suspensor, the embryogeny being like that of *B. simplex*.

In *B. obliquum*, Fig. 31G, H, a suspensor is present, the embryogeny is endoscopic and the embryo proper develops from the densely protoplasmic terminal cell. This cell divides by a wall of variable position, the hypobasal cell (adjacent to the suspensor) giving rise to a large foot, while the distal or epibasal cell gives rise to a somewhat inconspicuous superficial shoot apex and a bulky first leaf. Some time later the first root is formed endogenously near the centre of the embryo. As it grows it penetrates the foot. A vascular strand extends from the first leaf into this root. Root elongation is rapid, keeping pace with the growth of the first leaf, so that, according to Campbell (1940), 'the young sporophyte has a definite bipolar structure.' The first leaf eventually appears above ground. (*See* Campbell, 1911, 1940; Lyon, 1905; Bower, 1908, 1935.) An initial cell is present in the shoot apex. No vascular tissue is discernible below the shoot apex. A massive sheath develops at the base of the first leaf and encloses the apical meristem and the second leaf which is formed on the flank of the meristem. The vascular strand of the second leaf joins that already present, i.e. the vascular system in the shoot in *Botrychium* appears to be entirely of foliar origin.

In the specialised but evidently related group of organisms that constitute the genus *Botrychium*, it is a matter of considerable interest that a suspensor is present in some species but not in others. Moreover, we can see that in different species there are factors which have an effect on the initial growth and division of the zygote. These several specific developments afford evidence of differences in the biochemical pattern and reaction in the ovum or zygote. It may be that, within the genus, comparatively small differences in the hereditary constitution may account for the presence or absence of a suspensor.

HELMINTHOSTACHYS ZEYLANICA

While the early stages in the embryogeny of this species are imperfectly known, it has been demonstrated that a suspensor is present (Lang, 1902, 1910, 1914). The cylindrical prothallus grows vertically in the soil, the archegonia and later the young embryo being aligned in an approximately horizontal direction. The zygote elongates in the axis of the archegonium and extends into the prothallial tissue before any segmentation takes place. The first two walls are transverse: the small, innermost segment is the embryonic cell; the two larger cells constitute the suspensor, Fig. 31J–O. The outer suspensor cell may remain undivided or it may divide into a number of smaller cells. The second tier of the suspensor divides into several cells. The essentially axial embryo continues to grow straight for some time, the embryonic cell giving rise to a hypobasal segment, which develops into the foot, and an epibasal segment which gives rise to the shoot apex, the first leaf and probably the first root. The apex has its inception near the centre of the epibasal tier. As the growing embryo responds to the stimulus of gravity its axis becomes curved and the shoot assumes an erect position. At this stage the embryo is compact and fleshy and is reminiscent of the embryo in *Botrychium*. Later, the embryo consists of a somewhat elongated hypocotyl terminated by the shoot apex and a first, rudimentary leaf, a conspicuous fleshy foot embedded in the prothallus, and a first root, Fig. 31L. The second leaf is functional and according to Campbell (1940) resembles the first leaf in *B. obliquum*. He also considers that in *Helminthostachys*, in relation to 'the greater development of the axis and terminal bud,' the vascular strand which runs from below the apex to the root tip may be partly of axial or cauline origin. The shoot meristem has a truncated apical cell like that in *Ophioglossum*. The axis of the young sporophyte is at first upright but eventually becomes a horizontal creeping rhizome.

In discussing the embryology in the Ophioglossaceae as 'a very interesting problem in morphology,' Bower (1935) considers that the facts support the view that the presence of a suspensor is evidence of an archaic condition and that 'by its elimination the embryo has solved an awkward problem of orientation. So long as the suspensor anchors the embryo in relation to the archegonial neck, contortion of the sporeling would be necessary in order to secure an upright orientation of the shoot except in certain favourable cases.' It does seem probable that the suspensor is a primitive feature in ferns, but whether its presence has been as disadvantageous as Bower suggests is debatable. In gymnosperms and angiosperms, which are the most successful and progressive members of the Plant Kingdom, a suspensor has been retained throughout. The same is true of the large and successful genus *Selaginella*. From the evolutionary, genetical and causal points of view, the loss of a suspensor in different lines of descent is, of course, a matter of very considerable interest. For if the suspensor is ultimately a gene-determined organ, then, in different phyletic lines not closely related, there has been the same or a very similar kind of modification in the reaction system.

MARATTIACEAE

In these ferns the prothallus is superficial, green and fleshy, but it also has a mycorrhizic fungus in its tissue. The archegonia project downwards from the lower side of the prothallus, and, according to the species, the embryo may or may not have a suspensor. The first wall in the zygote is at right-angles to the archegonial neck and the embryogeny is vertical and endoscopic, whether a suspensor is present or not. The inner or epibasal segment gives rise to a large first leaf and to a somewhat insignificant shoot apex. The hypobasal segment gives rise to the foot. The primary root, which is usually formed some time after the first leaf, arises endogenously below it from the central tissue of the embryo. Although the shoot apex is inconspicuous and slow to develop, the first leaf is a dorsiventral structure with a normal orientation towards the apex. With some variations, then, the Marattiaceae are like the Ophioglossaceae and other ferns in respect of their fundamental embryonic pattern.

In all Marattiaceae thus far investigated (*see* Campbell, 1911, 1940, for a general survey) the zygote is divided by a transverse wall. In those species in which the segment adjacent to the archegonial neck does not develop into a suspensor, the next wall is at right-angles to the first yielding a regular quadrant stage. In *Angiopteris*, *Marattia* and *Kaulfussia*, the hypobasal cell, lying next the archegonial neck, gives rise to the foot, while the epibasal cell forms the stem apex and first leaf. The latter is the conspicuous organ, Figs. 30, 32, but close to its inner base the inconspicuous shoot apex, with a single 3- or 4-sided apical cell, is also present. On further growth the first leaf bursts through the upper surface of the prothallus. Campbell (1940) regards this stage as being comparable with that of *Ophioglossum moluccanum*, except that the apex in the Marattiaceae is more conspicuous.

After the octant phase, the initially squat embryo becomes globular and then elongated vertically and its bipolar character becomes apparent. The first root is formed endogenously near the centre of the embryo when the latter has attained to some considerable size, a group

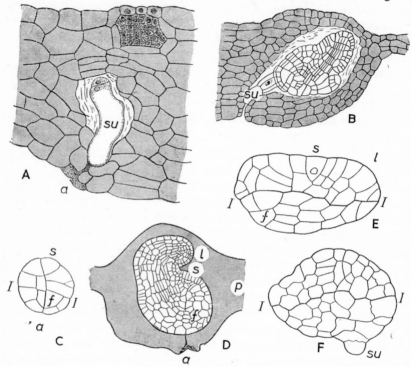

Fig. 32. Embryogeny in Marattiaceae

A, B, *Angiopteris evecta*. A, Endoscopic embryo, with elongated suspensor (*su*), and small embryonic cell as seen in a transverse section of the prothallus; the archegonium (*a*) is seen in l.s. B, A later stage, showing the embryo, with suspensor (*su*), pushing inwards to emerge on the upper side of the prothallus (after Land). C, D, *Marattia douglasii*. C, Young embryo; no suspensor is present, but the embryo is endoscopic; I–I, first partition wall; *s*, shoot; *f*, foot. D, An older embryo; *s*, shoot apex; *l*, leaf; *p*, prothallus; *a*, archegonium neck (× 100). E, *Angiopteris evecta*. No suspensor is present. F, *Danaea jamaicensis*. A small suspensor (*su*) is present; I–I, first wall of embryo; *s*, shoot apex; *f*, foot (C–F, after Campbell). (A, × 200; B, × 100; C, × 225; D, × 72.)

of cells dividing actively and becoming so organised as to constitute a root apex, with a single apical cell of variable form. As this root enlarges it penetrates downwards through the foot which becomes more or less obliterated, and through the lower side of the prothallus into the soil. This root development is more or less in organic continuity with the first leaf.

The second leaf is formed on approximately the opposite side of the apex to the first and has a vascular strand which becomes conjoined with the first leaf-root strand; and, as Campbell (1911, 1921, 1940) and others have shown in some detail, the vascular system subsequently developed in the young sporophyte shoot is apparently composed entirely of decurrent, fused leaf-traces. This seems to be true in all Marattiaceae so far studied; i.e. there appears to be no true axial or cauline stele, and the primary stele at the base of the shoot is not a true protostele. However, in *Danaea*, after the formation of about the seventh leaf, a single axial strand which is not of foliar origin can be traced in the pith to the shoot apical meristem (Brebner, 1896, 1902; Campbell, 1940).

Campbell has called attention to the insignificant size of the shoot apex in embryos of Marattiaceae, and to its belated appearance in the Ophioglossaceae. In his view, the shoot largely consists of coalescent leaf-bases, and in this he sees some confirmation of Delpino's theory that the leaves and not the stem are the primary organs, the so-called stem being an integrated construction of foliar members. The same idea underlies the various phytonic theories of shoot construction. Campbell (1921) further states that the young sporophyte of *Ophioglossum* 'has no stem at all, but consists simply of a single leaf and root, the stem arising secondarily as an adventitious bud.' While it is true that the leaves are the rapidly-growing and conspicuous organs in eusporangiate ferns—as indeed they are in all ferns—nevertheless we may note that, however insignificant histologically the shoot apex may be, and however late its appearance in the embryogeny, it is the centre and focus of the whole axial development, all the lateral members being formed in an orderly manner in relation to each other round that centre. Moreover, if the apex is destroyed the axial growth and the formation of new foliar members soon ceases (Wardlaw, 1949a).

The suspensor in *Danaea* is small; in *Macroglossum* it is large. The presence or absence of a suspensor in the Marattiaceae does not change the orientation of the embryo: it is always endoscopic and directed upwards through the prothallus. In the particular case of *Macroglossum*, Bower (1935, p. 529) remarks that the peculiar form assumed by the embryo 'gives the impression of its being held in place by its suspensor, but unable to penetrate the prothallus upwards. . . .' 'Possibly such difficulties as its form implies may have opened the way for the condition constantly seen in the leptosporangiate ferns, where the embryo without a suspensor emerges on the lower surface of the prothallus.' *Angiopteris evecta* is of interest in that it has been described as being with and without a suspensor in different specimens, Fig. 32A, B, E (Land, 1923). (For a general discussion of fern embryos, *see* end of Chapter X.)

Chapter X

EMBRYOGENESIS IN LEPTOSPORANGIATE FERNS

THERE is now a considerable literature on the embryology of lepto-sporangiate ferns. In 1842 Bischoff discovered the embryo enclosed within the tissue of the prothallus, and in 1849 Hofmeister demonstrated that it was formed within an archegonium. In his 'Comparative Investigations' (1851) he gave detailed accounts of the embryogeny in *Dryopteris* (*Aspidium*) *filix-mas* and *Pteridium* (*Pteris*) *aquilinum*. In 1863 Pringsheim followed with a study of *Salvinia natans* and in 1865 Hanstein dealt with *Marsilea salvatrix*. Other investigations appeared from time to time, some relatively complete, others of a more fragmentary character. Vladesco (1935) has summarised and evaluated the work to date and may be referred to for a comprehensive bibliography. His own work, which includes both morphological and experimental observations, has been drawn upon here for an account of the normal development in leptosporangiate ferns.

THE EARLY SEGMENTATION AND EMBRYOGENY

In *Dryopteris*, *Adiantum*, *Onoclea*, *Gymnogramme* and other leptosporangiate ferns, the archegonia are typically formed on the lower side of the heart-shaped prothallus and have their necks directed downwards, or obliquely downwards. The fertilised ovum is approximately spherical in shape, and the first partition wall, known as the *basal wall*, lies in the axis of the archegonium and at right-angles to the axis of the prothallus, Figs. 30D, 33–36. By the time this wall has been laid down, the polarity of the embryo has been irreversibly determined: the anterior segment, which lies towards the apex of the prothallus, is the *epibasal* segment and gives rise to the shoot apex and first leaf; the posterior or *hypobasal* segment gives rise to the first root and foot. The second wall is at right-angles to the first and it lies in the axis of the archegonium and of the prothallus; it is described as the *median wall*. The embryo now consists of *quadrants* which would be seen in plan by looking down on the under surface of the prothallus. The third wall is a transverse one, i.e. it is perpendicular to the archegonial axis and to the first two walls. The embryo now consists of *octants*. These initial divisions, and those which follow, usually take place in a very regular manner; indeed, they are in close agreement with the ideal segmentation pattern that would be obtained in a sphere dividing by walls of minimal

142

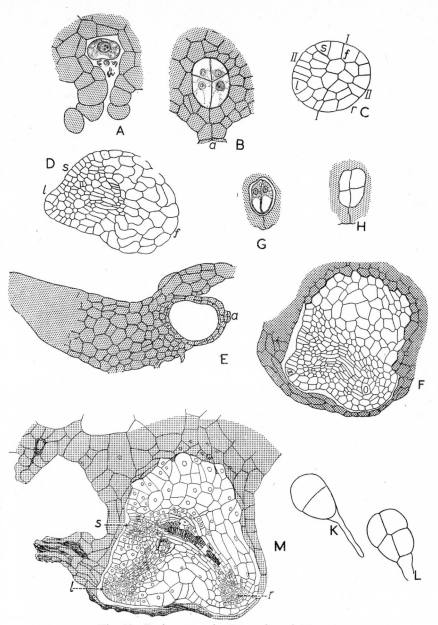

Fig. 33. Embryogeny in *Osmunda* and *Matonia*

A, *Osmunda cinnamomea*. Archegonium in l.s. with ovum at fertilisation. B–E, *O. claytoniana*. B, Archegonium (*a*) in l.s. showing embryo at octant stage. C, Older embryo; I–I, II–II, first and second partition walls of zygote; *s*, shoot apex; *l*, apex of first leaf; *r*, root; *f*, foot. D, Older embryo; note conspicuous development of foot. E, Transverse section of prothallus, showing lateral position of embryo (after Campbell). F–L, *O. cinnamomea*. F, Well-developed embryo, with large foot. G, H, Early stages (after Cross). K, L, Germinating spores (after Campbell). M, *Matonia pectinata*. Well-developed embryo in l.s. (after Stokey and Atkinson). (A, × 300, B, C, × 173; D, × 150; E, × 50.)

area (*see* D'Arcy Thompson, 1917, 1942; Thomson and Hall, 1933). The positions of the walls are not determined by external factors such as light or gravity but by factors within the zygote or adjacent prothallial tissue. Vladesco (1935) maintains that, with occasional exceptions, the sequence in wall formation described above is general in leptosporangiate ferns, this being contrary to the classical view that the transverse wall is laid down before the median wall. Hofmeister, Hanstein and Pringsheim held that the segmentation into quadrants by the basal and transverse walls was highly significant in determining the inception of the several organs of the embryo. Vladesco considers that this view should now be abandoned.

Leptosporangiate fern embryos have no suspensor. At the first division of the zygote, however, as in *Pteris serratula*, Fig. 35A, the epibasal segment may be slightly smaller than the other (Atkinson, 1894). In *Marsilea*, Fig. 36B, the hypobasal segment is the smaller (Campbell, 1918). Vladesco (1935) states that the epibasal segment is usually the smaller. If we regard the approximately spherical zygote as a reaction system, this unequal division would be indicative of cytoplasmic or metabolic differences at the anterior and posterior poles. Longitudinal sections of the embryo of *Gymnogramme* at the octant stage, in the plane of the transverse walls, show that it is ovoid and elongated along its polar axis, Fig. 34 (Vladesco, 1935).

Now, in the small sphere of meristematic cells illustrated in Fig. 35B, it is evident that a considerable amount of biochemical or physiological differentiation must already have taken place; for different regions—which can be indicated as the anterior-superior, the anterior-inferior, the posterior-superior, and the posterior-inferior quadrants—soon develop into (1) the shoot apex, (2) the first leaf, (3) the root and (4) the foot, respectively. In short, the main organographic regions are determined at an early stage.

The earlier investigators tried to relate the formation of the several organs to the individual quadrants in a more or less precise manner. A more critical scrutiny of the facts of the embryonic development, however, shows such views to be untenable. That individual quadrants do give rise to particular organs is not in question, but there is no close and obligatory relationship between the segmentation pattern and organ formation. Although the orientation of the walls during the division of the octants is such as to define what appear to be 'three-sided' apical cells, these do not, in fact, function as the apical cells of the leaf and shoot. Indeed, the delineation of the so-called epibasal and hypobasal discs (Vouk, 1877) is by no means constant: it is not found in *Scolopendrium vulgare*. The first leaf, as in *Gymnogramme sulphurea* (Vladesco, 1935), and many other ferns, originates equally from both of the

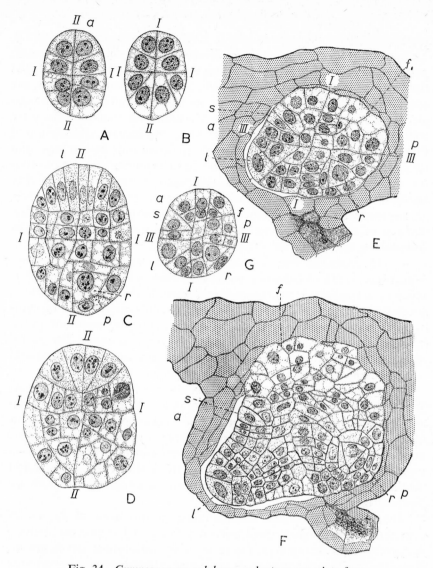

Fig. 34. *Gymnogramme sulphurea*, a leptosporangiate fern

A, B, Sections of 16-celled embryo, cut at right-angles to the archegonial axis; the sections traverse the inferior octants in A and the superior octants in B; the anterior octants are uppermost (× 380). C, D, E, Older embryos; in C and D the inferior and superior octants respectively have been cut parallel to the transverse wall; in E, the section is a longitudinal median one; i.e. it is cut parallel to the axes of the archegonium and the prothallus; C shows that the first leaf is derived from both octants; the root initial can be seen in one of the posterior octants; in E the first leaf, the shoot apex, the first root and the foot are distinguishable (× 380). F, A still older embryo in longitudinal median section. G, *Scolopendrium vulgare*. Longitudinal median section of embryo, showing the obliquity of the first partition walls in the anterior octants, no 'epibasal disc' being formed; I–I, first or basal wall; II–II, second or median wall; III–III, third or transverse wall; *l*, leaf; *s*, shoot apex, *r*, root; *f*, foot. (A–E, G, × 380; F, × 190; after Vladesco.)

anterior-inferior octants: it does not begin from the three-sided cell in one of the octants, with a concomitant suppression of the other. The root apex, which is formed precociously, originates from a single octant in relation to the normal pattern of segmentation. The shoot apex, like the leaf, is not formed by the growth of the three-sided cell in one of the anterior-superior octants, as has been generally thought: the apical initial is formed by the characteristic enlargement of one of the cells close to the median wall. This cell may be in one or the other of the two octants. It remains rather inconspicuous until the second leaf and the second root initials are becoming differentiated. The initial of the second leaf, which Vladesco considers to be independent of the shoot apex, and to pertain to the embryonic tissue mass, may occur in the same octant as the shoot apical cell, or in the other anterior-superior octant. The foot, which soon consists of enlarged vacuolated cells, does not only consist of the posterior-superior quadrant, but may also comprise some of the tissue derived from segments of the anterior-superior quadrant, as in *Pteridum aquilinum* (Hofmeister, 1851, 1857). Vladesco summarises the facts by saying that the octants as such have no organogenic significance.

As the embryo continues to enlarge within the protective sheath afforded by the venter, prevascular tissue becomes differentiated, a strand being typically observed between the leaf tip and root tip, this being conjoined with a strand which originates below the shoot apex. The first root is usually diarch, while a cross-section of the embryonic shoot about the level of the foot would reveal a small protostele. In many, though not in all, leptosporangiate ferns, there is a close correspondence between the number of leaves and of roots, one root being typically formed at the base of each leaf. This has been interpreted by Vladesco as giving strong support to the phyllorhize theory of Chauveaud (1921).

Phyllorhize Theory. A consideration of the later stages of the embryonic development leads to an analysis of the organisation of the young sporophyte plantling and its further orderly development. These studies have led to the formulation of conceptions such as that of the *phyllorhize*, a term used by Chauveaud, though various phytonic theories of plant construction have long been entertained (Wardlaw, 1952). Chauveaud recognises the spherical multicellular fern embryo as a meristematic or embryonic tissue mass, from which two rather different organs may be formed, namely the *phylle* (having the nature of a foliar organ) and the *rhize* (having the nature of a root or radical member). These two organs together constitute a unit, designated as the *phyllorhize*, which is held to be fundamental in the construction of vascular plants. At the point of union of these units in the first phyllorhize is the foot, by which the phyllorhize is attached to the prothallus. At the base of the *phylle* lies the residual meristematic mass, corresponding to the shoot apex, from which the second phyllorhize will be formed; and there is always a residuum of this mass available for the formation of further phyllorhizes. Chauveaud further

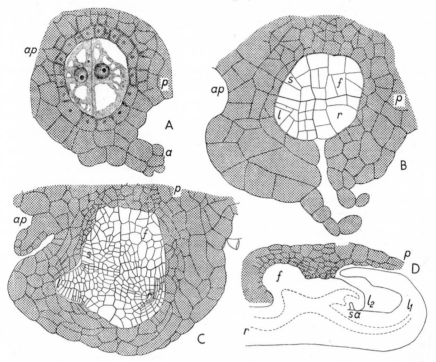

Fig. 35. Embryogeny in leptosporangiate ferns

A, *Pteris serratula*. First division of zygote, as seen in l.s. of the archegonium (*a*); the smaller segment is towards the prothallus apex (*ap*); *p*, prothallus. B, C, *Adiantum concinnum*. B, Post-octant stage, as seen in a longitudinal median section of the prothallus and archegonium; *ap*, direction of apex of prothallus; *s*, shoot apex; *l*, first leaf; *f*, foot; *r*, first root. C, Older embryo, still enclosed in the pro- thallus; lettering as before. D, *Onoclea sensibilis*. Fully formed embryo, with first and second leaves, l_1 and l_2; *sa*, shoot apex. (A, B, × 250; C, × 135; after Atkinson; D, × 48; after Campbell.)

recognises that the base of the *phylle* has a shoot-like character and this he designates as *caule*, the upper foliar portion being recognised as *feuille* (leaf). This theory of construction in the ferns rests on the following facts: (i) that in many ferns there is a very close correspon- dence between the number of leaves and of roots, e.g. young plants of *Alsophila australis*, *Gymnogramme sulphurea*, *Ceratopteris thalictroides*, *Scolopendrium vulgare*, *Polypodium vulgare*, and others, may show four, five or more perfect phyllorhizes; (ii) that the vascular tissues run from leaf to root; and (iii) that the shoot apex may be rather inconspicuous at first and may have little or no vascular tissue differentiated below it. The theory, which in some respects is evidently aptly descriptive for some species, is supported by Vladesco and others; but because of its serious defects and limitations it has been rejected by Bower (1923) and Bugnon (1921, 1924), and by the writer (Wardlaw, 1943, 1952) on the basis of experimental investigations. The facts seem to favour an axial theory of construction, the shoot apex being the primary morphogenetic region of the plant.

Fig. 35B, C, shows that the dispositions of the epibasal and hypobasal segments relative to the surrounding prothallial cells, from which nutrients will be absorbed, are closely comparable. As the epibasal region is directed towards, and the hypobasal region away from, the apex of the prothallus, the two regions may be differentially affected by metabolic gradients within the prothallus. In this connection Albaum (1938) has shown that a basipetal auxin gradient can be demonstrated in the prothallus: the epibasal segment of the embryo would thus be at a higher point on this gradient than the hypobasal segment.

In general, the embryonic segmentation pattern is more regular and exact in leptosporangiate than in eusporangiate ferns. Campbell (1940) has noted that each of the octants, which are like tetrahedra with one curved surface, shows what appears to be apical growth for a brief period, i.e. the divisions of each octant are such that a 'three-sided' apical cell is formed. But this, in fact, is exactly what would happen in the division of a tetrahedron by walls of minimal area, Fig. 35B. Vladesco (1935) has indicated that none of these three-sided cells functions as an apical cell, whether of the leaf or the shoot. In the root quadrant, in which the octant wall is somewhat oblique, the larger cell begins to function as the apical cell of the first root.

During its early development the embryo remains within the prothallus and obtains all its nutrition from it, probably by way of the foot. It is during this phase that the organisation of recognisable meristems, i.e. of shoot, leaf and root, each with a single apical cell, takes place in three of the quadrants. In the fourth quadrant the origina meristematic character is soon lost and it becomes a region of distended parenchyma-like cells and is recognised as the foot. There is a characteristic gradient of cell size from the foot into the shoot region, Figs. 33F, M; 35C. As soon as organ formation becomes sufficiently advanced, it can be ascertained that whereas the shoot and root are of radial symmetry, the first leaf, and all subsequently-formed leaves, are of dorsiventral symmetry and arise in a definite relationship to the shoot apex. It is difficult to account for the inception of this orderly development, or organisation, in the very young embryo, but such concepts as

(i) the existence of a distinctive biochemical pattern in the spherical embryo at, or soon after, the octant stage, (ii) the organisation of the shoot apical meristem as a morphogenetic region, (iii) the functioning of the apical cell (or apical cell group) as a growth centre whose physiological field affects the growth of the adaxial side of the leaf, and (iv) the effect of light, gravity and polarity in effecting characteristic accumulations of auxin in the leaf and root, i.e. the anterior- and posterior-inferior quadrants, may contribute to an understanding of the observed developments.

In the leptosporangiate ferns, as in other pteridophytes, the epibasal segment of the zygote, or distal pole, soon becomes a self-determining morphogenetic region, drawing nutrients to itself from the foot. It seems not unlikely that auxin, produced during the growth of the incipient shoot and leaf apices, diffuses backwards and is differentially distributed in the two hypobasal quadrants, promoting root formation and growth in one quadrant and parenchymatisation in the other.

In the young embryo, as in the adult fern, the leaves grow much more rapidly than the shoot. Nevertheless, in leptosporangiate ferns, the sporophyte may well be considered to be an axial structure from the outset. Apart from the first leaf, which originates simultaneously with the shoot, the shoot apex gives rise to the leaves and not vice versa.

BRIEF SURVEY OF LEPTOSPORANGIATE FERNS

Bower (1926) has placed the Osmundaceae in a central place among the Eusporangiatae, but notes that they show certain evolutionary upward tendencies: they are the contemporary representatives of an ancient phyletic line, somewhat intermediate in morphology between the eusporangiate and leptosporangiate ferns. Campbell (1895, 1918, 1940) has maintained that they belong to the Leptosporangiatae. The archegonium and embryogeny are like those of this subdivision, though there are some differences worthy of note.

In *Osmunda* an octant stage of some regularity has been observed (Campbell, 1918, 1940), Fig. 33. The first two walls are both in the axis of the archegonium; the third wall is transverse; and the inception of the primary organs from the quadrants and the post-octant segmentation pattern are as in the Polypodiaceae. The post-octant segmentation pattern, however, is considerably less regular, and comparative morphologists have regarded this as evidence of the essentially intermediate position between eusporangiate and leptosporangiate ferns occupied by the Osmundaceae. The *Osmunda* embryo, moreover, retains its globular form for a longer time, i.e. there is a delay in the inception of its primary organs, Fig. 33c, D, and it does not emerge from the calyptra until it has attained to a considerable size,

Fig. 33E, F. In short, the embryos of these ferns show growth and structural differences as compared with those of *Adiantum* or *Dryopteris*. To what extent some of the growth characters of the *Osmunda* embryo are related to the presence of an endophytic fungus in the green prothallus is a matter of interest, especially in view of the very slow growth and development of the embryo in eusporangiate ferns with holosaprophytic prothalli.

In the Gleicheniaceae the embryogeny is also intermediate in character. Precise information is lacking but according to Campbell (1940), who has figured embryos at various stages of development in *Gleichenia pectinata* and *G. linearis*, the initial divisions of the zygote, the general segmentation pattern, and the organogeny are as in the Polypodiaceae. The embryo, however, is characterised by a large foot, the axes of the first leaf and root are aligned and their vascular strands continuous, as in the Marattiaceae, and the shoot apex is initially small and inconspicuous but has a definite tetrahedral apical cell. The presence of a vascular strand below the apex has not been definitely ascertained, though its existence seems probable.

Little is known of the embryogeny in the Schizaeaceae. This is unfortunate, since in species such as *Schizaea pusilla* the prothallus is typically filamentous and the archegonium almost free, i.e. in contact with the prothallial tissue only at its base. It would be very interesting to know if, in these ferns, the embryogeny follows the same pattern as in *Adiantum* or *Onoclea*, where the developing zygote is surrounded by prothallial cells. In *Lygodium japonicum* Vladesco (1935) found that the sequence of divisions to the octant stage was as usual for leptosporangiate ferns. In *Aneimia phyllitides*, however, after the basal wall has been laid down, the anterior segment is divided by a median wall, whereas the posterior segment is divided by a transverse wall (Vladesco, 1935). The further development is, unfortunately, not known but Vladesco states that it does not appear to show any important divergences.

An incomplete and inexact account of the early development of *Hymenophyllum tunbridgense* was given by Janczewski and Rostafinski in 1875. Vladesco (1935) states that the arrangement of the primary organs appears to be normal for leptosporangiate ferns, but contrary to the account given by the two authors mentioned above, the first root develops normally, without any precocious disorganisation, and second and third roots are sometimes formed under their corresponding leaves. In many plantlings, however, only one root is formed. Vladesco states that this may be related to the humid environment in which this fern grows.

In the Hymenophyllaceae, the gametophyte in some species of

Trichomanes consists of a flattened thallus like that of many lepto-sporangiate ferns; but in other species it may be filamentous and branched like a moss protonema. In *Hymenophyllum* the prothallus is typically a branched, strap-like structure, usually one cell in thickness except for the cushions in which the archegonia are formed. The embryogeny in those species in which the prothallus is either filamentous, or in the form of a thin narrow ribbon, seems likely to be of special interest; for in them the effect of the gametophyte on the developing zygote may be expected to be somewhat different from that exercised by a more massive prothallus. Unfortunately, little is known about the embryogeny in the Hymenophyllaceae. However, Holloway (1930, 1944) has given an account of the prothallus and embryonic development in one species, *Cardiomanes reniforme* (*Trichomanes reniforme*). In this species the slowly growing gametophyte consists of narrow branching ribbons, often one cell in thickness. Completely filamentous forms were also observed. The form of the gametophyte is thus very variable, especially in its earlier stages of development. The archegonia are typically found in groups on the upper and lower sides of well-formed ribbons, Fig. 35 *bis* A. In all, Holloway has reported on the structural development of some eighty embryos, ranging from the fertilised ovum to the beginning of growth in the young sporophyte. All his illustrations, however, show the neck of the archegonium directed upward, though the configuration of some of the embryos portrayed suggests that they had been formed in downwardly directed archegonia. The main points which have emerged from this valuable study may be summarised as follows, Fig. 35 *bis*. (1) The first partition wall in the segmentation of the zygote may be at right-angles to the long axis of the archegonium, or obliquely inclined to it; but it is never quite in the plane of this axis, as in leptosporangiate ferns. In two associated archegonia, on opposite sides of the same cushion, one had the first wall obliquely transverse, while the other had it so strongly inclined as to be almost vertical. (2) The epibasal (or neck) segment and the hypobasal segment then divide by walls at right-angles to the first or basal wall; but some anomalous embryos consisting of a linear group of three cells were also observed. (3) After the quadrant stage there is no regularity in the ensuing divisions, and the apical cells of the primary organs cannot be distinguished until considerable further development has taken place, i.e. the embryo consists of a histologically undifferentiated globular or ellipsoidal tissue mass. (4) When at length the apical, or initial, cells of the first leaf (cotyledon) and first root can be distinguished, they are seen to be quite inconstant in their relation either to the neck of the archegonium or to the longitudinal direction of the gametophyte ribbon. A little later, the initial

6

cell of the shoot can be distinguished near the base of the leaf and away from the root initial, its position being clearly indicated subsequently by the cluster of associated hairs. (5) In some embryos it appeared that the shoot, leaf and root may all have originated from the epibasal segment, the hypobasal segment giving rise to the foot only; this point, however, was not definitely ascertained. The root is apparently endogenous in origin and in alignment with the leaf; it may sometimes emerge in proximity to the archegonium neck. (6) As in some other ferns, the shoot is slow in developing. Its associated stele is formed later than that which runs between the leaf and the root; it becomes conjoined with this strand. (7) Many embryos may develop on a gametophyte at the same time. In such cases it was observed that starch may accumulate round the half-formed embryo. (8) The foot is typically a large organ but in older embryos it tends to be in contact with the cushion only at its base. As a result, the embryo projects strongly.

If we assume that the rather tenuous parental prothallial tissue has relatively little regulative effect on the zygote, and also bear in mind that archegonia may be disposed on the prothallus with the neck pointing upward, downward or laterally (because of curvatures in the cushions), then the variable position of the first partition wall of the zygote is perhaps to be expected. It seems to be fairly clear that, as in other archegoniate plants, the polarity of the embryo is defined once this wall has been formed. From this beginning, the further organogenic development of the embryo is not unlike that in other leptosporangiate ferns; it is reminiscent of some eusporangiate ferns in the delay in the inception of the primary organs. Some of Holloway's observations suggest that in the nutrition of the young embryo there may be a preponderance of carbohydrates relative to the other substances required for sustained growth. This might account for the late inception of the leaf, root and shoot apices. In the illustrations in Fig. 35 *bis*, the present writer has given the embryos the orientation which he thinks they may have had during their actual growth.

The Matoniaceae occupy a position related to, but somewhat in advance of, the Marattiaceae and Gleicheniaceae (Bower, 1926). Stokey and Atkinson (1952) have cultured the spores and obtained prothalli, embryos, and eventually young plants of *Matonia pectinata*, Fig. 33M. During its development from the spore the gametophyte passes through a typical filamentous stage, organises a distal apical cell and widens out to form a thalloid plant body with distinctive features as compared with the typical heart-shaped prothallus. The neck of the archegonium, which arises on the lower side, is tilted towards the apical end of the prothallus. The first division of the zygote is by a wall

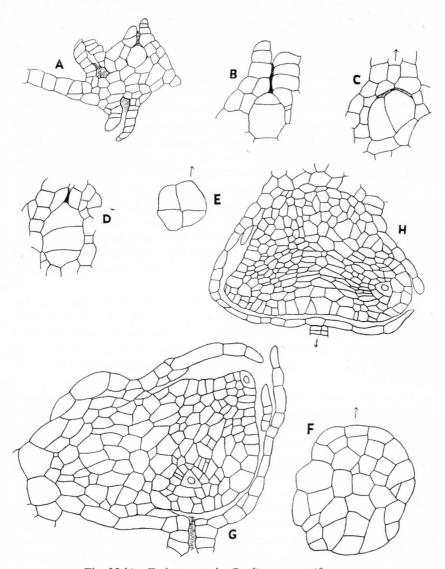

Fig. 35 *bis*. Embryogeny in *Cardiomanes reniforme*

A, Section across a marginal cushion, showing archegonia on both sides (× 120). B, L.s. of a two-celled embryo, the partition wall running obliquely in the plane at right-angles to that illustrated. C, L.s. of a two-celled embryo showing an almost vertical partition wall. D, L.s. of an anomalous embryo. E, Four-celled embryo in l.s. (the arrow indicates the position of the archegonium neck). F, L.s. of an older embryo, about the stage when the leaf initial cell can be distinguished (Figs. B–F, × 220). G, Still older embryo showing initials of the first leaf and of the endogenous root; the shoot apex, not seen in this section, would lie just to the left of the leaf apex; note also the considerable foot (× 175). H, Fully formed embryo showing the considerable foot and the shoot apex, leaf, root and incipient vascular tissue (× 150). (All after Holloway; Figs. H and G have been inverted by the present author.)

in the axis of the archegonium and at right-angles to the axis of the prothallus. The two daughter cells are not quite equal in size, a condition that appears to be general for leptosporangiate ferns. The further embryonic development also appears to be in accord with that of other leptosporangiate ferns. *Matonia pectinata* has long been of special interest to morphologists because of the presence of a very distinctive polycyclic solenostele in the adult rhizome. Stokey and Atkinson found that in a quite young embryo there is a solid core of xylem at the centre, the conducting tissue being well differentiated before the embryo is large enough to burst through the enlarged venter or calyptra. In this species, in short, there is apparently a precocious development of vascular tissue. The vascular tissue is continuous from below the apices of the shoot and the first leaf backwards to the first root, Fig. 33M. In its general appearance and somewhat massive construction, this embryo is not unlike that of *Osmunda cinnamomea*, Fig. 33F.

Dryopteris filix-mas. The embryogeny of this classical species was investigated by Hofmeister. More recently Becquerel (1931) has followed the embryonic development by growing prothalli bearing embryos in mineral culture solutions. Several archegonia on the same prothallus may be fertilised and begin to develop embryos ('polyembryons') but usually all but one abort. However, it is not rare to find two sporophytes on a single prothallus. Vladesco (1935) cultured the prothalli of this fern on burnt soil and noted that the co-existence of several embryos on the same prothallus had no effect in modifying either the orientation or the sequence of the partition walls. He also noted that in some cases the basal wall dividing the zygote was not so much perpendicular to the prothallial axis but strongly inclined towards the prothallial apex. The posterior segment appeared to be the larger of the two segments. In this species, Hofmeister stated that the zygote divided by a basal, a transverse and a median wall in that sequence. Vladesco has corrected this statement and maintains that the second wall is the median wall, as in most leptosporangiate ferns. Moreover, in the posterior segment, the two quadrants may be of unequal size— evidence of biochemical heterogeneity or of unequal forces, e.g. pressures, acting on different sides of the hemisphere. Vladesco has also noted other irregularities in the division of the zygote. Whilst still in the globular post-octant phase, the inception of the several organs begins to be apparent. The first root occupies a median position relative to the first leaf. The foot not only comprises the posterior-superior quadrant, but also part of the anterior-superior quadrant. The general organogenic development is comparable with that of *Gymnogramme*, Fig. 34.

Dryopteris parasitica is generally like *D. filix-mas*. Vladesco (1931) has figured an interesting case of two embryos developing within the same archegonium.

In *Scolopendrium vulgare* two or three sporophytes may be found on vigorous individual prothalli (Vladesco, 1935). The zygote is spherical but sometimes elongated along the axis of the prothallus. The post-octant divisions in the epibasal segments are somewhat different from those found in other leptosporangiate ferns. The partition walls run from the basal wall to the curved outer surface, and no 'epibasal disc' is therefore formed, Fig. 34. In other Polypodiaceae, such as *Athyrium filix-foemina*, *Blechnum orientale*, *Woodsia ilvensis*, etc., the details of the embryonic development are typically those of leptosporangiate ferns (Vladesco, 1935). The same is true of such Cyatheaceae, e.g. *Alsophila australis* and *Cibotium* sp., as have been investigated and of *Ceratopteris thalictroides* (Parkeriaceae).

In the heterosporous order, the Marsileaceae, comprising *Marsilea* and *Pilularia*, the large oval megaspores undergo development on being shed from the sporocarp. The apical region of the megaspore becomes organised as a reduced prothallus with, usually, a single projecting, short-necked archegonium, Fig. 36. After fertilisation, the embryonic development takes place very quickly—in *M. vestita* the first wall appears within one hour of fertilisation and the first leaf can be seen within 24 hours—and is closely comparable with that of homosporous leptosporangiate ferns. As the embryo develops, the cells of the surrounding venter are stimulated to grow and divide by periclinal walls, the enlarging venter thus forming a two-layered calyptra which continues to ensheath the embryo until the formation of the root and first leaf is well advanced. Campbell (1940) states that the limits of the root and foot are not clearly defined and indicates the probability that the whole embryonic region contiguous with the food resources in the prothallus 'no doubt functions as a haustorium.' Thomson (1934) has shown experimentally that the form of the haustorial foot can be modified by excising the young embryo.

The first leaf in *Pilularia* and *Marsilea*[1] is non-laminate or awl-shaped, but the later-formed leaves of *Marsilea* are bifid and tetrafid; in *Pilularia* all the leaves are awl-shaped; in *Regnellidium* the adult leaves are typically bifid. The further development of the embryo of *Marsilea* under controlled conditions has been studied in some detail by Allsopp (1951–1953).

In the other order of heterosporous ferns, the Salviniaceae, including *Salvinia* and *Azolla*, the archegonium in the latter is formed in the small prothallus which occupies the apical end of the megaspore. The

---

[1] In some species of *Marsilea* the first leaf is somewhat spatulate.

lower or inner portion of the megaspore is filled with food reserves. On further growth the prothallus breaks through the spore membrane and some chlorophyll develops. If the first archegonium in *Azolla* is fertilised, no other archegonium is differentiated; otherwise several others may be formed. In *Salvinia* the prothallus is large, with more green tissue and more archegonia. The initial development of the archegonium is as in the homosporous ferns, but at maturity the neck is shorter.

In both genera the megaspores float with the prothallus and archegonia directed upwards. In *Azolla filiculoides* the zygote elongates vertically and its first division is usually by a transverse wall, i.e. the basal wall is at right-angles to the neck of the archegonium, Fig. 36G, H. More oblique divisions, however, have also been illustrated, Fig. 36F. The next wall is at right angles to the first, the two epibasal quadrants giving rise to the shoot apex and first leaf, and the two hypobasal ones to the foot and root, Fig. 36H, J. A 'two-sided' apical cell is formed by the first division of the stem quadrant; this cell persists in the adult sporophyte. The leaf quadrant divides by a median wall, and this, according to Campbell (1918), foreshadows the two lobes found in older leaves. The first leaf, in fact, becomes a funnel-shaped sheath within which lies the shoot apex. The first root is formed as in the Polypodiaceae. The foot is a large organ and becomes elongated below the root-base. The second leaf originates from the first segment of the shoot apical cell, each successive segment forming a new leaf. Vascular tissue can apparently not be distinguished until the second leaf has grown considerably, the strands from the first and second leaves and from the primary root being conjoined near the centre of the shoot, Fig. 36J. No vascular tissue can be detected below the shoot meristem. The embryogeny of *Salvinia* resembles that of *Azolla* but no roots are formed. According to Yasui (1911) a root rudiment is present in the early embryogeny but it does not develop further and becomes merged with the tissues of the foot.

Although the segmentation pattern and organogenic developments in *Azolla* and *Salvinia* are closely comparable with those in the Polypodiaceae, we may note that it is the two upper segments, next to the archegonial neck, which give rise to the shoot apex and first leaf respectively: in leptosporangiate ferns, the corresponding two segments give rise to the first leaf and first root respectively. These facts suggest that gravity may be one of the factors which affects the biochemical pattern underlying the embryonic development.

Parthenogenetically formed embryos of *Marsilea drummondii* are strictly comparable with the normal embryo (*see* next Section).

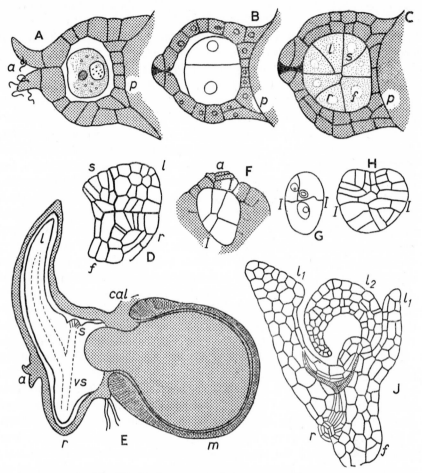

Fig. 36. Embryogeny in heterosporous ferns

A, *Pilularia globulifera*. Archegonium in longitudinal median section containing recently fertilised ovum; the archegonium (*a*) is shown in what is probably its natural orientation. B–D, *Marsilea vestita*. Stages in the development of the embryo, showing the differentiation of the shoot (*s*), leaf (*l*), root (*r*), and foot (*f*) regions; *p*, prothallus. E, *Pilularia globulifera*. Fully developed embryo in l.s., still attached to the prothallus and megaspore (*m*), and enclosed in the calyptra (*cal*); *vs*, vascular strand; other lettering as before (semi-diagrammatic). F–J, *Azolla filiculoides*. F, Young embryo as seen in l.s. of archegonium; the first partition wall, I–I, is obliquely vertical. G, H, Young embryos in l.s. in which the first wall is transverse to the archegonial axis; in H, the epibasal segment is forming the apices of the shoot and first leaf; the first root initial can be seen in one of the hypobasal quadrants, as in homosporous leptosporangiate ferns. J, Well-developed embryo in l.s., after it has broken through the prothallus; lettering as before (all after Campbell). (A, × 300; B, C, × 525; D, × 260; E, × 75; F–H, × 350; J, × 100.)

APOGAMOUS DEVELOPMENTS

In many fern species the sporophyte may be formed from the prothallus without the fertilisation of an ovum. The relevant literature has been reviewed by Bower (1923, 1928, 1935), Smith (1938) and Manton (1950). This phenomenon, known as *apogamy*, has relevance to studies of embryogenesis. Apogamously produced sporophytes may have their inception in a single cell or in a group of cells of the gametophyte, in one or more cells adjacent to the base of the archegonium, or in the ovum in an unopened archegonium (parthenogenesis). In the cases of apogamy which have been critically examined cytologically, the prothallial cells are already diploid. However, the apogamous sporophyte originates, its organogenic development resembles that of a normal embryo. This can be seen in *Pteris cretica*, in *Nephrodium molle*, or in *Marsilea drummondii*. In each instance the nutrition of the young sporophyte is drawn from the cells of the prothallus. Thus, the young sporophyte, whether produced apogamously or after normal fertilisation, manifests a specific organisation from an early stage. The tentative conclusion may therefore be drawn that the size and the relative development of the organs are determined by genetical factors as the general or pervasive underlying cause, and by the nutritional status of the prothallus, environmental and other factors, as the proximate cause —a view that is justified by such experimental studies as have so far been undertaken.

Pellaea viridis is well known as a species which typically reproduces apogamously (Steil, 1918; Vladesco, 1935). Antheridia and archegonia are formed in the normal way on the heart-shaped prothallus. There is evidence that the spermatozoids enter the archegonia and that normal fertilisation occurs. An initial, normal zygotic segmentation has been observed; the later segmentation is irregular and the embryo subsequently aborts. A sporophyte, however, is formed by the active cell division of the prothallial cushion tissue in the vicinity of the archegonia. Whether chemical stimuli from the latter promote the apogamous growth is not known, but active meristematic activity, and later the formation of tracheides, are closely associated with the archegonia. The irregular divisions of the embryo are thought by Vladesco to be due to the pressure of the actively meristematic, adjacent gametophyte tissue.

Steil (1939) has given a comprehensive review of apogamy, apospory and parthenogenesis in the ferns. With regard to the apogamous development of the young sporophyte, an early and usually unmistakeable indication is the appearance of tracheides just behind the apical indentation of the prothallus. In different instances, various morphological and histological developments take place close to the prothallus indentation, e.g. a tongue-like or cylindrical outgrowth may appear, or a group of prothallial cells may become pale in colour and tracheides are differentiated within. The very young apogamous embryo, i.e. one in which the first leaf has not yet appeared, is typically surrounded by multicellular hairs and sometimes by scales; it forms a shoot, leaf and root but not a foot; but in all other respects it closely resembles the embryo produced as a result of fertilisation. In short, the development of an apogamous embryo is very much like that of a sporophyte bud.

EXPERIMENTAL INVESTIGATIONS

Thus far the experimental investigation of leptosporangiate fern embryos is not in any way commensurate with the importance of the subject, but a beginning has been made. There are, of course, serious technical difficulties but they should not be regarded as insuperable. Experimental fern embryology, indeed, affords a challenging but relatively unworked field, and seems likely to yield important results to the investigator who can bring new ideas and new techniques to bear on it.

The following aspects have been investigated by experimental methods: (i) the effect of gravity, light and other physical factors on the early segmentation and disposition of the embryo; (ii) the effect of excising the embryo; (iii) the effect of nutritional factors; and (iv) regeneration.

The Effect of Physical Factors. Sadebeck (1879) held the view that the orientation of the first partition wall in the zygote was determined by factors in the external environment, notably by gravity. In attempts to ascertain the effect of gravity on embryonic development, Leitgeb (1878) used the megaspores of *Marsilea*, which are large enough to be picked up and placed in different positions, rotated on a kleinostat, and so on. He showed that the first wall could be induced to occupy different planes but these were always about the axis of the archegonium, the wall being horizontally disposed. As a result the epibasal segment was directed upwards. The first wall, however, could not be induced to form in any plane other than that of the archegonial axis. Thus, while gravity exercises some effect in this species, factors intrinsic to the zygote-archegonium complex appear to be the master factors in the embryonic development. Some of the earlier studies of this aspect have recently been reviewed by Wetter (1952).

Several investigators have shown that the dorsiventrality of the fern prothallus is essentially a light-induced effect and the same factor apparently determines the position and orientation of the archegonium. In experiments with *Ceratopteris thalictroides*, in which prothalli with fertilised archegonia were variously orientated and rotated, Leitgeb (1880) found that the positions of the basal wall and of the several nascent organs were not altered. The action of light and of the substrate was also ruled out; in short, external factors were apparently not primarily involved. Heinricher (1888) illuminated the dorsiventral prothalli of *Ceratopteris* firstly from above, so as to induce archegonia on the lower or shaded side, and then from the lower side so that archegonia were induced on the upper side. As Fig. 30E shows diagrammatically, the leaf and root quadrants are directed upwards in the left-hand archegonium, in which light and gravity are acting in opposite directions, and downwards in the right-hand archegonium where the directions of light and gravity coincide. In both archegonia the root and leaf quadrants are adjacent to the neck; also, in both, the epibasal segment, which comprises the shoot and leaf quadrants, is directed towards the apex of the prothallus. These experimental results seem to show that external factors such as light and gravity have little or no effect on the differentiation of the embryo. Wetter (1952) considers that this finding for *Ceratopteris* probably holds good for all leptosporangiate ferns. All the attendant circumstances support the conclusion, with which the present writer is in accord, that the polarity of the zygote is determined by gradients in the parent prothallial tissue, the position of the first nuclear spindle and of the basal wall being evidence of that polarity and not the cause of it (A. Lang, 1949; Wetter, 1952). It is not impossible that auxin or some other growth-regulating substance, formed at the prothallus apex and moving basipetally, as demonstrated by Albaum (1938), is the primary determiner of polarity. Alternatively, both acropetal and basipetal metabolic gradients in the prothallus may determine not only polarity, but also the biochemical pattern in the egg or in the zygote. Wetter calls attention to the fact that the orientation of apogamous sporophytes is essentially the same as that of the normal embryo.

The Effect of Excising the Embryo. Ward (1950) has shown by the use of a surgical technique that the embryonic development of *Polypodium aureum* can be modified. By incising the prothallial tissue close to a fertilised archegonium, he effected the partial release of the young embryo. This embryo outgrew the calyptra much earlier than did a normal embryo of comparable size. The treated embryo developed as a slow-growing embryonic mass, at first lacking appendages and without definite shape, but later it differentiated a stem and leaf as in the normal embryogeny. There was, however, no root development. The extreme effect observed in these released embryos was the production of an enlarged slow-growing tuberous mass of parenchymatous tissue of indefinite form and lacking vascular tissue. Several such masses eventually gave rise to three plants with apparently normal stems and leaves. Other curious developments were also noted. Embryos isolated from the apex of the prothallus were notably slow in development as compared with those isolated in other ways, this being attributed to the interruption of the basipetal auxin gradient. Ward considers that the morphological developments which ensued upon the artificial release of the young embryo from the restraint of the prothallial tissue indicate that formative effects are normally exerted on the developing embryo by the archegonium and derived calyptra.

As already mentioned, Thomson (1934) showed that when young embryos of *Marsilea* were excised and grown in culture solution changes could be observed in the shape of the foot.

The Segmentation Pattern. The regular system of cell cleavages has been attributed by various investigators to the changing energy relationships in enlarging cells and to the action of surface forces. So far as the writer is aware, these ideas have not been tested experimentally in the ferns.

Nutritional Factors and Embryonic Developments. Practically nothing is known of the effect of nutritional factors on the early embryonic development in leptosporangiate ferns: the relationship between the zygote and the adjacent cells of the prothallus is evidently a very intimate one.

Klebs (1916) showed that the morphology of the prothallus can be varied according to the composition of the culture solution and the incidence of the factors of light and temperature (for a review of this aspect, see Williams, 1938). Becquerel (1931) tried to use the method of pure culture of prothalli in mineral solutions to study the early embryogeny. Vladesco (1935) used similar methods and found that in *Gymnogramme sulphurea* the first divisions of the zygote were closely comparable whether the prothallus bearing it was growing on moist burnt soil, floating on a culture solution, or submerged in it. In some submerged embryos, the epibasal segment appeared to be larger than the hypobasal segment, this being a reversal of the usual condition in leptosporangiate ferns. Moreover, whereas the subsequent divisions took place normally in the epibasal segment, development was delayed in the hypobasal segment and the orientation of the partition walls was atypical. These observations would appear to indicate that the biochemical pattern of the zygote had been somewhat modified by its development under submerged conditions (probably diminished supply of oxygen and light intensity). Vladesco also records that a root initial was very rarely differentiated in submerged embryos, the plantling being rootless or with a small abortive root. By contrast, it was rare to find that a root failed to develop, or became abortive, in prothalli growing on the surface of the culture liquid. These latter sporophytes were closely comparable with those produced on burnt soil, except that the first leaf was of smaller size and simpler form; the succeeding leaves were also reduced and they had no attendant roots, i.e. plantlings with several leaves had but a single root. In submerged plantlings the first leaf gave rise to aposporous prothalli, while the second leaf developed into an indefinite organ, intermediate in character between a leaf and a prothallus. When such plantlings were placed on moist soil, the shoot apex renewed its normal activity and new leaf and root primordia were formed. When zygotes of *Dryopteris parasitica* were cultured in solutions under various conditions, and in various positions, the orientation of the embryo in the archegonium was not altered (Vladesco, 1935). Plants grown on cotton wool, kept continuously moist with culture solution, developed one root for each leaf: prothalli floating at the surface of the same solution, on the other hand, bore embryos which developed very slowly, were of smaller stature, and showed a diminution in the number of roots: and submerged plantlings were still more reduced. Submerged plantlings of this species, however, yielded no aposporous prothalli. In *Ceratopteris thalictroides*, an aquatic species, the plantlings produced on floating prothalli were almost as vigorous as those obtained on moist soil, but there was some reduction in size in those which developed fully submerged. In all these cultures of *Ceratopteris*, leaf formation was accompanied by root formation—exemplifying the phyllorhize condition in its classic form.

Some interesting correlations between the supply of nutrients, including sugars, nitrogen-containing compounds, vitamins, growth-regulating substances, etc., and morphogenesis in older embryos, have been established by Allsopp (1950, 1951, 1952, 1953) and Wetmore (1950, 1951).

In *Marsilea* the first leaf is small, non-laminate and awl-shaped, but those subsequently formed show a progressive increase in size and form bifid and tetrafid laminae. This kind of observation has been regarded as supporting the theory of recapitulation. Goebel (1908) pointed out that the primordia of the young fern sporophyte and of the adult plant are essentially alike, and that the size and complexity of the fully developed leaf are the direct result of the nutritional status of the subtending apex. This view is now supported by a considerable body of evidence (Wetmore and Wardlaw, 1951; Wardlaw, 1952). By growing young embryos of *Marsilea drummondii* and other species in sterile media, using the methods of tissue culture, Allsopp (1951, 1952, 1953) has shown that the rate of growth of the embryo, and the size and complexity of its leaves, are primarily determined by the supply of nutrients. By varying the concentration of sugar, it is possible to maintain embryos so that they produce a succession of the awl-shaped leaves, or of bifid leaves, or they can be induced to form the large tetrafid leaves precociously. Also, plants which have been forming normal tetrafid leaves can be made to produce awl-shaped leaves by appropriate changes in the composition of the culture medium. Closely comparable results have been obtained with *Adiantum* (Wetmore, 1950; Wetmore and Wardlaw, 1951). Various departures from the normal development of the leaves and roots of *Marsilea* can also be induced by the addition of certain growth-regulating substances to the culture media.

Regeneration. Goebel (1908) showed that if the first leaf of the sporophyte of various ferns is cut off and placed on moist soil, it may either yield an aposporous prothallus, or a bud, or a formation of intermediate or indeterminate character. Relevant data for various fern species are cited by Vladesco (1935). Goebel advanced the view that the kind of regeneration obtained is determined by nutritional factors. Beyerle (1932) held that only when the first leaves of some species were excised could they be induced to form buds or prothalli. The regenerations originate from epidermal cells and may arise at various points; the smaller the leaf, the more will it tend to yield a prothallus rather than a bud. Also, external conditions do not, apparently, modify the nature of the regeneration.

In studies of regeneration, Vladesco (1935) used young sporophytes of *Gymnogramme sulphurea* and found: (i) that isolated first or second leaves, excised a little above their junction with the shoot, and placed on moist soil, did not form buds; (ii) that a phyllorhize (i.e. a leaf and its attached root) without attached stem tissue, when planted in moist soil, also failed to yield buds; (iii) that a very young first leaf, excised so that the shoot apex remained attached to it, yielded an almost normal plantling; the root formed in conjunction with the second leaf anchoring the plant to the soil; (iv) that the removal of the first root did not greatly affect the subsequent development of the embryo, an unusually robust second root being formed precociously; (v) that the removal of the first leaf led to a reduction in the size and to a simplification of the second leaf, and to a suppression of the second root; (vi) that the removal of the first leaf and first root was followed by the formation of the second leaf and its root, both being somewhat reduced; (vii) that when the shoot apex was excised, about the level of the anterior region of the foot, there was regeneration at the cut surface of both foot and vascular strand, the organisation of one or more new meristems, and the subsequent development of one or more buds and small plantlings. When very young embryos, still without vascular development, were cut so as to remove the apical portion, the root primordium continued to develop whilst the cut surface developed several ill-defined meristematic outgrowths: some of these became inhibited or abortive, but two or three of them became organised as buds, each with a leaf, the vascular strand of which extended to the primary root. In some cases a single bud became predominant. Excellent regeneration was obtained with very young embryos of *Cibotium sp.*

Young Sporophytes and Induced Buds. The young sporophyte of leptosporangiate ferns is typically protostelic, i.e. with a solid xylem core surrounded by phloem and pericycle. During the ontogenetic obconical enlargement of the shoot, the stele enlarges, becomes medullated, then solenostelic, with characteristic leaf-gaps in the cylindrical vascular column, and eventually dictyostelic or meshlike, as new leaves are formed in close phyllotactic sequence on the shoot. In lateral shoots, which are either formed normally or can be induced, the progressive stelar elaboration is closely comparable with that of the developing sporophyte (Wardlaw, 1943 etc.; 1952). This is especially true of the small lateral shoots formed from bud rudiments, or detached meristems (Wardlaw, 1943), in old, mature regions of the shoot: the base of the lateral shoot is typically protostelic, and the first leaves are small and simple with a transition of more elaborate adult leaves as the shoot increases in size. On the other hand, when lateral buds are induced to develop close to the large shoot apex in *Dryopteris aristata*, they are of large size and solenostelic from the outset and have leaves which, though still small, have some of the elaborate pinnation characteristic of adult leaves. In short, as in the nutritional experiments with embryos of *Marsilea*, the morphology and anatomy of natural or induced buds reflect the nutritional status of the tissue region from which they are formed. A considerable body of experimental evidence supports this conclusion. Such findings impose caution on the application of the theory of recapitulation to plants (*see also* Chapter XVI).

GENERAL DISCUSSION OF FERN EMBRYOGENY

Zygote and Embryo Organisation. Woodger (1945) has emphasised the need for a theory of zygote structure to explain embryological data. This theory would include concepts relating to cytoplasmic organisation. In his view, the early stages in embryo development are to be explained in terms of the production and mutual interaction of parts—'of cell parts in the first instance, of cells and cellular parts later.'

A study of zygote development in ferns suggests the existence of biochemical pattern in the zygote and at the two-celled and quadrant stages. By inference, a heterogeneous distribution of metabolites may already have taken place in the egg before fertilisation. While the cells surrounding the venter may be closely comparable in their metabolism, they are probably not identical. A basipetal auxin gradient within the prothallial tissue has been demonstrated (Albaum, 1938), and there may be acropetal gradients of carbohydrates and other metabolites having their source in the older region of the prothallus. Thus there may be physiological differences on opposite sides of the ovum. These may be small but they may be none the less important. They may account for the fact that the embryonic axis is typically aligned on the axis of the prothallus, the epibasal segment being invariably towards the prothallus apex. A conception of this kind may provide a working hypothesis relating to the cytoplasmic organisation of the ovum and zygote and to the subsequent cleavage pattern and organogenic development. A hypothesis along these lines would also be in general accord with contemporary biochemical conceptions of morphogenesis, i.e. that different specific substances, or different concentrations of them, may be involved in the inception of the different organs. The need for concepts which will relate embryonic development and metabolism becomes evident when we contemplate the organisation of the post-octant embryo, in particular the positions of the primary organs relative to the archegonium and the prothallus.

Our knowledge of the ontogenetic growth pattern is almost entirely based on the 'stages of development' as ascertained in anatomical studies. These 'stages' are distinctive for the species and they occur with great fidelity in the normal development. In the ferns, each octant undergoes several divisions and the embryo becomes a spherical mass of histologically similar meristematic cells. Yet, at this early stage, the main pattern of development, or organisation, has already been established: the shoot apex, the first leaf, the first root, and the foot have been determined, and the orderly development of the sporophyte has begun. In short, it would appear that in the post-octant embryo there is a patternised distribution of metabolites, different morphogenetic substances, or different concentrations of the same substances, being present in each of the quadrants. As an over-simplification, we might perhaps say that a 'leaf-forming substance' has accumulated in the leaf quadrant, a 'root-forming substance' in the root quadrant, and so on. But however we may describe these events, the ultimate problem is to explain how the characteristic patternised distribution of metabolites is brought about in an initially homogeneous system (*see* Chapter III).

In a fern embryo entering on the post-octant phase of development, the basic pattern might be modified in various ways, e.g. by changes in the gene-controlled metabolism, the cells both of the embryo and of the prothallus being affected, or by environmental factors. Thus mycorrhizic nutrition of the prothallus may not only modify the nutrition of the embryo in a general way: it may affect one quadrant more than another and lead to its precocious development, or to its delayed or inhibited development. This, indeed, is what seems to happen in fern and lycopod species with saprophytic prothalli.

In the normal development, as in the embryogeny of *Dryopteris*, *Onoclea* or *Adiantum*, the primary organs, shoot, leaf and root, are formed almost simultaneously and grow in a mutually regulated or harmonious manner; and in all the subsequent growth and organogenesis, including the sustained growth of the adult over many years, this developmental harmony is apparent, i.e. a specific pattern of development is maintained throughout. The embryonic developments, in fact, lead on naturally and conformably to those that follow. But, in that the adult fern plant is a considerably more complex structure than the embryo, it may be inferred that in the ontogenetic development there is a continuous elaboration of the underlying biochemical pattern.

The Embryo a Spindle or Filament. In all fern embryos polarity is determined at the outset. In species with a suspensor, the young embryo typically undergoes some elongation and is filamentous in character. Where no suspensor is present, the zygote becomes an enlarging sphere, or spheroidal body, dividing successively into hemispheres, quadrants and octants. In species with a suspensor, the distal embryonic cell develops in an essentially similar manner. From a general survey of plant embryos, especially those of Bryophyta and Pteridophyta, Bower concluded that all were initially more or less spindle-like and were 'based on the ultimate type of a transversely septate filament' (1923). In his view, the two-celled stage of the leptosporangiate fern embryo could be regarded as a filamentous stage, this reflecting a primitive ancestral state. While there may be substance in such a view, we should, perhaps, be chary of accepting it out of hand. The shape of a growing zygote depends on allometric growth, i.e. on the relative growth development in different directions. If it grows rapidly along one axis only, a spindle, or filament, will necessarily result, and this will normally tend to divide by transverse walls. If its rate of growth is equal along all three axes it will become spherical; and equatorial, quadrant and octant divisions are likely to follow. Until more is known of the nature of the reaction systems that yield the different distributions of growth, views as to the relative evolutionary status of filamentous and spherical embryos must necessarily remain speculative. Nevertheless, it is a fact that the most filamentous and alga-like fern embryos, i.e. those with a suspensor, belong to eusporangiate species which on other grounds are held to be of ancient and primitive stock. As Bower has pointed out, no leptosporangiate fern is known to have a suspensor and there is no evidence of the formation of that organ *de novo*. The Ophioglossaceae and Marattiaceae afford evidence that the suspensor is an organ which, in different fern groups, may have been lost or eliminated in the course of descent. We should note, however, that a suspensor is consistently present in the seed plants.

Gametophyte and Sporophyte. Considerations of the embryogeny prompt a reference to similarities and differences in the development of the gametophyte. Each of the alternating generations begins from a single cell and affords evidence of polarity from the outset; in each there is an orderly segmentation pattern, a distal apical meristem, or growing point, being organised at an early stage. In the gametophyte, however, the 'continued embryogeny' and physiological dominance of the apical cell group are usually not retained as they are in the sporophyte. The very different developments of the gametophyte and sporophyte must be attributed to intrinsic differences. Yet it is not simply a question of chromosome number: a diploid prothallus still has the characteristic gametophyte morphology. Ultimately, as it seems, there must be some over-riding metabolic difference, or difference in the biochemical constitution or organisation, of the zygote as compared with the spore. Any satisfying biochemical theory of organismal pattern must be able to account for the very different developments of the gametophyte and the sporophyte.

Segmentation Pattern and Organogeny. In any general discussion of embryonic development in ferns, the distinctive segmentation pattern, especially during the early stages, naturally attracts attention, the more so as the several primary organs can be related to the segmentation at the octant stage. This indeed, led the earlier embryologists to postulate a direct causal relationship between segmentation and organ formation; or, as Goebel (1918, p. 978) called it, a kind of 'mosaic-theory' of plant embryogeny. In a critical analysis of this conception and its origins, Bower (1923, p. 300) has pointed out that 'instead of accepting a general embryology as based on cell cleavages, it would be more natural to regard the embryo as a living whole; to hold that it is liable to be segmented according to certain rules at present little understood: that its parts are initiated according to principles also as yet only dimly grasped: and that there may be, and sometimes is, coincidence between the cleavages and the origin of the parts, but the two processes do not stand in any obligatory relation one to the other.' That the developing zygote should be envisaged as a whole seems indisputable. Its specific, gene-determined reaction system, and the incident biophysical and environmental factors, are responsible for the distribution of growth and therefore for both the segmentation pattern and the pattern of organ formation. These two phenomena will be broadly, and some-times closely, coincident. As to the relative positions of the primary organs, the foot may be inconstant in position. This led Bower (1923) to the view that it is an organ which is formed 'only where it is required for the first stages of development and nutrition of the embryo.' Goebel (1898, 1905) had already stated (i) that the relative positions of the primary organs (shoot, leaf, root and foot or haustorium) are not the same in all vascular plants, (ii) that external factors do not determine the early embryonic developments, (iii) that the arrangement of parts is due to internal factors, and (iv) that the positions of the primary organs are such as to be the most appropriate for their function. The essentially organographic view expressed in (iv) was not fully acceptable to Bower: he considered that embryos do not show the plasticity implied in Goebel's statement. In the development of all pteridophyte embryos (and indeed of all plant embryos), Bower regarded the formation of a polarised filament, spindle or axial body, as the prevailing and presumably obligatory initial condition—a development 'based on the ultimate type of a transversely septate filament' (1923, p. 301). He did not consider that all the developments observed in fern and lycopod embryos are such as to be 'the most beneficial for their function': on the contrary he held that some of them, e.g. the formation of a suspensor, reflect a somewhat unprogressive hereditary constitution and impose more or less severe handicaps on the young sporophyte. The reality of the alleged disadvantages may be questionable. Such conceptions are difficult to test scientifically and it will probably remain largely a matter of opinion whether or not a suspensor is a drawback to the developing embryo. Its presence in the embryo of seed plants suggests that if it does not possess functional importance, it is at least not detrimental.

The Suspensor. When the morphologist asserts that the suspensor is a primitive organ found in some modern survivors of ancient stocks, it may well be that he has seized upon a truth. It is a genetical character which happens to become manifest in the early embryogeny and in the determination of which only a few genes may be specially involved. The genic action which leads to the formation of the suspensor may possibly be seen in those differential protoplasmic changes which occur in the elongating zygote. Even if we accept the view that physical factors determine the way in which a zygote divides, the metabolic material which generates some of the forces, and on which forces must work, is a specific protoplasm in a specific prothallial matrix.

Comparison of Embryogeny within the Filicineae. If we accept the view that the ferns are a varied but essentially coherent group—a 'brush' of phyletic lines originating in a common ancestral group, as Bower described them—it is cogent to consider what community or diversity of organisation they show in their embryogeny. Already we have seen that both in *Lycopodium* and *Selaginella* there may be considerable variation in the embryonic development from species to species. In the Filicineae, in which there are not merely generic but also familial, ordinal and sub-class differences, a still wider embryonic diversity might well be expected. To some extent this expectation is realised. There are, indeed, differences between eusporangiate and leptosporangiate embryos; and within some families, and sometimes even genera, such differences as the presence or absence of a suspensor are found. Other differences, such as the size and position of the foot and the tardy organisation of the shoot apex, are of the kind already encountered in *Lycopodium*. The extent of the vascular development below the shoot apex also differs in different genera. No vascular tissue is formed below the shoot apex in the embryo of the Marattiaceae and Ophioglossaceae. In *Matonia pectinata*, on the other hand, a strong and precocious vascular development can be discerned while the embryo is still within its calyptra (Stokey and Atkinson, 1952). Of the two groups of heterosporous ferns, both of which show specialisation in their spore-producing members, the Marsileaceae have an embryogeny which is essentially the same as that of leptosporangiate ferns, whereas the Salviniaceae have an exoscopic embryogeny. The Salviniaceae, however, are highly modified in several respects.

In general, the embryological data support the phyletic seriation based on the morphology of the adult plant. Furthermore, as the data of this and the preceding Chapter show, all fern embryos have much in common in the major aspects of their organogenic development and organisation.

Comparison with Other Pteridophytes. In view of modern trends in taxonomy, a comparison of ferns with other pteridophytes should be deferred until the data for all the classes of vascular plants have been reviewed. Some points of comparison with other pteridophytes may, however, be considered at this point.

An evident matter for consideration is the orientation of the embryo relative to the archegonium. *Equisetum, Psilotum, Isoetes, Ophioglossum, Botrychium, Azolla* and *Salvinia*, are all characterised by exoscopic embryogeny. In *Lycopodium, Selaginella, Botrychium obliquum, Helminthostachys, Danaea* and *Macroglossum* the embryogeny is endoscopic. In *Marattia* and some related genera, in which the archegonia are formed on the lower side of the flat prothallus, the embryo is endoscopic but has no suspensor. In leptosporangiate ferns, the embryo is neither exoscopic nor endoscopic: it is lateral, i.e. its axis is at right-angles to that of the archegonium. The orientation and initial segmentation of the zygote appear to be primarily determined by inherent or intra-prothallial factors, but the magnitude of these factors, and their true significance in the embryonic development, have yet to be assessed.

In lycopods, *Selaginellas, Equiseta* and ferns, a leaf is usually formed early in the embryogeny, though in some instances it may be delayed; there may also be a delay in the organisation of the shoot apex. These parallel cases of delay in organ formation appear to be referable to similar nutritional relationships between embryo and prothallus. No doubt they have a genetical basis. *Psilotum* and *Tmesipteris* are unique among pteridophytes in that no leaf or root is formed during the embryogeny, though older plants of *Tmesipteris* form scale-leaves and then vasculated leaves. Whether *Psilotum* is a leafless and rootless plant *ab initio*, or whether these organs were once present in the race and have been eliminated during descent, is not definitely known, though the balance of evidence has been considered by many morphologists to support the former view. In the highly modified, aquatic, heterosporous fern genus *Salvinia*, a rudimentary root is said to be discernible in the early embryogeny but becomes merged in the parenchymatous foot as the embryonic development proceeds.

The Filicineae differ from all the other classes of Pteridophyta in their possession of large or *megaphyllous* leaves, in contrast to the small or *microphyllous* leaves of lycopods, *Selaginellas*, and horsetails. If only the early embryogeny were considered, however, it is doubtful if this distinction could be maintained: in respect of their origin and positional relationship to the shoot apex, the first leaves of microphyllous and megaphyllous types are not unlike. As the sporophyte enlarges, however, and forms its second, third, and fourth leaves, the difference between the two foliar types becomes very conspicuous. Some observers consider that there is a fundamental difference between the megaphyll and the microphyll (Bower 1935; Hamshaw Thomas, 1932), i.e. that they are not, or are probably not, truly homologous organs. The present writer does not subscribe to this view. It is true that megaphyllous species have a capacity for leaf-growth that is not shared by microphyllous species; but in all the basic organogenic relationships—formation near the basiscopic margin of the apical meristem, dorsiventrality, vascularisation and phyllotaxis—there is no fundamental difference between megaphylls and microphylls: they are alike in being lateral foliar members, formed at the shoot apex.

From this discussion, no clear view emerges as to the relationship between the ferns and other pteridophytes. That their patterns of embryonic development show many similarities is evident, but whether these similarities are due to community of origin, or whether they are to be regarded as parallelisms of development, cannot be decided on the evidence thus far available. From the embryological data it appears that megaphyllous and microphyllous groups, though quite distinct, do not necessarily exemplify fundamentally different kinds of organisation.

Chapter XI

EMBRYOGENESIS IN GYMNOSPERMS:
CYCADALES AND GINKGOALES

GENERAL INTRODUCTION

IN the evolution of plants, the gymnosperms occupy a unique position between the still amphibious pteridophytes and the flowering plants. The gymnosperms are seed plants and include members of great antiquity. In their organisation they exhibit characters which remind us of their archegoniate or pteridophyte ancestors, on the one hand, and of the more highly evolved flowering plants, on the other. In the gymnosperms, we shall be concerned with the development of embryos borne within seeds and nourished by the parent sporophytic plant; we shall also have to survey a considerable and varied assemblage of species of which the systematic and phylogenetic relationships are by no means clear. That the Gymnospermae is a class of Pteropsida (or Filicopsida) is generally accepted by contemporary systematists; but the origins of the class are still obscure and uncertain. Some taxonomists, indeed, have suggested an origin from Lycopsida. At the other end of the scale a not dissimilar difficulty presents itself: there is no clear and generally accepted view as to how the angiosperms may have originated from gymnospermous ancestors, if that indeed was the evolutionary sequence. It is against this general background that this survey of embryogenesis in different gymnosperm orders, families and genera has been undertaken.

Contemplation of the facts of reproduction in a gymnosperm such as *Pinus*, in a lycopod such as *Selaginella*, and in a heterosporous fern like *Marsilea*, suggests that the gymnosperms may have originated from some early pteridophyte stock, or still more ancient proto-pteridophyte stock. In their somatic organisation and their reproduction, however, the gymnosperms have made important advances: they are true seed plants, adapted to a land habitat, widely distributed, and in some regions constituting the predominant vegetation. Considerable and, thus far, unbridged phyletic gaps separate the gymnosperms from the pteridophytes on the one hand, and from the angiosperms on the other. Nevertheless, comparison with these groups seems natural. The essential features in the life cycle are common to them all. In the assumed evolutionary sequence from pteridophyte to gymnosperm to

171

angiosperm, there is a progressive reduction in the development of the female gametophyte, a loss of motility in the male gamete, and elaboration in the retention, nourishment and protection of the embryo on the sporophyte plant and in the maturing of resistant, encapsulated germs.

The main homologies relating to the embryonic development may be briefly indicated at this point. The megasporangium of *Marsilea* or *Selaginella* corresponds to the nucellus of *Pinus*, the protective integument in *Pinus* being a new development not found in pteridophytes. The nucellus and its integument constitute the ovule which is borne on the upper side of a fleshy scale. In the nucellus of *Pinus*, as in the pteridophyte megasporangium, meiosis takes place: the four cells with haploid nuclei form a linear series, of which only the innermost develops. It corresponds to the single megaspore in a pteridophyte and becomes transformed into the embryo sac. But whereas the thick-walled pteridophyte megaspore is usually shed at maturity, or soon after, by a rupture of the sporangial wall, the megaspore in *Pinus* is retained on the parent plant. As Bower (1948) has said, all these facts 'point to the conclusion that the thin-walled embryo-sac of *Pinus* is a retained megaspore, and that we see in it a derivative state which has been universally adopted by seed-plants.' The retention of the mega-spore in the ovule gives it the biological advantage of continued nutrition. Just as the pteridophyte megaspore, e.g. that of *Selaginella* or *Marsilea* produces a prothallus, or female gametophyte, with archegonia at the apical end (or proximal face), so also in *Pinus* the megaspore or embryo-sac enlarges, its nucleus undergoes many divisions and a cellular prothallus (the so-called endosperm) is formed. Three to six archegonia become differentiated in this prothallus, the necks of the archegonia being directed towards the base of the scale, i.e. towards the axis of the cone. In a majority of living gymnosperms, fertilisation of the ovum within the archegonium takes place by a non-motile male gamete, or male nucleus, which is conveyed to the neck of the archegonium by means of a penetrating pollen-tube. In the Cycadales and Ginkgoales, however, the germinating pollen grains, i.e. microspores, develop tubes, but the male gametes still have the organisation of large motile spermatozoids. These are two in number in *Ginkgo*, *Zamia* and *Cycas*, but they are numerous in *Microcycas*. The young embryo grows downwards through the base of the arche-gonium into the prothallus (or 'endosperm') so that the embryo in the mature seed is embedded in nutritive tissue. Thus, in *Pinus*, as compared with heterosporous pteridophytes, the only new structure in the reproductive mechanism is the integument in the ovule, all the other features, as Bower has said, being 'modifications in accordance with

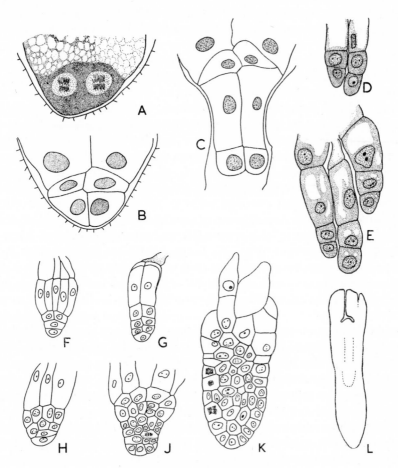

Fig. 37. Embryogeny in *Pinus*

A–E, *P. lambertiana*. A, First division of free nuclei. B, Three-tiered proembryo.
C, Four-tiered proembryo. D, Two of the four primary embryos have delimited the
primary suspensor initials. E, Primary embryos delimiting third segments. F–J,
P. ponderosa. F–J, Four successive stages in the development of the young embryo.
K, *P. nigra*. Older embryo, with apical cell. L, *P. radiata*. Median l.s. of mature
embryo. (A–E, × 160; F–J, × 120; K, × 95; redrawn from Johansen.)

life on land, of parts already present. . . . The biological probability of the several steps disclosed by this comparison is such as to justify their acceptance as evolutionary history.'[1] In a later Chapter we shall have occasion to consider the homologies that exist between the embryosac in flowering plants and that in the gymnosperms. Lastly, it may be noted that, in the gymnosperms, several archegonia may be fertilised, and that polyembryony, a feature already noted in some pteridophytes, is of very general occurrence.

In passing it may be noted that some investigators have stressed that heterospory is not a necessary postulate in a theory of origin of seed habit but rather heterothally (Thomson, 1927; Doyle, 1953). Doyle, indeed, suggests that the terms androspore and gynospore should be used instead of microspore and megaspore. There is increasing palaeontological evidence, however, of the incidence of heterospory in ancient pteridophytes.

Outline of Embryogenesis in Pinus. The details of embryogenesis in different gymnosperm groups are variable; they may also be somewhat complicated. In *Pinus*, to give a preliminary and simplified indication of development in one type, the zygote nucleus within the archegonium divides at once, and then again. The four nuclei so formed move to the basal end of the archegonium and lie in a single plane, Fig. 37. Further nuclear divisions follow so that four tiers of four nuclei are formed, each nucleus being subsequently separated from its neighbours by thin cell walls. The basal cells, i.e. those lying at the base of the archegonium, are the *embryonic cells;* the cells of the adjacent tier elongate to form the *suspensor,* or suspensors. In *Pinus* and some related genera, this cell complex at the base of the archegonium may cohere to form one single large embryo, or each linear series of cells may separate, with the result that four separate embryos are formed side by side. Although at first several embryos may be present, sooner or later one embryo in each ovule secures the ascendancy and the others become inhibited and absorbed. The enlarging embryo is thrust by its suspensor down into the prothallial tissue and there it matures into a germ with an apical growing point, numerous cotyledons, a hypocotyl and a massive root. The prothallus, which persists and functions as a nutritive 'endosperm,' enlarges and crushes the nucellus against the hardening integument which becomes the seed coat. (For a fuller account of the Pinaceae, *see* p. 190.)

Classification. The taxonomic and phylogenetic seriation of the gymnosperms is difficult and many important problems still await solution. The evidence suggests that the gymnosperms originated in ancient pteridophyte ancestors as two main lines of descent, the

---

[1] The pollen tube is, of course, also very significant in the evolution of seed plants.

Cycadophytes and the Coniferophytes. For these groups Sahni (1921) introduced the terms Phyllospermae and Stachyospermae respectively.

CYCADOPHYTES (or PHYLLOSPERMAE)	Pteridospermae (Cycadofilicales) Bennettitales Cycadales
CONIFEROPHYTES (or STACHYOSPERMAE)	Cordaitales Ginkgoales Coniferales Gnetales

(The underlined orders consist of, or include, living genera; the others are known only from fossil remains.)

Recently Eames (1952) has indicated that *Ephedra, Welwitschia* and *Gnetum*, hitherto included in the Gnetales, do not constitute a coherent and related group. Johansen (1950), who has given a valuable survey of gymnosperm embryology, follows Hagerup (1933) and others in the view that the group is not a natural one and describes his materials under the headings: Cycadophyta, Ginkgophyta, Coniferophyta and Ephedrophyta.

THE ENVIRONMENT OF THE OVUM

The gymnosperm ovum differs markedly from that of any of the pteridophytes in that its encasing archegonium is deeply-seated within a massive ovule. The developing ovum and embryo thus participate in the nutritional resources of the adult, sporophytic plant. As one example, it will be convenient to consider here the ovum in the cycads. As the megaspore enlarges to form the prothallus it becomes still more deeply embedded in the nucellar tissue. When eventually the several archegonia are formed, they are surrounded on all sides, except for the small region of the neck, by cells densely stored with reserve materials. The egg is of very large size and at maturity contains a conspicuous nucleus. During the phase of free nuclear division in the formation of the gametophyte (prothallus or 'endosperm'), a surrounding, tapetum-like, nutritive layer, one or two cells thick, and known as the endosperm jacket, is differentiated. Evidence of the existence of physiological gradients is afforded by the formation of walls in the gametophyte from the external nutritive wall progressively inwards towards the centre. The inception of the archegonium initials at the micropylar end suggests that there is a polarised distribution of metabolites within the prothallus. In this development the possibility of a stimulus from the pollen or pollen tube being involved should, perhaps, also be considered. In *Cycas*, for example, the pollen has already been received while the female gametophyte is still in the free nuclear stage. This late differentiation of the female gametophyte is very general in gymnosperms. In some genera, e.g. *Microcycas* the archegonium initials may occur round the sides and even near the base of the prothallus, but only those at the micropylar end become fully developed and functional (Reynolds, 1924). The ventral cell of the developing archegonium, almost all of which will become the ovum on maturation, enlarges rapidly, and becomes highly vacuolated. This would indicate the abundant presence of substances which increase osmotic pressure. A rapid inward movement of protein-forming substances then follows and a protoplasmic reticulum, with a centripetal gradient of small to large vacuoles, is formed. Meanwhile, the nucleus, which has also enlarged, divides, the daughter nuclei becoming the ovum nucleus and the ventral canal nucleus. The latter soon becomes disorganised. It has, however, occasionally been observed to enlarge like the egg nucleus and it may, in some instances, function as a male gamete, fusing with the egg nucleus (Sedgwick, 1924; Chamberlain, 1935). The archegonial neck in gymnosperms is very small, and, by comparison with that in bryophytes would be regarded by morphologists as being very much reduced.

As the ovum enlarges, it becomes surrounded by a tapetal-like layer of cells known as the archegonial jacket. As this jacket becomes more highly differentiated, the egg-membrane in contact with it becomes progressively more thick and tough, so resistant indeed that it remains firmly attached to the suspensor in maturing seeds. During its early development the egg-membrane in *Cycas* has numerous large pits, each covered by a thin membrane. These tend to be thrust by the turgid protoplasm of the egg into the adjacent jacket cells as haustorium-like processes. As the maturing egg becomes more turgid, these processes are protruded still further into the jacket cells, the separating lamellae and walls are broken down, and direct contact is established between the egg protoplasm and that in the jacket cells. At this stage the cells of the prothallus are densely packed with starch, protein and probably other reserve materials. These are the materials which are being actively drawn upon by the ovum through its peripheral haustoria. According to Chamberlain: 'The turgidity of the female gametophyte (in the cycads), and later, the turgidity of the central cell, and, still later, the egg cell, is extreme,' and he adds that if small cuts are made in the prothallus near the egg membrane, 'the liquid contents of the egg will spurt out, sometimes to a distance of 20 cm.' This is indeed a remarkable physiological situation, quite unmatched in any of the lower groups. In these observations, something of the biological significance of the seed habit, especially in its nutritional aspects, begins to be apparent: the ovum, and the germ formed from it, have a nutritional endowment that is quite unequalled in any pteridophyte, where the young embryo is dependent on the slender resources of an insignificant prothallus. This, of course, is a general observation; it is intended to emphasise a particular aspect but it requires some qualification. As we shall see in later chapters, there are many angiosperms in which the seed is very small and its contained germ ill-developed.

On the completion of the mitosis which gives rise to the egg nucleus and the ventral canal nucleus, and with the dissolution of the latter, the ovum enters on its final phase of maturation. The nucleus now moves towards the centre of the ellipsoidal egg, and becomes very large, up to 500μ in the cycads (Chamberlain, 1935). The cytoplasm becomes very dense, most of the vacuoles disappear, leaving what has been described as a kind of fibrillar appearance, and densely packed storage materials, including starch, oil and proteins, can be identified. This is the condition of the ovum as it awaits fertilisation.

In *Pinus*, also, the ovum is of considerable size and is surrounded by a nutritive archegonial jacket; but in some other Coniferales the ovum may be quite small, as in *Sequoia* (*see* Chapter XII).

The shapes and relative positions of the prothallus and archegonia are such as to indicate that physiological gradients not only operate between the periphery and the centre of the ellipsoidal ovum but also along its main axis, these making for important differences in reaction at the outer, or micropylar end, and the inner, or basal, end. Such polarity may indeed have been established before, or during, the formation of the linear tetrad of megaspores. In all gymnosperms the embryogeny is typically endoscopic: the *embryonic cells* which give rise to the *shoot apex* lie adjacent to the *basal* end of the archegonium, the suspensor being formed towards the micropylar end. The young embryo grows downwards into the prothallus (or 'endosperm') during its subsequent development.

Terminology. For convenience, the region of the zygote adjacent to the neck of the archegonium will be referred to as the *upper region*, or *upper end*, and the opposite end as the *basal region* or *end*. The embryo apex is always formed at the basal end and is endoscopic, i.e. develops away from the archegonium neck.

THE CYCADALES

The order Cycadales comprises some 85 living species, these being the contemporary representatives of a conspicuous and important group of plants that flourished in the Mesozoic Period. The genera include *Cycas, Stangeria, Bowenia, Dioon, Zamia, Encephalartos, Macrozamia, Microcycas* and *Ceratozamia*.

The large mature ovum is as described in the previous Section (p. 175). In these plants we encounter the very unusual and interesting phenomenon of fertilisation of the ovum being effected by motile spermatozoids. Moreover, the pollen tube is essentially a haustorial structure which penetrates the nucellus and supplies nutrients to the spermatozoids: it is not a carrier of the male gametes as in angiosperms. The spermatozoids are thrust into the ovum with such force that their ciliate region is stripped off, apparently because of the resistance offered by the dense cytoplasm of the ovum. The whole situation is of great physiological interest. Some observations which shed light on the constitution of the ovum may be noted here. At the time of fertilisation, the archegonial cavity, Fig. 38, is moist, but not filled with liquid. At the beginning the spermatozoids swim in the pollen-tube liquid in which they are discharged from the greatly swollen and highly turgid tubes. This pollen-tube liquid probably contains high concentrations of sugar solution; at any rate, it is known that the spermatozoids can move about freely in a 30 per cent solution of cane sugar. It is held that when this pollen-tube liquid of high osmotic pressure comes into contact with the turgid neck cells of the archegonium, it withdraws water from them, reduces their turgor pressure and permits some of the contents of the egg to pass into the archegonial chamber, 'leaving large vacuoles at the top of the egg' (Chamberlain). The spermatozoid is then drawn violently into the egg cytoplasm. In *Bowenia serrulata*, according to Lawson (1926), each archegonium secretes a drop of liquid through the neck cells, and this, together with the liquid from the pollen-tube, enables the spermatozoids to swim in the archegonial cavity. The neck cells are also said to swing open with a hinge-like movement, whereby the spermatozoids gain access to the ovum. These reactions may induce changes in the constitution of the upper region of the egg which are important in the subsequent embryonic development. Having gained access, the male nucleus moves into the centre of the ovum, and fuses with the female nucleus.

The Proembryo. The fertilisation of the ovum nucleus is followed by free nuclear division. This initial phase of development leads to the formation of the *proembryo*. At the beginning of this phase, all the nuclei are seen to be dividing simultaneously; their numbers thus increase in an approximately geometrical manner, 7, 8, 9 and 10 simultaneous divisions yielding 128, 256, 512 and 1024 nuclei respectively. At about the seventh division, not all the nuclei divide and departures from the theoretical numbers have been observed. There is evidence of polarity in the behaviour of the groups of nuclei associated with the upper and lower regions of the zygote. Division of nuclei of the lower group is always accompanied by division in the upper group but the converse is not always found. From this it could be inferred either that there is a gradient of a stimulatory substance from the archegonium

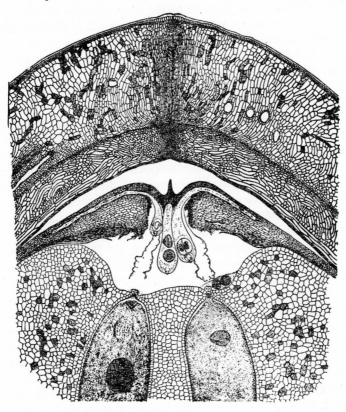

Fig. 38. Fertilisation in *Dioon edule*

Reconstruction of an ovule, as seen in longitudinal section, with its prothallus and two of the archegonia at the time of fertilisation. Motile spermatozoids are discharged from the ends of the pollen-tubes into the archegonial cavity. A sperm has entered the egg on the left; the egg on the right still shows the ventral canal nucleus; two sperms, immediately above, are ready to enter this egg (after Chamberlain).

base to the neck, or that there is a gradient of inhibitory substance in the opposite direction. During the earlier phase of zygotic development many more nuclei are to be observed at the upper end. The extent of free nuclear formation varies in different genera and species. In the large ovum of *Dioon edule*, which may be as much as 5 mm long, some 1000 nuclei are present (the corresponding theoretical number would be 1024); in *Zamia floridana*, with a 3 mm ovum, 256 nuclei have been recorded; but in *Bowenia serrulata* there are only 64 (Lawson, 1926). These data are of interest for comparison with those of gymnosperms with small zygotes. For example, in *Sequoia*, only four nuclei are present, a wall being formed at the first division. *Cycas* and *Stangeria* are characterised by a second phase of simultaneous free nuclear division at the base of the zygote, these nuclei being subsequently organised into the embryo apex and suspensor.

The numerous free nuclei are at first fairly uniformly distributed in the zygote, each nucleus being surrounded by a comparatively small amount of cytoplasm. Before wall-formation begins there is usually some movement of the nuclei towards the basal end. This is particularly noticeable in *Stangeria*: the cytoplasm at the basal end of the zygote becomes dense and contains many nuclei, whereas the cytoplasm in the upper region becomes vacuolated and thinly populated with nuclei. Important but as yet little understood biochemical and biophysical processes underlie these developments. Cell formation now begins to take place, the manner of this process being somewhat specific. After the free nuclear phase in *Encephalartos, Macrozamia* and some species of *Cycas*, the embryo becomes cellular throughout, this development being considered to be phylogenetically primitive. In *Dioon* and *Stangeria*, the deposition of the permanent walls is preceded by an evanescent segmentation throughout the whole zygote, both processes having their inception at the lower end and subsequently progressing towards the upper, i.e. neck end. In some others, cell formation takes place in the lower region while the upper region still remains in the free nuclear state, e.g. in *Bowenia*. After some hundreds of cells, with dense protoplasmic contents, have been formed, the visible organisation of the embryo begins. The oval cell mass, or partial cell mass, is known as the *proembryo*. This term is used to include the early embryonic development up to the point where the distal embryonic region begins to form the distinctive organs of the embryo proper.

Fig. 39. Embryogeny in Cycads

A–D, *Zamia umbrosa*. A, Formation of cellular proembryo at end of second phase of simultaneous nuclear division. B, Cellular proembryo; wall formation is completed but there is as yet no regional differentiation. C, Beginning of differentiation; young cap cells can be distinguished, also beginning of elongation of suspensor cells. D, Differentiation of proembryo completed; cap meristem, suspensor cells and buffer cells are now clearly differentiated (A, C, × 40; B, D, × 35; after Bryan). E, F, *Macrozamia spiralis*. E, Development of proembryo; the elongation of the suspensor cells has forced the embryo down into the prothallus; an enzymic digestion of that region is taking place. F, Five embryos derived from five archegonia; the suspensors are coiled and closely entangled; all but one of the embryos have become abortive; note the persistent egg membranes (E, × 33; F, × 2·4; after Brough and Taylor). G, *Bowenia serrulata*. Developing embryo with suspensor (× 75, after Lawson).

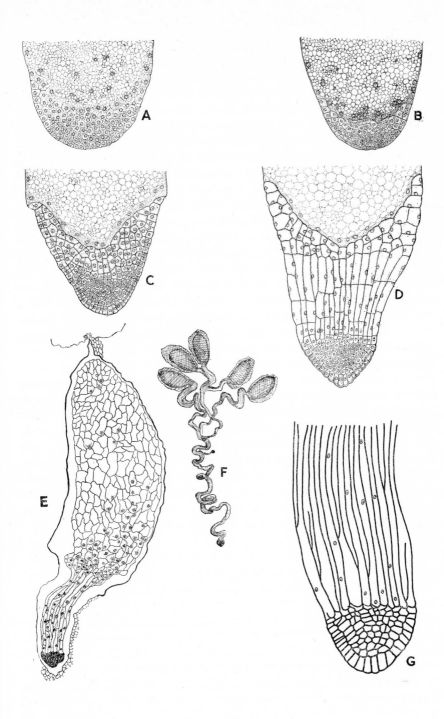

The coherent mass of densely protoplasmic cells which occupies the basal end of the archegonium will in due course develop into the body of the embryo proper. This region of the proembryo will here be referred to as the embryonic region. In the subjacent cells, which will develop as the suspensor, the first evidence of differentiation can be seen, Fig. 39, in that they begin to elongate conspicuously in the axis of the proembryo. The proembryo thus affords evidence of differential metabolism, the end adjacent to the base of the archegonium becoming the locus of apical growth and morphogenetic activity. Further evidence of differential metabolism is seen in the formation of mucilage cavities which begin to appear about this time.

Bryan (1952) has illustrated in detail the early embryonic development in *Zamia umbrosa*, Fig. 39. Following the phase of free nuclear division, a cellular proembryo is formed at the base of the archegonium. This proembryo differentiates into four regions, namely: (i) a distal meristem whose outer cell layer eventually forms (ii) a conspicuous cap; (iii) a suspensor, subjacent to the distal meristem; and (iv) buffer cells subjacent to the suspensor and extending for some distance up the sides of the archegonium. The cap cells become conspicuously enlarged in the axis of the embryo and have a haustorium-like appearance. They have densely granular contents, large nuclei and thick cell walls. The posterior region of the meristem continually adds new elongating cells to the suspensor which eventually becomes coiled and twisted. When eventually the cap cells disintegrate, the meristematic region enters on an active phase of growth. While cap cells have not previously been reported in the Cycadales, Bryan considers that on critical examination they will probably be found in other genera. Similar cap-like developments are known in various conifers. As the suspensor cells continue to divide and elongate to a remarkable extent, the embryonic region is thrust down into the tissue of the prothallus. Even more remarkable suspensor developments have to be recorded. As we have seen, several archegonia are present at the micropylar end of the prothallus; the ovum in each of these may be fertilised and the pro-embryonic and embryonic developments indicated above may ensue. One embryo, however, becomes predominant, and it alone becomes fully developed, all the others sooner or later being inhibited, Fig. 39 (Brough, 1940; de Silva and Tambiah, 1952). But the several suspensors, some of which are short and some considerably elongated, grow side-by-side and become twisted and coiled together. This compound structure is topped by the upper region of the suspensor of the single embryo that eventually attains to full development. In these developments, which are reminiscent of the interweaving of fungal filaments in the formation of complex fructifications, evidence of the organising capacity of the distal embryo apex may be discerned. Chamberlain records that the living suspensor in *Ceratozamia* can be pulled out to a length of some 7–8 cm.

Polyembryony within a single archegonium has also been observed, e.g. in *Macrozamia reidlei*, there may be one to three additional lateral embryos. These arise like the main embryo, each owing its formation to a small group of actively dividing cells at the basal periphery of the

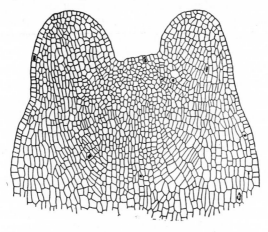

Fig. 40. *Dioon edule*

Embryo in longitudinal section, showing an early stage in the formation of cotyledons. The enlarged basal region is the coleorhiza. The shoot and root apical meristems are not yet clearly differentiated (after Chamberlain).

proembryo. The primary suspensor may also fork and give rise to equal embryos. A similar branching of the suspensor has also been seen in *Encephalartos*.

The Embryo. Contemporaneously with these suspensor developments, the embryonic region has been growing slowly. The differentiation of the rather uniform mass of meristematic cells takes place very gradually, but two cotyledons are eventually formed, while below them, in the bulky basal region known as the coleorhiza, an endogenous root has its inception, Fig. 40. In the early stages of this embryonic development, when the whole of the apical region is still growing, both periclinal and anticlinal divisions take place in the cells of the outermost tissue. The distal, superficial layer, which by virtue of its position becomes the dermatogen, appears to assume a haustorial function, Fig. 40, but whether the main nutrition of the embryo is by way of this tissue region, or acropetally by way of the suspensor, is still a matter for conjecture. After the formation of the cotyledons, the sunken shoot apex gives rise to the first leaf and to one or more associated

7

scales. The embryo, which is now deeply embedded in the prothallus, extends the whole length of the seed; the coleorhiza has become hard; the long suspensor is coiled and packed in the micropylar region; the nucellus has practically disappeared, its substance having been transferred to the prothallus, which functionally is now the 'endosperm' surrounding the germ; and the seed coat has hardened and matured in characteristic ways. The mature seed is fairly uniform throughout the group. In *Cycas, Macrozamia* and *Ceratozamia*, the seeds have already been shed before the embryo has formed its cotyledons.

The cotyledon number may be variable. Where two are present, they may be of unequal size. *Encephalartos* is reported as having three cotyledons. In *Ceratozamia*, which usually has one, the single cotyledon always develops on the side next the ground. If, however, the seeds are revolved in a klinostat throughout the development of the embryo, two cotyledons are typically formed (Dorety, 1908). The basal regions of the cotyledons are conjoined and form a kind of tube. The lobed or divided cotyledon tips have suggested to some observers that more than two cotyledons are potentially present.

The cycad seed has no resting stage. On germination, the coleorhiza bursts through the seed coat; the root-tip digests and forces its way through the base of the coleorhiza and begins to grow rapidly downwards; the cotyledons begin to protrude from the seed; and the new leaf formed at the apex slowly grows out. The greater part of the cotyledon(s) remains within the seed, serving as an absorbing or haustorial organ.

The vascular anatomy of the seedling is quite complex. In *Dioon edule*, both of the cotyledons have four evenly distributed vascular strands; these become concurrent in the short shoot and, together with whatever cauline vascular tissue there may be, constitute a four-sided vascular plate. Protoxylem groups are present at each corner. Conjoined with the corners of this plate, and seemingly decurrent from its lower side and continuous with its protoxylems, are the four protoxylem strands of the first root. The first and second leaves which are duly formed at the apex have each four separate vascular strands (Thiessen, 1908); these become conjoined in the protoxylem regions of the vascular plate. The vascular strand of the young sporophyte shoot is protostelic but with the enlargement of the shoot it becomes an endarch solenostele (siphonostele). In *Microcycas*, however, the vascular plate is an endarch siphonostele from the outset (Dorety, 1909). The anatomical developments in these cycad embryos and young sporophytes thus afford many interesting points for causal investigation. Here it is worth referring to some remarkable petrified embryos of Bennettitales which are dicotyledonous. The seeds appear to be exalbuminous—a remarkable condition in gymnosperms (Wieland, 1906; Scott, 1923).

Relationships. Chamberlain (1935) has argued that the Filicales, Pteridospermae (Cycadofilicales) and Cycadales may be regarded as a genetic line sufficiently well established by the morphological facts of fossil and living species. He points to the very fern-like character of the leaf in such genera as *Stangeria* which was once placed in the Polypodiaceae. He also attempts to explain the very considerable difference between the spore-producing members of ferns and cycads on the grounds that 'extremely rapid changes may take place in reproductive structures without any noticeable change in the leaves.' It is certainly a fact that there are well marked similarities between eusporangiate ferns, pteridosperms and cycads, while the probable evolutionary sequence in the elaboration of the ovule (p. 172) will not readily be set aside. But to show, on a strictly factual basis, at precisely what point the divergence between the ferns and pteridosperms took place, and to specify the morphological characters of the common ancestor, are tasks of very great difficulty, the more so when the possibilities of parallel evolution are borne in mind.

In the foregoing survey, the nutritional status of the ovum at and after fertilisation has been treated in some detail; for there is good support for the view that nutrition is a major factor in the embryonic development. If we assume that the cycads evolved from a eusporangiate fern source, then among the critical genetical changes would be those which determined the differentiation of a single megaspore and its retention within the sporangium. Thereafter the nutritional status of the prothallus, ovum and zygote would be radically modified. The genetical changes envisaged, though of great importance, were not necessarily of very great magnitude; but in the circumstances indicated above, they could be productive of very extensive changes in the embryonic development. For whereas the eusporangiate fern embryo has its inception in a small ovum, nourished by a small thalloid gametophyte, the embryo of the nascent cycad would have its inception in a large ovum, and would draw upon the nutritional resources of a relatively massive, vascularised sporophyte during its development.

GINKGOALES

It is purely as a matter of convenience that the Ginkgoales are treated at this point: any relationship between this group and the Cycadales is a very ancient and remote one. Chamberlain (1935), and more particularly Florin (1949), have associated the Ginkgoales with the Coniferophytes.

The ovum nucleus in *Ginkgo biloba* is fertilised by the nucleus from a motile spermatozoid. Proembryo development then follows, the phase of free nuclear division continuing, with a progressive diminution in nuclear size, until about 256 nuclei have been formed. These nuclei become uniformly distributed in the cytoplasm and after one or more general nuclear divisions—the eighth or ninth—wall formation takes place simultaneously throughout the proembryo. One nucleus is enclosed in each of the approximately equal cells, Fig. 41. This cellular homogeneity in the spherical embryo, however, masks an underlying polar differentiation. The cells at the basal end of the archegonium soon begin to divide actively and continue to function as meristematic cells, whereas those towards the central and upper regions divide infrequently, become relatively large and vacuolated, and may even undergo some dissolution. At this stage the embryo is characterised by a marked gradient of cell size. According to Johansen (1950), no true suspensor is formed in this species, but Radforth (1936) states that the proembryo elongates into a conical suspensor. The actively dividing cells at the base of the archegonium now become organised as an apical meristem and in due course two protuberances, the cotyledons, can be distinguished and other leaves are subsequently formed. In the compactly cellular region below the shoot apex the primary root has its inception, Fig. 41. Each cotyledon has an apical growing point consisting of a number of small meristematic cells. Like the shoot apex, this meristem is of the eusporangiate, or bulky, type of organisation. Embryos with three cotyledons are of frequent occurrence. Anomalous developments have also been recorded. Thus some differential growth has been observed as between the two cotyledons: one may be longer than the other and notched at the apex, while the other is deeply bifid; but at maturity the two are of equal length.

The first procambial strands originate in the cotyledons and can be traced basipetally into the young shoot or axis. The next strands are those of the first two leaves, which are decussate with the cotyledons, the constitution and form of the shoot stele being determined by these two sets of strands. In embryos with two cotyledons the stele is elliptical in transverse section; with three cotyledons it is triangular. In the root meristem in the former the plerome is wedge-shaped; in the latter it is bluntly pyramidal. The fully developed embryo usually

Fig. 41. Embryogeny in *Ginkgo biloba*

A, Proembryo with sixteen free nuclei, of which seven can be seen; *a*, archegonium neck. B, Cell formation in the proembryo is completed. In A and B, as in the other illustrations, the shoot apex is uppermost (× 70; redrawn from Johansen). C, Young embryo showing gradient of cell size from the basal into the apical region (× 120, after Lyon). D, Upper part of older embryo in l.s. showing the shoot apex, the cotyledons and the beginning of tissue differentiation (× 40). E, Nearly mature embryo (× 7·5). (D, E, after Coulter and Chamberlain.)

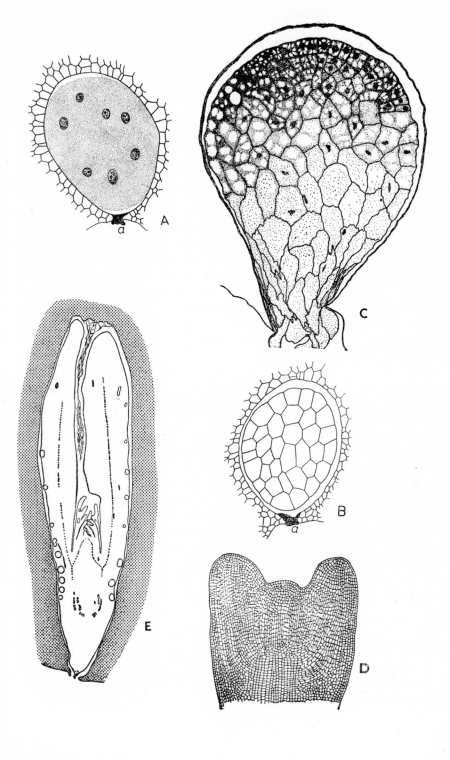

has five leaves, the first two being decussate with the cotyledons, the other three being irregularly disposed. On germination, the cotyledons have a haustorial function; the first leaves are deeply lobed; and the strong first root grows down into the soil.

Experimental Investigations. Steward and Caplin (1952) have shown that a growth-regulating substance, analogous to the 'coconut-milk factor' present in the watery endosperm of coconuts, is present in the developing gametophyte in the ovule of *Ginkgo biloba.*

Tsi-Tung Li (1934) and Radforth (1936) have reported on the culture of *Ginkgo* proembryos in various sterile synthetic media. Radforth found that there is a noticeable difference between embryos grown *in vivo* and *in vitro*, the latter having a diameter nearly twice that of equivalent proembryos grown *in vivo.* The *in vitro* embryos were symmetrical, whereas those grown *in vivo* were asymmetrical, i.e. the formation of the suspensor can be artificially delayed. The cultured embryos also gave other indications of responses to nutritional factors. Having thus obtained evidence that extrinsic factors, i.e. substances in the culture solution, can modify the form and development of the embryo, Radforth concludes that, under natural conditions, the suspensor 'is also the result of reaction to external influence,' i.e. to the surrounding prothallial tissue, and should therefore be regarded as 'a secondary feature imposed upon the symmetrical three-dimensional growth which characterises the earlier stages of proembryo development. As such it cannot have the significance of primitiveness ascribed to it by both Bower and Lang, who regard the axial single filament type of suspensor as even more primitive than the conical.' Nor can the embryo of *Ginkgo* be regarded as a 'primitive spindle.'

Phylogeny. Ginkgo biloba, like the living cycads, has been described as a 'living fossil.' *Ginkgo* and related genera are recognisable in Liassic (Lower Jurassic) strata, while other evidently ancestral forms flourished in Permian times. The embryo is unspecialised and of the bulky eusporangiate type. The simple leaves, with their parallel open venation, are very fern-like. Most members of the order have been extinct since the end of the Mesozoic: *Ginkgo biloba* is the only species that has persisted to the present day. Chamberlain (1935) considers that *Ginkgo* may have come from the Cordaitales, a purely fossil order, or that both may have originated from the same ancient pteridophyte stock; but Florin (1949) takes the view that the Ginkgoinae, Cordaitinae, Coniferae and Taxinae belong to the same natural group, the Stachyospermae or Coniferophyta, and that they constitute parallel evolutionary lines which probably had already separated in Upper Devonian or Carboniferous times.

Chapter XII

EMBRYOGENESIS IN GYMNOSPERMS: CONIFERALES AND 'GNETALES'

CONIFERALES

THIS very considerable assemblage of gymnosperms is believed to have sprung from a Palaeozoic coniferous ancestry, the latter possibly originating from some proto-pteridophyte stock. The order Coniferales has been variously classified, the principal families, according to several authors, being set out in the accompanying Table.

Families in the Order Coniferales

Chamberlain (1935)	Buchholz (1946)	Johansen (1950)	Florin (1951)	Lawrence (1951)
Abietaceae	Pinaceae	Pinaceae	Taxodiaceae	Taxaceae
Taxodiaceae	Araucariaceae	Araucariaceae	Pinaceae	Podocarpaceae
Cupressaceae	Taxodiaceae	Sciadopitaceae	Araucariaceae	Araucariaceae
Araucariaceae	Cupressaceae	Taxodiaceae	Podocarpaceae	Cephalotaxaceae
Podocarpaceae	Podocarpaceae	Cupressaceae	Cupressaceae	Pinaceae
	Cephalotaxaceae	Saxegothaeaceae	Cephalotaxaceae	Taxodiaceae
Taxaceae	Taxaceae	Podocarpaceae	Taxaceae	Cupressaceae
		Pherosphaeraceae		
		Cephalotaxaceae		
		Taxaceae		

Florin (1951) considers that, on the basis of the female reproductive organs, all the recent genera usually included among the conifers should be referred to two quite distinct subdivisions—the true Coniferae and the Taxinae.

In the present survey the writer has followed the arrangement of Buchholz (1946) and Johansen (1950). Technical methods for the examination of embryos have been given by Buchholz (1938).

Certain features are of very general occurrence in the embryogeny of conifers, in particular, the extensive development of the suspensor and polyembryony. Accordingly, some of the main embryonic developments will first be considered, and this will be followed by a general survey which will aim less at completeness than at a sampling of features of special interest.

The morphology of the ovule in the Coniferales, with its integument, nucellus, prothallus and archegonia is in agreement with the general account already given (p. 172). As the ovum in *Pinus* and other genera enlarges to its mature, pre-fertilisation state, it becomes highly vacuolated, some of the vacuoles being said to contain protein. It accumulates abundant food reserves and is surrounded by a conspicuous tapetal-like sheath or 'jacket.' The process of fertilisation, and the first and second mitoses of the fusion nucleus, have not only important biological aspects: they also present a range of biochemical and biophysical problems of great interest but on these we have practically no information whatsoever. The details of the discharge of the contents of the pollen tube into the ovum vary. Sooner or later a male nucleus moves down into the ovum and fuses with the female nucleus. The other nuclei near the archegonial neck degenerate. The four free nuclei formed by the first two divisions of the zygote at first occupy a central position in the proembryo. Soon fine fibrils are formed in the surrounding cytoplasm; these increase in diameter and length, become aligned along the axis of the proembryo and eventually extend to its base. Some of the fibrils then apparently become adpressed and attached to the archegonial membrane and 'soon the nuclei become pulled to the base of the archegonium by means of the tractive force exerted by the fibrils' (Johansen, 1950). This curious phenomenon is undoubtedly related to the polarity of the proembryo, for it has been observed that these fibrils have the same basipetal alignment, irrespective of the orientation of the cone or ovuliferous scale.

The eggs in the Coniferales, as compared with those of the Cycadales, are comparatively small and the number of free nuclear divisions is greatly reduced. An extreme case is found in *Sequoia* where there is no free nuclear stage, the egg being little larger than that of a pteridophyte and a cell wall being laid down at the first nuclear division, Fig. 44. In general, however, a free nuclear proembryo is characteristic of the Coniferales.

PINACEAE

In *Pinus*, which has been fully investigated, the zygote nucleus undergoes mitosis; this is immediately followed by a second mitosis, the four free nuclei thus formed being situated about the middle of the proembryo. This is the full extent of the free nuclear phase. The four nuclei now move to the base of the archegonium where a third division takes place, this last terminating with wall formation, Fig. 37 (*see also* p. 174). However this basipetal nuclear movement may be explained, it suggests the existence of polar gradients due to a biochemical differentiation within the proembryo. The nuclei, in fact, have moved to what will become the primary morphogenetic region of the embryo. The eight nuclei at the base of the proembryo are now disposed in two tiers each of four nuclei, with walls between. The cells of the upper tier again divide, three very regularly arranged tiers being thus formed. A division in the lowest tier completes this proembryo phase of development, Fig. 37. The lowermost tier will give rise to the embryo proper, the middle tier to the primary suspensor, the third tier to the rosette, while the uppermost tier which is unwalled on its upper surface will soon degenerate. The rosette is thus adjacent to a wall described as the basal plate which separates the embryo from the unorganised remains of the proembryo. Rosette cells are present in *Pinus, Cedrus, Tsuga* and *Pseudolarix*; but in *Abies, Picea* and *Larix*, in which they are initially present, they soon degenerate. Both the distal embryonic cell tier and the rosette tier may give rise to embryos, the development of the latter taking place more slowly. We shall return to them later.

Attention must now be directed to the lowermost tier, for it gives rise to all the organs of the embryo proper, including the shoot, cotyledons, leaves, roots and secondary suspensor cells, the upper three tiers contributing nothing to these developments. These tiers, nevertheless have important functions. The uppermost tier, of which the distal ends are in open contact with the egg cytoplasm, is apparently active in transmitting nutrients to the growing embryo below; and this appears to continue as long as any food reserves remain in the micropylar end of the proembryo. The cells of the tier below this absorptive layer, known as the 'rosette' because of its appearance in vertical view, are actively meristematic and often develop into embryos. The cells of the penultimate basal tier undergo a quite remarkable elongation and constitute the primary *suspensor*. At this stage in the development, where the embryonic region is about to be thrust down into the prothallus, the proembryo phase may be considered, arbitrarily but conveniently, to have come to an end.

Polyembryony is a very general phenomenon in the Coniferales. It may be due to the development of several fertilised eggs, this being said to constitute *simple polyembryony*: or it may result from the longitudinal subdivision and separation of several embryos from a single proembryo, this being described as *cleavage polyembryony*. Both types are of wide occurrence: simple polyembryony is general in *Larix, Picea, Pseudotsuga* and *Abies*; while cleavage polyembryony is a constant feature in *Pinus, Cedrus, Pseudolarix* and *Tsuga*. Buchholz (1933) has made the distinction between *determinate* and *indeterminate* cleavage polyembryony in conifers. In the latter there are no indications that any one of the several embryos, derived from a single zygote, has a distinct advantage during development. In the former, one embryo, usually the terminal one, is more favourably situated than the others, and tends to be the one which comes to maturity in the seed. The position of the various cleavage embryos is thus important in determining which will survive. This distinction can be applied to the embryonic development in several families of the conifers. Buchholz considers that the evolutionary steps may have been as follows: (i) indeterminate cleavage polyembryony; (ii) determinate cleavage polyembryony; (iii) simple polyembryony, with vestigial traces of (ii); and (iv) simple polyembryony without traces of (ii). The embryogenies of *Pinus, Cedrus, Tsuga, Cryptomeria, Biota* and *Chamaecyparis* exemplify indeterminate cleavage polyembryony: that of *Dacrydium* illustrates determinate cleavage polyembryony.

To return to *Pinus*: the four basally-situated embryonic cells, each with its subjacent suspensor, become slightly separated from each other, but the four short filaments so constituted remain attached to the rosette tier. In each of the cleavage embryos, the suspensor now begins to elongate rapidly, with the result that the embryo is thrust downwards into the gametophyte tissue. The distal embryonic cell, or apical cell, has meanwhile enlarged and divided by a transverse wall. The subapical cell so formed begins to elongate conspicuously to form what has been described as an *embryonal tube* or *secondary suspensor*. A second cell cut off from the apical cell also elongates and is transformed into an embryonal tube, and this process may continue till there are three or more embryonal tubes in linear sequence, all adding to the length of the suspensor region of the embryo, Fig. 37. As a consequence of these developments, the embryo has been thrust deeply into the richly stored cells of the prothallus. The production of the so-called embryonal tubes, which constitute the secondary suspensor, is evidently due to physiological processes similar to those which give rise to the primary suspensor with which they are continuous. Johansen notes that the elongation of the suspensors is so rapid that it is greater than the rate of the dissolution of prothallus tissue in front of the embryo apex; and hence the suspensor and embryonal tubes become coiled and convoluted, the first-formed suspensor cells soon collapsing.

Meanwhile, the apical cell has undergone divisions in other planes; a bulky meristematic tissue mass is gradually built up, the identity of the original apical cell being lost, Fig. 37. The presence of a distal apical cell in the early embryogeny in *Pinus* has attracted a considerable amount of attention. This cell grows, divides, and gives rise to the tissues of the young embryo in the same way as does the shoot apical cell in many pteridophytes. As the embryo enlarges, however, the apical cell disappears, the shoot meristem then consisting of an apical cell-group. In *P. banksiana* the apical cell persists for a considerable part of the embryonic development, and in *P. montana* it is stated to be evident in the mature embryo. The usual condition in *Pinus*, however, is that the apical cell becomes indistinguishable before the cotyledons appear. In the presence and persistence of an apical cell, morphologists have claimed support for the idea of a pteridophyte ancestry of the Coniferales.

The growing embryonic tissue both withdraws materials from the prothallus and secretes enzymes into it. As a result the prothallial tissue becomes disintegrated and liquefied, a zone of plasmatic material typically surrounding the embryo apex. Also, starch disappears from the prothallial cells before the embryo encroaches on them. As the prothallial tissue offers some resistance to the passage of the embryos, the suspensors come apart and become closely coiled and compressed and fill the disintegration cavity round the embryo. After the embryo has attained its maximum length, the suspensor and the remains of the egg and nucellus form a dry cap which may protect the root and basal end of the embryo when it breaks through the testa at germination (Chamberlain, 1935).

It may be inferred that while the embryo proper still consists of undifferentiated meristematic cells, the biochemical pattern that underlies and precedes the visible structural development is, nevertheless, beginning to be determined, Fig. 37. At any rate, soon after this stage, the distal region of the embryonic mass begins to differentiate into the shoot apex and cotyledons, while the proximal region becomes organised as a root. In the inception of the primary root, a small group of root initials can first be distinguished, and as these grow and divide the tissues of the periblem, root-cap and plerome become differentiated, Fig. 37L. A dermatogen is not recognisable in the early embryogeny. In *Pinus* many cotyledons are formed. Some investigators, e.g. Hill and de Fraine (1906–1910), have suggested that this is a derivative condition from a dicotyledonous ancestor, but others have taken the opposite view (Dorety, 1917; Chamberlain, 1935). Recent comprehensive investigations by Buchholz (1918–1933) indicate that polycotyledony is the primitive condition, the smaller cotyledon numbers being due to fusion. The several cotyledons in *Pinus* appear as primordia round the shoot apex before any vascular strands associated with them can be observed, Fig. 42 (Chamberlain, 1935).

In *Pinus*, the mean number of cotyledons is eight. *P. banksiana* (a species with an apical cell in the mature embryo) has three to six, and *P. contorta* from two to eight. On the other hand *P. lambertiana* has from twelve to eighteen, and *P. sabiniana* from seven to eighteen. It would be interesting to know, from a morphogenetic study of these and other species, if the small cotyledon number is associated with a small apex and the large number with a large apex, i.e. indicating a size and form correlation. Such information would be important in relation to Turing's (1952) diffusion reaction theory of morphogenesis (*see also*

Wardlaw, 1954). In *Pinus ponderosa*, Buchholz and Stiemert (1945) and Buchholz (1946) have demonstrated that there is a close and direct correlation between seed size, endosperm size, embryo size and cotyledon number. The embryos of large seeds, at the time of differentiation of the shoot apex and the cotyledon primordia, are much larger than those of small seeds, and have many cotyledons. The number of cotyledons may range from 6 to 16, embryos with these numbers being

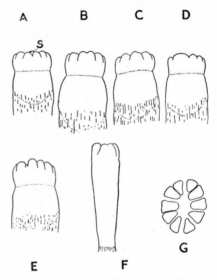

Fig. 42. Variable cotyledon number in embryos

A–E, *Cedrus libani*. A, Ordinary embryo with no fusion of cotyledons. B, C, Earlier and later stages in fusion. D, A large cotyledon that appears to have arisen by fusion. E, Evidence of cotyledon abortion. F–G, *Pinus banksiana*. F, Fusion of two cotyledons. G, Transverse section of a group of cotyledons; *s*, shoot apex (× 16, after Buchholz).

found in seeds with a volume range from 50–140 cu. mm. (*see also* Butts and Buchholz, 1940).

Embryonic Selection. Buchholz has shown that for a period of about five weeks during the early embryogeny little differentiation takes place, the several embryos within the ovule competing for survival. This has been described as the period of embryonic selection. Once predominance has been attained by one embryo, it grows rapidly and differentiates all its organs in 10–12 days; seed ripening is completed in a few weeks with little change in seed size. When the embryo eventually attains to its full size, Fig. 37, it is surrounded by the enlarged female gametophyte which has grown so as virtually to fill the remainder of the seed cavity, the whole being enclosed within the hard stony layer which constitutes the testa or seed coat.

So much for the single main embryo that comes to maturity. The proembryo in *Pinus* may, however, give rise to four filamentous cleavage embryos. Moreover, the four cells of the rosette remain meristematic and each may give rise independently to a filamentous embryo. The organisation of these embryos is like that of the distal embryos, but soon—at about the twelve-cell stage—their further development is restricted and they become abortive. Elongated suspensors are uncommon in rosette embryos. Well developed rosette embryos have been observed in *P. montana*. A single fertilised egg may thus yield eight young embryos; and since three eggs are sometimes fertilised, a single ovule may contain up to twenty-four embryos. Still larger numbers are possible and have, indeed, been observed. Usually only one of these embryos develops to maturity, though occasional seeds may yield two fully formed embryos.

Most species of *Pinus* have several archegonia, from two to six, but in *P. radiata* and some other species, only one is present, this being held to be an advanced and specialised condition.

With modifications of detail, which can be referred to the size and nature of the ovum, and to the distribution of growth in the embryo, the foregoing account of the embryogeny of *Pinus* is applicable to many of the Coniferales.

Phylogenetic Aspect. Johansen follows Buchholz in the view that species with a single, entire embryo have been derived from species in which cleavage embryos were normally present, i.e. cleavage polyembryony was the primitive condition. In this view, *Pinus* probably exemplifies the most primitive embryogeny among the Coniferales and cleavage polyembryony may have originated in the ancestry of this genus. This curious embryonic development, which is general in the conifers, is modified in various ways in the more advanced members of the group. The apical cell, which is a conspicuous histological feature in the early embryogeny of *Pinus*, may be a character derived from the original pteridophyte ancestors.

Embryogeny and Classification. Classifications which were accepted at an earlier stage have been modified in the light of later taxonomic, anatomical and palaeontological studies. Buchholz has suggested a classification based on embryology but so far this has not been co-opted into any modern and generally accepted taxonomic system. Although the Coniferales have many embryonic developments in common, distinctive features occur in the several families and genera. The facts of embryogeny may eventually enable botanists to indicate some of the lines of evolutionary advance and thus afford a basis for a phylogenetic classification.

In the Pinaceae, *Pinus* is considered to exemplify the most primitive

type, on the grounds of the abundant occurrence of cleavage polyembryony, the formation of rosette embryos, and the presence of an
apical cell. On the other hand, in *Pseudotsuga*, there is simple polyembryony and no single apical cell; also, there are no rosette cells and
therefore no rosette embryos. On these grounds it is recognised as the

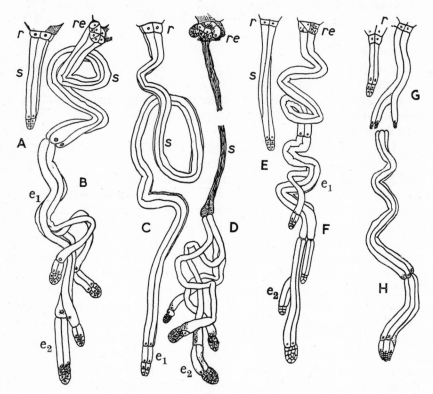

Fig. 43. Comparative series of embryos of Pinaceae

A, B, *Pinus laricio* (*P. nigra*). C, D, *Cedrus libani*. E, F, *Tsuga mertensiana*. G, H,
Pseudolarix amabilis. J, K, *Abies balsamea*. L, M, N, *Picea excelsa*. O, P, *Larix
kaempferi*. Q, *Pseudotsuga taxifolia*. *s*, primary suspensor; e_1, e_2, embryonal tubes;
r, rosette cells, which may give rise to rosette embryos, *re* (after Buchholz).

most derivative type. And between *Pinus* and *Pseudotsuga*, genera with
embryos showing various intermediate features are known, Fig. 43.
This is the basis of the conception advanced by Buchholz in 1931.
Until we have more knowledge of the factors involved in the inception
and development of the various embryonic features, and some clue
as to how these features change under the impact of genetical change,
it will be difficult to determine finally the taxonomic relationships. A
sufficiently detailed account of the various embryonic conditions in the

Pinaceae has been given by Johansen (1950), following the work of Buchholz (1918 *et seq.*). From the causal standpoint the basic questions would appear to include: How do known genetical changes affect (i) the distribution of growth, (ii) cellular differentiation, and (iii) organ formation, in the embryonic development?

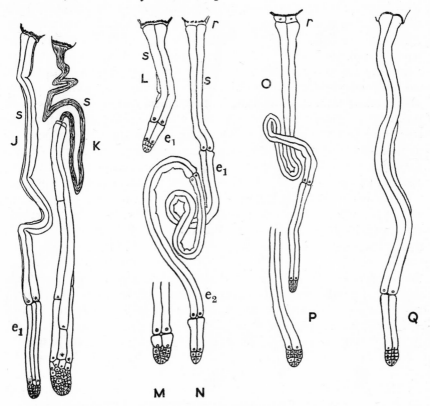

Fig. 43 (*contd.*)

ARAUCARIACEAE

The embryogeny of *Araucaria* and *Agathis* is notably different from that of all other Coniferales (*see* Eames, 1913; Burlingame, 1915; and Johansen, 1950). In *Araucaria angustifolia*, the 32–45 free nuclei become uniformly or concentrically distributed through the sub-spherical proembryo. In *Agathis* the free nuclei number 32–64. With the onset of wall formation in *Araucaria*, a polar elongation of a curious kind begins: those cells which later will give rise to the embryo proper occupy a central position, with elongated suspensor cells on the micropylar side and a layer of considerably enlarged cap cells on the distal side, Fig. 44. The initial simple polyembryony, involving 3–4 proembryos, is superseded by the strong development of one embryo and the disintegration of the others. There is no evidence of cleavage polyembryony, though seeds with two subjoined mature embryos have been observed. After a period of inactivity, the central embryonic cells begin to grow, this new phase being also marked by the disintegration and crushing of the primary suspensor cells and cap cells. At first all the cells of the small embryonic mass grow and divide about equally, but soon those on the proximal side elongate and form a secondary suspensor, while those on the distal side form a subspherical mass of small-celled embryonic tissue—in fact, the morphogenetic region of the embryo. The growth of the apical region now slows down and organ formation begins. A root apex is differentiated near the suspensor end, the adjacent region being recognised as the hypocotyl: at the distal end the nascent shoot apex appears to be inert, but two cotyledons are formed on its flanks. They continue to grow and differentiate and become very large relative to the rest of the embryo.

The origin and function of the proembryo cap have given rise to some speculation. It has been suggested that it protects the embryonic cells, provides the digestive enzymes, and so on. Johansen (1950) notes that, immediately after free cell formation, elongation takes place simultaneously in both the upper and lower groups of cells adjacent to the embryonic cells: if polar gradients are present, it is not surprising that the suspensor and cap cells react somewhat differently. The embryo apex in *Araucaria* is endogenous, a condition found in conifer root apices and in the shoot apices of some ferns (*see* Chapter IX; and Wardlaw, 1953). It has a multicellular, massive construction from the outset.

TAXODIACEAE

The embryonic development in *Sciadopitys verticillata*, Fig. 45, is in general like that in the Pinaceae (Buchholz, 1931). When the first four free nuclei move to the base of the archegonium, they divide and form 32 nuclei which become arranged in three tiers, i.e. an embryonic, a suspensor (described as a prosuspensor) and a rosette tier. Briefly, the subsequent development is characterised (i) by the very great elongation of the prosuspensor, its collapse, disorganisation and replacement by a so-called primary suspensor derived from the embryonic initials; (ii) by subsequent additions to the suspensor of embryonal tubes; (iii) by marked cleavage polyembryony described as the most extreme example of this phenomenon in the conifers; (iv) by the abortion of the apical cell in the individual embryo; (v) by the formation of some rosette embryos; (vi) by the occurrence of occasional mature twin embryos; and (vii) by the formation of occasional bud embryos which do not,

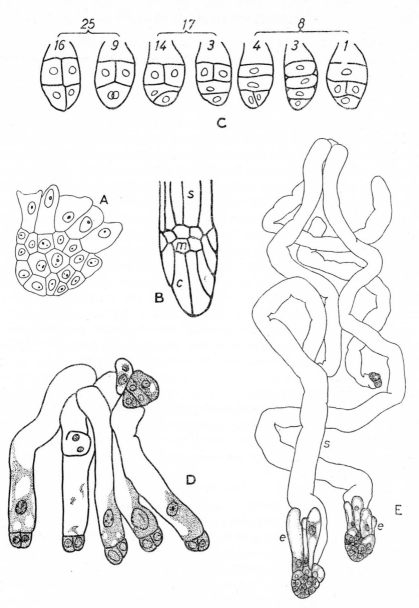

Fig. 44. *Araucaria angustifolia* (*A. braziliana*) and *Sequoia sempervirens*

Araucaria. A, Late proembryo, showing beginning of elongation of suspensor initial cells (× 485). B, Proembryo with cap cells (*c*) and portion of suspensor (*s*); meristem cells, *m* (× 235) (A and B after Johansen). C–E, *Sequoia sempervirens.* C, Diagrams indicating frequency of distribution of variations in cell arrangement in 50 four-celled embryos. D, Eight embryo units (some aborting) derived from the fertilisation of two adjacent archegonia. E, A later stage in the embryonic development; note the long suspensor (*s*) and the embryonal tubes (*e*) which are beginning to form the secondary suspensor (D, E, × 70; C–E, redrawn from Buchholz).

however, attain to full maturity. Buchholz (1931) regards the embryo of *Sciadopitys* as a type to which the embryos of the Cupressineae and Taxodineae may be referred.

Sequoia sempervirens, Fig. 44c–e, shows an unusual, indeed, quite exceptional, embryonic development. The archegonium and ovum are small, the spindle of the dividing zygote nucleus is aligned in the axis of the archegonium, and a transverse wall is laid down. There is, in fact, no free nuclear phase in this genus. The two nuclei again divide, their products being separated by longitudinal walls. Some slight variations have been recorded in the initial segmentation pattern (Buchholz, 1939), Fig. 44c. Each of the four cells can function as an embryo initial and give rise to a filamentous embryo. Some observations seem to indicate the presence of an apical cell, others that the division of the embryonic cell is typically by a longitudinal wall. The subsequent development is characterised by typical cleavage polyembryony, by the great elongation of the suspensor, the formation of a secondary suspensor, the development of embryonal tubes, and by embryonic growth initially by a single apical cell, this being soon transformed into a more massive apex. Rosette cells are usually absent. The single embryo which comes to maturity has usually two cotyledons (*see below*). The later stages in the embryogeny of *Sequoia*, in short, are of the general gymnospermous character.

In *Sequoiadendron giganteum* (*Sequoia gigantea*), the first walls appear when eight free nuclei, which fill the lower half of the archegonium, have been formed. Simple and cleavage polyembryony may both be present. A rosette is also conspicuous. The young embryo grows by an apical cell, but this is soon replaced by a group of initial cells. The subsequent developments are generally like those in *Sequoia sempervirens*. When in due course the single embryo has become considerably enlarged, it is cylindrical in shape and has a massive distal region consisting of the shoot apex and two to six, usually four, cotyledon rudiments (*see below*). The embryonic development is very protracted in this species, some two years elapsing between fertilisation and the maturation of the seed. Fertilisation in *Sequoiadendron giganteum* takes place in August. The embryo is still in a very immature state at the onset of winter but develops to maturity during the following season (Buchholz, 1937). During the first month the embryo is very small: at the two-celled stage after the division of the zygote, Buchholz estimates that it is 20,000 cubic microns. As the large tree which develops may eventually have a volume of 1640 cubic metres, the organism thus enlarges 82×10^{15} times.

In a statistical study of cotyledon number in *Sequoia* and *Sequoiadendron*, Buchholz (1940) has shown that in the former the range is

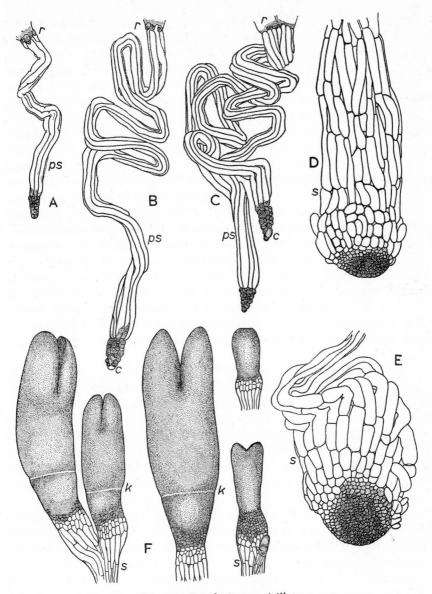

Fig. 45. *Sciadopitys verticillata*

A, Early stage showing prosuspensor (*ps*) and rosette cells (*r*). B, Embryo with
fully elongated prosuspensor and aborted cap cell (*c*) at tip. C, Embryo complex,
composed of two adjacent embryo systems; the embryo at the right has an aborted
cap cell (*c*). D, E, Development of individual embryos; the apex has broadened
and the secondary suspensors (*s*) have become multicellular. F, Embryos showing
various stages in the formation of the two cotyledons; note twin embryos connected by a common secondary suspensor; k, margin of root cap. (A–C, × 33;
D, E, × 50; F, × 17; all after Buchholz.)

from 2–3, with 90·4 per cent with two cotyledons, whereas in the latter the range is from 2–6, with 33·3 per cent with three cotyledons, and 62·8 per cent with four cotyledons. Differences in genetical constitution are thus reflected in the embryonic development. While the general developmental pattern is comparable in the two species, there are differences in the proembryo cytology, in the rosette development, in the number of cotyledons formed, and so on. These differences are indicative of both quantitative and qualitative differences in the growth processes of the two species. A consideration of the gametophytic and embryological differences in *Sequoia sempervirens* (Redwood) and *Sequoiadendron giganteum* (the Big Tree) has led Buchholz (1939) to the view that they should not only be regarded as belonging to distinct genera, but that they are probably descendants of widely separated genera—a view that is said to be supported by the fossil evidence.

In the other sub-family of the Taxodiaceae, including the genera *Taxodium*, *Cryptomeria* and *Cunninghamia*, the embryogeny, with various differences of detail, is generally like that in the Pinaceae. *Cryptomeria japonica* has two to four cotyledons, *Taxodium distichum* has two to nine, *T. mucronatum* has three to five, *Cunninghamia lanceolata* has two to four, and *Taiwania cryptomerioides* has two or three, (for details, see Johansen, 1950; Buchholz, 1932, 1940).

CUPRESSACEAE

The several genera included in this family show marked differences in the details of their embryonic development. In *Thuja*, which stands apart from other members of the family, there is no cleavage poly-embryony and only one embryonal initial undergoes further develop-ment—a marked simplification of the general embryonic process in gymnosperms, Fig. 46A–C. The early embryogeny is characterised by the presence of a distinctive apical cell, but this disappears before organ formation begins.

Libocedrus, *Biota* and *Chamaecyparis* form a coherent group, very different from *Thuja*, and with several distinctive features including the variable disposition of the free nuclei and the initial wall formation at

---

Fig. 46. Embryos of Cupressaceae, etc.

A–C, *Thuja occidentalis*. A, Four-celled proembryo; the ventral nucleus is seen above. B, Older embryo; the subapical tiers are elongating into the suspensors. C, Suspensors and young embryo; the distinctive apical cell in B is no longer in evidence (redrawn from Land). D–G, *Actinostrobus pyramidalis*. D, Walls have been formed in the four-nucleate proembryo. E, After some further nuclear divi-sions, the embryonic initials have been delimited. F, The suspensors have now elongated. G, A four-celled embryo (× 250; D–F, after Saxton; G, after Looby and Doyle). H–M, *Juniperus communis*. Stages in the development of the cleavage proembryos (*see* Text) (redrawn from Cook). N, *Saxegothaea conspicua*. Walled proembryo (× 215, after Looby and Doyle).

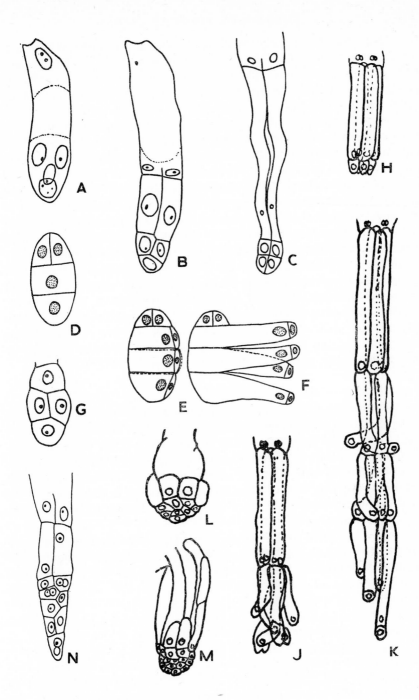

the base of the archegonium. The nuclear dispositions seem to be determined by the shape and size of the archegonium. Cleavage polyembryony is general and is evident at an early stage. The mature embryo has two cotyledons (Buchholz, 1932; Doak, 1937; Sugihara, 1938, 1939).

The section of the Cupressaceae represented by *Actinostrobus* and *Callitris* shows some curious and interesting variants of the general pattern of gymnosperm embryology. In *Actinostrobus* (Saxton, 1913), the archegonia, in groups of twenty-five to thirty, are formed laterally in the gametophyte, i.e. the transverse plane of the archegonium is aligned with the axis of the gametophyte. The microgametes traverse the nucellus laterally, two adjacent archegonia being fertilised by the contents of one pollen tube. Many of the archegonia remain unfertilised and soon degenerate. When the zygote nucleus divides, the two daughter nuclei are aligned on the long axis of the archegonium. The further nuclear divisions are such as to yield two cells next the archegonial neck (which undergo no further development and soon disappear), and four embryonic initials, Fig. 46D–G. These four cells appear to be polarised in the transverse plane for each of them forms a small distal initial cell and four very large suspensor cells, Fig. 46F, four embryos being usual in this genus. The details obtained by Looby and Doyle (1940) for the proembryo of *Callitris* are somewhat similar. The further development of *Actinostrobus* is characterised by the very great elongation of the suspensor, by the absence of a rosette, by the division of the embryo initial cell by two vertical walls, so forming a tier of four cells (no apical cell has been recorded), and by the elaboration of the secondary suspensor. The cotyledon number is usually two and the shoot apex is broad and massive. The peculiar features of the embryonic development, then, appear to be largely consequential on the position of the archegonia. From the developments outlined above, the physiological gradients in the axis of the prothallus appear to be more potent in the embryonic development than are gradients in the long axis of the archegonium. In a recent comprehensive account of *Callitris* Baird (1953) has noted that the ovule is pollinated long before the appearance of the megaspore mother cell, that the mature prothallus is long and narrow, that the archegonia are formed laterally and aligned along the pollen tube and that the embryogeny is essentially the same in *Actinostrobus* and *Callitris*.

In *Juniperus communis* there are no unusual features in the proembryo development: it consists typically of three tiers with four distal initial cells. Some curious and unique developments, however, have been observed in the four cleavage embryos. The terminal and subterminal cells, which in other gymnosperms would comprise the small embryo initial and the enlarging subjacent suspensor respectively, both elongate, Fig. 46H–L. Johansen (1950) regards each of these cells as a potential embryo initial. Sometimes the cells of the subterminal tier grow more rapidly and push aside those of the terminal tier, but usually the latter hold their own. They elongate and become lobed distally. Nuclear division, providing a nucleus for each lobe, may follow, or the nucleus may enter one lobe which then grows ahead of the other lobes. After a cell has elongated, the nucleus divides; one daughter nucleus occupies the small distal cell, the other the elongated suspensorial segment. In this way the distal cell may add new elongated segments to the intertwined suspensor, Fig. 46K. These developments impose a delay in the organisation of the embryo proper. However, the distal cells of those embryos which have penetrated deeply into the prothallus eventually enter on a new phase. This is characterised by the formation of a mass of meristematic cells and is the beginning of definitive embryo formation. The actively growing apical cell produces a broadening mass of meristematic cells, below which the single suspensor cell becomes greatly distended radially, Fig. 46L. As the embryo enlarges, cells in the subapical region elongate and form the massive secondary suspensor, Fig. 46M. The latter more or less effectively obliterates the embryos which lie behind it. Mature embryos have usually two cotyledons (see Cook, 1939).

PODOCARPACEAE

In *Saxegothaea conspicua* the archegonium is an elongated structure with a narrow pointed base. The four free nuclei from the first two mitoses of the zygote nucleus move into this basal region and again divide twice, the sixteen nuclei (approximately) being disposed in somewhat irregular tiers (Looby and Doyle, 1939; Doyle and Looby, 1939). These tiers, which occupy only a small part of the archegonium, include an upper one of three to five nuclei, open above to the cytoplasm of the proembryo, an adjacent tier of three to five cells which will elongate and become the primary suspensor, and a conical mass of some six to ten embryonic cells at the base of the archegonium, the most distal cell being an apical initial, Fig. 46N. Some of these cells become binucleate and persist for some time in this condition, but partition walls are eventually laid down. The subsequent embryogeny is usually characterised by the absence of cleavage polyembryony— though that may sometimes occur—by the elongation of the suspensor cells and the early collapse of some of them, and by the early formation of abundant embryonal tubes.

In several species of *Podocarpus* there is the unusual feature that fertilisation only takes place after the 'seeds' are shed from the plant,

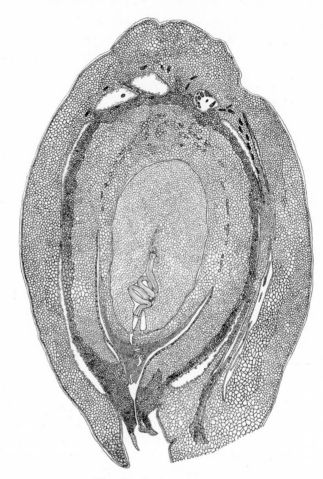

Fig. 47. *Podocarpus totarra*

Longitudinal section of ovule, showing developing embryo with suspensor penetrating the prothallus ('endosperm') ($\times$ 22, after Buchholz).

Fig. 48. Embryos of Podocarpaceae

A, B, *Podocarpus urbanii*. A, Two embryo systems with prosuspensors (*ps*) bearing two and three binucleate cells. B, Three embryo systems, the longest with three embryos developing massive secondary suspensors from embryonal tubes (*et*); many small embryos are present at the ends of prosuspensor cells ($\times$ 45). C, *P. totarra*. A later stage in the embryogeny, characterised by the formation of a massive distal region and secondary suspensor ($\times$ 80). D, E, *P. hallii*. Later stages in the organisation of the embryo proper (after Buchholz). F, G, *Phyllocladus alpinus*. Four- and eight-nucleate proembryos ($\times$ 925; from Johansen, redrawn from Kildahl).

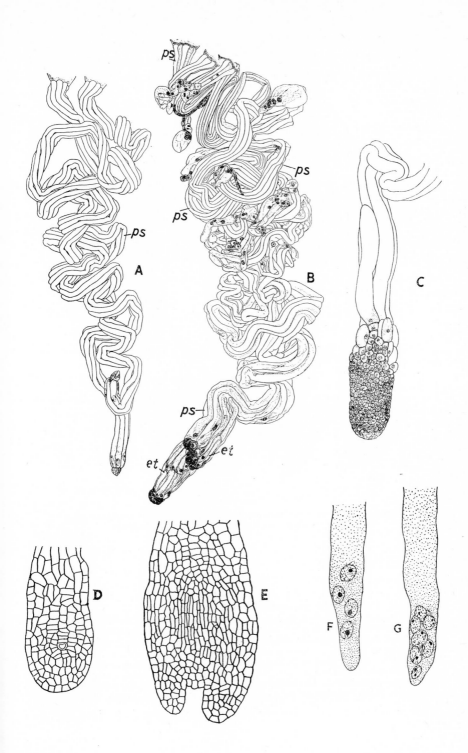

but pollination has already taken place. In the proembryo phase, eight free nuclei are present in the base of the archegonium. The several species of *Podocarpus* show differences in the arrangement of

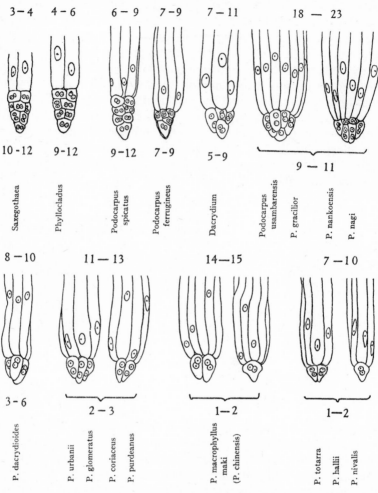

Fig. 49. Podocarpaceae

Comparison of young embryos, showing variations in the number of prosuspensor cells (numerals above figures) and in the number of binucleate embryonic cells (numerals below figures). *Podocarpus* includes the widest range of variation found in any genus of Coniferales. (All diagrams are approximately to same scale; after Buchholz.)

the proembryo cells. In *Phyllocladus*, eight free nuclei are present at the base of the narrow, saccate archegonium, Fig. 48F, G; after a further division the sixteen nuclei become arranged in tiers like an inverted pyramid, and on the completion of wall formation there are tiers of 5, 4, 3, 3, 1 or 6, 4, 3, 2, 1 cells, the uppermost 5 or 6 being cells which are open above to the cytoplasm of the proembryo. All the nuclei again divide: the upper tier produces five or six prosuspensor (suspensor) cells, and an equal number of nuclei which degenerate; the nine to eleven cells below, which on the elongation of the pro-suspensor are seen to constitute the embryo proper, become binucleate, a feature already noted in *Saxegothaea*. This binucleate condition of the embryonic cells is also common to *Podocarpus* and *Dacrydium*. Comparative studies show that the principal differences in the embryo-geny of the several genera and species can be referred to the relative developments of the suspensor and the binucleate embryonic cells. This is illustrated in Fig. 49 and in the accompanying Table (after Buchholz, 1941): the larger the suspensor, the smaller the number of distal embryonic cells.

Species	Number of parallel suspensor cells	Number of bi-nucleate embryonic cells
Saxegothaea	3–4	10–12
Phyllocladus	4–6	9–12
Dacrydium	7–11	5–9
Podocarpus spicatus	6–9	9–12
Podocarpus ferrugineus	7–9	7–9
P. dacrydioides	8–10	3–6
P. usambarensis	18–23	9–11
P. nankoensis	18–23	9–11
P. urbanii	11–13	2–3
P. coriaceus	11–13	2–3
P. macrophyllus maki	14–15	1–2
P. totarra hallii	7–10	1–2

Rosette cells are rarely observed in this group, but they do occur and may form small embryos in *Podocarpus urbanii*. Simple and cleav-age polyembryony occur though in some, e.g. *P. macrophyllus maki*, no cleavage takes place in the terminal embryo. In this species some of the prosuspensor cells may become detached and form small embryonic cells distally (*see also* Brownlie, 1953).

CAPHALOTAXACEAE AND TAXACEAE

The Taxaceae are held by some botanists to be the most advanced order in the Coniferales, but others, e.g. Saxton (1934) and Florin (1939, 1951), consider that both the fossil evidence and the morphology and life history of the living genera indicate the Taxaceae as an ancient phyletic line, distinct from the Coniferales, though probably sharing a common ancestry. The more primitive order, the *Cephalotaxaceae*, will be treated first.

The archegonia of *Cephalotaxus*, usually four in number, are long, narrow, and pointed at the basal end. At the thirty-two celled stage, the proembryo of *Cephalotaxus drupacea* is long and narrow, is closed in by walls at the upper end, and is without regular tiers, Fig. 51D, E. The upper cells constitute a rosette; the adjacent cells function as suspensor cells; and the distal embryonic region of the proembryo has a longish sterile cap cell which subsequently degenerates. The embryo apex is multicellular. There is no cleavage polyembryony, but the rosette cells may give rise to small embryos, these being without terminal caps. The presence of the distal cap cell has been associated with the suppression of cleavage polyembryony. The later development shows no exceptional features, two cotyledons being usual. The shoot apex is the last region of the embryo to be differentiated (*see* Strasburger, 1897; Lawson, 1907; Coker, 1907, Buchholz, 1925).

Taxus baccata, *Torreya* spp. and *Austrotaxus* are sometimes treated as the Taxaceae, with *Cephalotaxus* in a distinct but related family. In their gametophytic and embryonic developments, *Taxus* and *Torreya* exemplify a high level in gymnosperm organisation. In both *Taxus baccata* and *T. canadensis* the female gametophyte may or may not, in different instances, have become cellular when the pollen tube reaches it (Dupler, 1917; Saxton, 1936). The pollen tube may be in contact with the prothallus when the free nuclei are still in the course of becoming arranged round the megaspore membrane. A common but exceedingly interesting development in this group consists in the upward outgrowth from the prothallus of a multicellular tubular organ—described as the prothallial tube—which meets the downwardly advancing pollen tube in the nucellar tissue. This curious structure is mentioned or figured by various investigators, e.g. by Dupler (1917) in *Taxus canadensis*, by Saxton (1936) in *T. baccata*, by Coulter and Land (1905) in *Torreya taxifolia*, by Sahni (1921) in *Cephalotaxus*, and by Saxton (1934) in *Austrotaxus*. In short, it is of occasional occurrence in all Taxaceae. The interest of the prothallial tube lies in the fact that it closely resembles the very curious and unique prothallial tubes in *Welwitschia* (*see* p. 219). It may further be noted that no trace of a ventral canal nucleus has ever been observed in any species of *Taxus*, or in *Torreya taxifolia* (Coulter and Land, 1905), but it has been observed in *Torreya californica* by Robertson (1904).

The archegonia of *Torreya* are very small, those of *Taxus* a little larger, and those of *Austrotaxus* twice as large and comparable with those of *Cephalotaxus*. The number of archegonia is small, only one per ovule being present in *Torreya taxifolia*. On the other hand, in

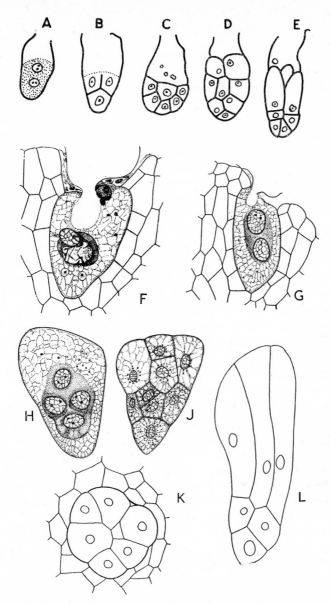

Fig. 50. *Torreya nucifera* and *T. taxifolia*

A, Proembryo with two nuclei (× 165). B, Four-celled proembryo (× 180). C–E,
Older proembryos, with ten to eighteen cells, and showing the beginning of elongation in the cells of the suspensor (C, × 180; D, E, × 165; after Buchholz). F–L,
Torreya taxifolia. F, Fertilisation; the male and female nuclei are in contact, the
cytoplasm of the male cell being closely applied to the egg nucleus; the cavity in the
egg cytoplasm is caused by the inrush of the pollen-tube contents; the non-functional
male cells, and the tube and stalk nuclei, are seen above. G, Two-celled proembryo. H, Four-celled proembryo, with beginning of wall formation. J, Proembryo shortly after partition walls have been laid down; the proembryo passes the
winter in this state. K, Cross-section through the suspensor cells. L, Proembryo
showing the elongation of the suspensor cells on the renewal of growth in Spring
(F–L, × 150; after Coulter and Land).

Austrotaxus (Saxton, 1934), *Taxus baccata* (Mirbel and Spach, 1843; Hofmeister, 1851; Jäger, 1899; Robertson, 1904; Saxton, 1936), *Taxus canadensis* (Dupler, 1917), several gametophytes may be formed, i.e. as a result of the development of several megaspores. In *Torreya taxifolia* and other species, wall formation takes place at the four free nuclear stage of the proembryo. In *Austrotaxus* nuclei in the basal group become walled in about the 8–16 nuclear stage, while the others remain as a free group in the cytoplasm above. *Taxus baccata* has a similar proembryonal condition. In *Torreya taxifolia* the proembryo completely fills the small archegonium; in other species it fills from one half to two thirds but subsequently elongates to fill the whole space. Except in *Austrotaxus*, this is the normal winter resting condition and has been designated the *hibernal embryo*. On further development, the uppermost cells, as in *A. spicata*, may constitute a rosette tier; the adjacent cells elongate and form the suspensor whilst the distal end consists of three multicellular tiers capped by a single apical cell. The further embryogeny is not known. *Taxus baccata* shows comparable developmental features, but the uppermost tier of cells degenerates contemporaneously with the elongation of the suspensor (Jäger, 1889; Johansen, 1950). In *Torreya nucifera*, Fig. 50, and *T. taxifolia*, the proembryo may consist of six to sixteen cells. On the renewal of growth, apart from various anomalous developments, there is characteristic cleavage polyembryony. The distal apex is typically multicellular and produces many enlarging embryonal tubes, a thick secondary suspensor being thereby formed, Fig. 51. The mature embryo has two cotyledons (*see* Coulter and Land, 1905; Buchholz, 1940; Tahara, 1940; Johansen, 1950).

Torreya and *Taxus* are highly specialised genera: Buchholz (1940) regards the mature ovule of *Torreya* as 'the largest and most specialised of those of all the conifers.' *Torreya taxifolia*, with only one small archegonium per ovule, and various distinctive embryonic features, is the most specialised species of the genus. Saxton (1934), in a phylogenetic scheme of the Taxaceae, considers that the five component genera were all derived from the same prototype, *Cephalotaxus*, *Taxus* and *Torreya* being indicated at the ends of three separate branches; *Amentotaxus* leads on to *Cephalotaxus*, and *Austrotaxus* appears as a connecting link to *Taxus*. *Taxus*, *Austrotaxus* and *Cephalotaxus* are characterised by simple polyembryony, though *Cephalotaxus* has determinate polyembryony in its small rosette embryos. Only in *Torreya*, has cleavage polyembryony been retained. The prototype of the order was probably characterised by cleavage polyembryony. Saxton (1934) regards the Taxaceae as a distinct and well-defined family of conifers, not closely related to any other family.

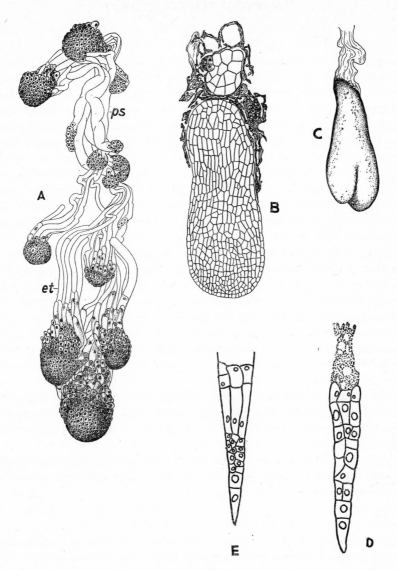

Fig. 51

A, *Torreya californica*. Complex embryo system dissected from a fully enlarged ovule; *ps*, prosuspensor cells; *et*, embryonal tubes, giving rise to suspensors (× 37). B, *T. taxifolia*. L.s. of older embryo on secondary suspensor, with remains of smaller embryos resulting from cleavage polyembryony. C, *T. californica*. Embryo from fully matured seed (× 18; all after Buchholz). D, E, *Cephalotaxus fortunei*. D, Proembryo of thirty-two cells, just before elongation of suspensor cells (× 120). E, Slightly older stage; suspensor cells elongating (× 100) (C, D, from Johansen, redrawn from Coker).

GENERAL COMMENT ON CONIFER EMBRYOLOGY

Buchholz (1950) has summarised the general state of knowledge of conifer embryology as follows. Of the 50 or more genera of living conifers, the embryogeny of about 80 per cent has been investigated to some extent. The same general pattern of development is found in all species of a genus, and in closely related genera the same pattern may also be observed. *Podocarpus* is exceptional. In this large genus many diverse types of embryogeny occur; but within the sections of the genus the relationships are comparable with those that obtain in the genera of other families. The Podocarpaceae which have been described as separate genera, *Acmopyle, Pherosphaera, Dacrydium, Saxegothaea,* etc., have embryogenies that fit into the series shown by the different sections of *Podocarpus*. Thus, the embryological data may be used as criteria in the taxonomic diagnosis of genera, though several genera may have embryogenies that are essentially alike. In the Araucariaceae, all members of the family have the same type of embryogeny, with simple polyembryony. As far as is known, the Podocarpaceae are characterised throughout by the presence of peculiar binucleate cells in the early embryo. Extensive embryological investigations have shown that most conifers, formerly supposed to develop through simple poly-embryony, have some form of cleavage polyembryony. Only the Araucariaceae and certain scattered genera such as *Thuja* (excluding *Biota*), several genera in Pinaceae, in Podocarpaceae and the Taxaceae, develop with simple polyembryony. Cleavage polyembryony has not afforded a precise taxonomic criterion as intermediate conditions are known to occur. The origin and explanation of this phenomenon have prompted considerable discussion and some disagreement, especially on the question of whether it is indicative of a primitive or advanced condition.

EPHEDRA, WELWITSCHIA AND GNETUM

The three genera *Ephedra, Welwitschia* and *Gnetum* have been placed in one order and one family by some taxonomists because they share a number of important characters in common, namely, the presence of vessels in the secondary wood, a compound strobilis in both male and female, the extension of the inner integument into a long micropylar tube, opposite leaves, absence of resin canals, and embryos with two cotyledons (Chamberlain, 1935). In the contemporary view, however, the Gnetales (or Ephedrophyta) of earlier classifications do not constitute a natural group (Eames, 1952), a view expressed by Bertand nearly eighty years ago. There is justification for raising them to ordinal rank. Each genus is probably the contemporary survivor of a line of some considerable antiquity. The fossil evidence, however, is conspicuous by its absence.

EPHEDRACEAE

There is only one genus in this family; some 32–35 species have been described. Strasburger (1876), Land (1904, 1907), Berridge and Sanday (1907), Berridge (1909), Khan (1943) and Johansen (1950) have contributed to our knowledge of the gametophytic and embryonic development. The ovule, typically with two archegonia, is a complex structure with two integuments and a deep pollen chamber. Initially the young archegonium has a neck cell and a central cell. The neck cell gives rise to a neck of four, or even eight regular tiers, and after the anticlinal walls have been formed the neck may consist of some 32 small cells somewhat irregularly disposed. The nucleus of the central cell divides but no wall separates the ventral canal cell nucleus from the egg nucleus. The ventral canal nucleus may remain near the neck or may move down into the centre with the egg nucleus (Land, 1904; 1907; Chamberlain, 1935).

Johansen (1950) has extended the account of the embryogeny of *Ephedra trifurca* as given by Land (1907). Eight free nuclei, described as being somewhat unequal in size, are formed from the zygote nucleus. These nuclei do not move to the basal region of the archegonium but are unevenly distributed in the protoplasm. Three to five of the nuclei become individually enclosed in somewhat irregular walls which later become globular. Each of these globular cells is an embryo (or pro-embryo); i.e. there is polyembryony without the cleavage phase that is characteristic of so many gymnosperms. The nuclei which are still free become arranged in a row down the centre of the archegonium, or become scattered within it. The lower walled cells usually form embryos successfully, and those near the micropylar end may also give rise to embryos (Johansen, 1950).

In the globular proembryo the nucleus divides, the more basal of the daughter nuclei becoming larger than the other, Fig. 52κ. The two nuclei now move towards the basal end of the cell and in proximity to each nucleus a small protuberance develops. The protuberance opposite the larger nucleus grows out into a tubular structure—described as the suspensor tube—while that opposite the smaller nucleus disappears. If the embryo cell is at the base of the archegonium, this suspensor tube will penetrate downwards into the prothallus: if the cell is higher up, the tube may grow outwards and then downwards. Both nuclei now move into the tube and a transverse wall is laid down, Fig. 52L. The upper nucleus moves backwards in the tube and disintegrates. A considerable elongation of the suspensor tube now takes place, the nucleate proembryo initial being thrust deeply into the prothallial tissue. The embryonic cell divides, the proximal cell giving rise to the suspensor (the secondary suspensor, according to Johansen). This cell divides by a longitudinal wall, and the distal embryonic cell by two intersecting obliquely longitudinal walls, an apical cell being thereby constituted. As the result of further cell division the distal region becomes more massive, Fig. 52M, N, the apical cell seemingly functioning for some time but eventually losing its identity. Cells at the proximal end of the embryo elongate to form suspensor cells. At about this stage the suspensor tube loses its turgor, collapses and disintegrates. Johansen regards this point as marking the transition from the proembryo to the embryo proper. While several of the embryos may grow for some time, usually only one comes to maturity. It is a dicotyledonous embryo of which the root is differentiated in proximity to the suspensor. Under favourable conditions there is immediate germination and the seedling becomes established during the same season.

In other species of *Ephedra* there are differences in the details of the development and segmentation of the suspensor tube. In *E. foliata* only one suspensor tube is initiated, the nucleus remaining undivided prior to tube formation. *E. altissima* is characterised by a very long tube.

The order to which *Ephedra* belongs is widely separated from the Welwitschiales and Gnetales (*sensu stricto*). It may have been derived from Cordaite stock or from an ancestral stock common to both the Cordaitales and Coniferales (Schoute, 1925; Florin, 1939; Eames, 1952).

GNETACEAE

The embryogeny in *Gnetum*, of which some 30 species are known, presents technical difficulties and consequently differences in interpretation have arisen. Differences between species have probably contributed to this state of affairs. In the ovulate flower, the nucellus is surrounded

---

Fig. 52

A, *Gnetum funiculare*. Branching of suspensor tubes (from Johansen, after Haining). B, C, E, *Gnetum gnemon*. Developing embryos (× 175; after Bower). D, *G. moluccense*. Several celled proembryo (after Thompson). F–J, *Welwitschia mirabilis*. F, Three-celled proembryo. G, Nine-celled proembryo, with four initial cells. H, Older stage; the cells of the inner ring are now considerably elongated, and those of the outer cortical ring are beginning to grow. J, A slightly older stage (*see* Text); *p*, pollen tube; *ic*, initial cells; *icr*, inner cortical ring; *ocr*, outer cortical ring; *c* cap cells (× 230, after Johansen, from Pearson). K–N, *Ephedra trifurca*. K, Proembryonic cell, with two nuclei and suspensor tube. L, The next stage, showing a partition wall in the suspensor tube. M, Beginning of formation of embryo proper; the distal region of the suspensor tube has divided by transverse and longitudinal walls. N, A later stage; the distal cells have divided by periclinal walls (K, L, × 950; M, N, × 470; after Johansen).

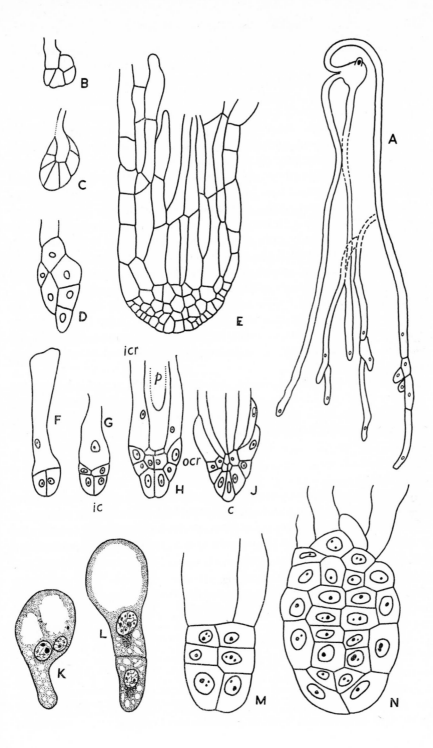

icr

p

ic

ocr

c

by three tissue sheaths or envelopes: by some investigators these are referred to as an (inner) integument and two perianth members; by others, as three integumentary structures; and by yet others, as perianth and outer and inner integuments. The growth of the inner integument is such as to make for a long micropylar tube, as in *Ephedra*.

The gametophyte and embryogeny have been studied in some detail in *Gnetum gnemon*. The megaspore (or embryo sac) nucleus divides repeatedly within an enlarging cell, the free nuclei becoming distributed in the wall layer of cytoplasm which encloses a large central vacuole. This free nuclear condition persists, at least in the upper region of the gametophyte, until after fertilisation, but some cellular tissue may be formed at the basal end (Thompson, 1916; Chamberlain, 1935). An extensive nutritional tissue is formed below the base of the gametophyte which lies deeply within the nucellus (Coulter, 1908). There is no formation of archegonia in *Gnetum* but a number of nuclei near the micropylar end become isolated within a cytoplasmic wall or sheath and function as eggs. Male nuclei discharged into the female gametophyte fuse with these egg nuclei, and this apparently acts as a stimulus to the rapid formation of a cellular endosperm-like tissue throughout the gametophyte, the cellular mass being particularly dense at the basal end. There is no evidence that the 'endosperm' formation is the result of a double nuclear fusion as in the formation of true endosperm in angiosperms. The ensuing embryonic developments are still insufficiently known, but a free-nuclear stage appears to be lacking. The zygote develops into a two-celled body which grows out in several conspicuous filamentous suspensors, Fig. 52A. Some of these may branch and all have a densely protoplasmic apical region at which a small distal embryonic cell is distinguishable. In parenthesis, it is at about this stage that the seed is detached. The definitive embryo is formed by the further development of one of the terminal embryonic cells, but in the earlier stages a polyembryonic condition prevails. In a species of *Gnetum* described by Thompson (1916), the fertilised egg divides to give two or three cells, each of which grows out into a long, usually uninucleate, downwardly penetrating filament. (To call these long tubular structures 'suspensors,' as if they were suspensors and nothing else, is misleading. The growing end of each such tube is potentially embryonic; so each 'suspensor' is comparable in its morphogenetic potentiality with a cleavage embryo in coniferous embryology.) In *G. moluccense* the suspensors grow beyond the gametophyte into the tissue at the base of the nucellus. Embryos, however, are developed only within the endosperm. In *G. gnemon* and *G. funiculare*, Fig. 52A, the filamentous embryos ramify widely throughout the gametophyte tissue and are thus not in close association with each other, as are the cleavage embryos of conifers. Hence it is understandable that the predominance of one particular embryo may only be established at a much later stage. Polyembryony, at least during the early stages, is a prevalent condition in *Gnetum*.

The segmentation pattern shown in Fig. 52B–E has been observed in the early development of the embryonic cell. The young definitive embryo in *G. gnemon* has an apical cell which may apparently persist for some considerable part of the further development. In this species also, concomitantly with the development of the two cotyledons, a lateral outgrowth appears on the side of the hypocotyl lying next to the ground. This protuberance, which becomes a cylindrical suctorial organ, appears to be of both exogenous and endogenous origin, for, according to Johansen, tissues of the hypocotyl epidermis, cortex, vascular tissue and pith all participate in its formation. At a later stage the embryo becomes cylindrical and has a somewhat massive many-celled apical region, with elongating cells behind. The single embryo which comes to maturity has two cotyledons, a long hypocotyl and a massive lateral suctorial, or haustorial organ, described as a foot (Campbell, 1940).

Several of the pre- and post-fertilisation developments in the Gnetales are strongly reminiscent of the corresponding developments in angiosperms. It is unlikely, however, that the two groups constitute a sequence within a single phyletic line, but rather that parallel evolution is involved.

WELWITSCHIACEAE

The very remarkable features shown in the vegetative development and mode of life of the single species *Welwitschia mirabilis* are matched by features in its fertilisation and embryonic development. In the ovulate flower, the nucellus is encased within an integument which becomes extended acropetally into a long micropylar tube, this in turn being enclosed within a sheath consisting of two broad perianth scales conjoined at their margins (Chamberlain, 1935; Campbell, 1940). The development of the gametophyte, or embryo sac, which exhibits some very peculiar features, is still rather imperfectly known. The work of Pearson (1909, 1910) suggests that only one embryo sac is formed. Within this enlarging cell there is abundant free nuclear division, so that eventually a thousand or more (approx. 1024) free nuclei are distributed through the enlarged ellipsoidal gametophyte. A majority of these are subsequently found towards the basal end. Cell walls now begin to appear, these dividing the embryo sac into large multinucleate cells. Archegonia are not formed. The multinucleate cells show a number of curious developments: the nuclei may divide, but more typically they fuse to form a single nucleus which may subsequently divide. The uppermost cells of the gametophyte, which may be regarded as being functional eggs, now begin to send out each an upwardly directed tubular process. These processes penetrate the nucellar tissue and eventually make contact with a pollen tube. The act of fertilisation is said to consist in a movement of the female nucleus into the pollen tube and a fusion there with a male gamete. The zygote thus formed elongates and divides into two cells, that towards the micropyle being recognised as the primary suspensor and the lower, or innermost and downwardly directed cell, as the embryonic cell. There is thus no free-nuclear phase. Still later, the organisation of the embryo is as is shown in Fig. 52F–J. The tier labelled *inner cortical ring* grows basipetally (relative to the embryo apex) and surrounds the primary suspensor. The *outer cortical ring* cells then grow in a similar manner to those of the inner cortical ring and in due course surround that tissue layer; i.e. a cross-section would show the primary suspensor surrounded by two rings of eight and sixteen cells respectively. A third and later, a fourth, sheath of cells may be added to the suspensor, Fig. 52J. The cap cells at the apex of the embryo undergo division but are later cast off, as in *Cephalotaxus*. The several organs of the embryo are subsequently formed from an inner plate of meristematic cells, Fig. 52J, situated below the cap.

DISCUSSION OF EMBRYOGENESIS IN GYMNOSPERMS

In attempting to distinguish factors which may be specially involved in embryogenesis in gymnosperms, we may note that the following observations and inferences have a general application.

(i) There is evidence of basipetal physiological gradients in the female gametophyte, i.e from the micropylar end (which is usually the archegonial neck end) to the basal end. These gradients may be important in determining the polarity and orientation of the proembryo and subsequently of the embryo.

(ii) At the time of fertilisation the ovum affords evidence of protoplasmic differentiation, i.e. of structural or metabolic heterogeneity, as between the upper or neck end and the basal end, the latter having the greater morphogenetic potentiality.

(iii) The extent of free nuclear division is directly related to the size of the ovum: where the latter is small, as in *Sequoia* and some other genera, there is no phase of free nuclear division.

(iv) Both the proembryo and the embryo show polarity from the outset. The proembryo is aligned along the axis of the prothallus; the embryonic pole adjacent to the base of the archegonium becomes the apical region, and the embryogeny is endoscopic.

(v) The initial development of small embryos, i.e. those with no free nuclear division, and of cleavage embryos, is essentially, and sometimes conspicuously, filamentous, the distal end being the region of sustained protein synthesis and morphogenetic activity.

(vi) With the exception of the Cycadales, Ginkgoales and Gnetales, cleavage polyembryony is a very general phenomenon. Abundant nutrition no doubt makes polyembryony possible, but the phenomenon should probably be referred to the action of gene-controlled enzymes.

(vii) In all gymnosperms, large amounts of nutrients are available in the gametophyte and nucellus. The ovum is sometimes of very large size and densely packed with storage materials; but even where the ovum is small, the proembryo and embryo are surrounded by, and can draw on, abundant supplies of nutrients during growth. The nutritional status of the embryonic environment thus seems likely to be of great importance in determining the development of the embryo. The very extensive formation of suspensors is probably an indication not so much by their functional importance as of the quantity and quality of nutrients available during the initial post-fertilisation phase. Only later, when a readjustment in the balance of nutrients may have been effected, does the definitive embryonic development proceed, this involving the formation of a bulky meristematic tissue mass. The delayed formation of the definitive embryo in the gymnosperms is reminiscent of the slow or belated organogenic development in some pteridophyte embryos.

(viii) Size and form correlations are evident in gymnosperm embryogenesis. Direct correlations have been observed between the size of the seed, the size of the embryo, and the number of cotyledons. The initial presence of an apical cell in some species and its disappearance later may also be indicative of a size-structure relationship.

PHYLOGENETIC ASPECTS

No close resemblances can be indicated between the embryos of gymnosperms and pteridophytes. Again, while some embryonic developments in gymnosperms are of an angiospermous character, the actual details are not to be matched in angiosperms: they suggest parallel evolution rather than descent from a common ancestor (*see* Chapter XVI, p. 323). While maintaining a strictly conservative attitude in these difficult problems of phylogeny, an attempt should nevertheless be made to indicate views that are not merely negative and unconstructive. To this end we may note, in the first instance, that gymnosperm embryos share the same *general* features as all other embryos, i.e. the early determination of polarity, axial development and a conspicuous meristematic and morphogenetic distal pole. On the general embryological data, then, the gymnosperms could share a common ancestry with other vascular plants, the concensus of morphological evidence pointing to ancient ferns, or possibly ancient fern prototypes, as the ancestors of the Phyllospermae. In their embryonic shoot apices, these gymnosperms show the eusporangiate type of construction. Other gymnosperm embryos are reminiscent of those pteridophytes with apices of an intermediate character between the eusporangiate and leptosporangiate organisations.

The inception of the gymnospermous phyletic lines may have taken place during the Lower Devonian or even in Silurian times. In a very general way we may perhaps envisage the ancestral forms as members of a prototypic pteridophyte stock, some of which were in a state of active mutation and therefore had a considerable potentiality for morphological innovation. Some descendants from this ancestral stock became elaborated as the eusporangiate ferns and others which showed still more advancement along the same general lines became the leptosporangiate ferns. There is evidence that some of these early ferns soon advanced to the heterosporous condition, e.g. *Archaeopteris* and *Stauropteris*. Among these ancient ferns, and also in species in other lines in which the elaboration of the shoot rather than the leaf was the conspicuous morphological innovation, were some in which *early* genetical changes led to the differentiation of sex in separate spores and sporangia, to heterospory, and to the retention of the megaspore. Given these innovations *at an early stage in the evolution of vascular plants*, important changes in the nature of the megaspore and in the morphological development of the embryo would necessarily follow, largely in relation to the impact of nutritional factors. And assuming further genetical changes of other kinds, it becomes possible to envisage how a number of lines, or phyla, of seed-bearing plants could have originated from an early pteridophytic stock.

Chapter XIII

EMBRYOGENESIS IN FLOWERING PLANTS:
GENERAL SECTION

INTRODUCTION

EMBRYOGENESIS in flowering plants has long been a subject of special interest to botanists. Historical accounts are available in the writings of Sachs (1890), Souèges (1934), Johansen (1950), and Maheshwari (1950). In the present book, considerations of space make it essential that some selection be made from the vast amount of information now available. The method adopted here has been to consider the embryonic development of flowering plants in its more general aspects as a first stage, then to sample different orders, families and genera of particular taxonomic or other interest. Embryos showing special features, anomalous and aberrant developments, etc., are then considered. Developments which illustrate the effect of genetical change, or the impact of factors which can be specified, are also examined, together with relevant experimental data. Finally, the data are considered in their causal and phylogenetic aspects. The writer's task has been eased by the comprehensive surveys of angiosperm embryology by Schnarf (1929) and Souèges (1934–1951) and by the recent publication of Maheshwari's *An Introduction to the Embryology of Angiosperms* (1950), and Johansen's *Plant Embryology* (1950). Maheshwari's book, written in the tradition of Coulter and Chamberlain's *Morphology of Angiosperms* (1903), gives an account of the morphology, histology and cytology of the antecedent events as well as of the embryogeny proper. Readers are accordingly referred to this work for an account of the development of the microsporangium and megasporangium, the male and female gametophytes, fertilisation and endosperm formation. Johansen's book is strictly confined to the details and analysis of the embryonic development and is important in that it affords a comprehensive survey of the embryology in all groups of seed plants.

THE ENVIRONMENT OF THE EMBRYO

The environment of the embryo is the embryo sac, the surrounding cell layer, and the tissues of the nucellus and integuments. The ovule may be variously orientated with respect to its stalk, while the embryo sac may be ellipsoidal or elongated, or bent round in various degrees.

A longitudinal axis of the embryo-sac may be specified as passing through the chalazal and micropylar ends, or through the antipodal group of nuclei, the central fusion nucleus and the egg apparatus. The micropylar end is morphologically the upper or distal end of the embryo sac. There is support for the view that polar gradients have a real existence in the embryo sac and that they are probably important in the development of the embryo.

The embryo sac may be enclosed within a tapetum of specialised cells, and these are probably important in the nutrition of the embryo sac, the developing endosperm and the embryo. Although we know little about physiological conditions within the embryo sac—our information being mainly of an inferential character, based on anatomical and cytological observations—it seems improbable that the distribution of metabolic substances in it is homogeneous. In *Lobelia trigona*, for example, the nuclear condition and the cytoplasmic vacuolation are noticeably different at the two ends of the elongated embryo sac.

Maheshwari (1950, p. 86) has illustrated diagrammatically several different types of embryo sac, these varying in the number and distribution of their nuclei (from four to sixteen). In that the nucleus controls the metabolism of the cytoplasm—it certainly produces important effects in its own immediate vicinity—metabolic differences in different regions of the embryo sac are to be expected. It may be noted that not all embryo sacs contain nuclei of identical chromosomal and genetical constitution and that they are not always disposed in the same manner. In fact, a considerable diversity in the distribution of nuclei in the embryo sac is found in different species. Moreover, some female gametophytes are monosporic, some are bisporic and some are tetrasporic in origin, according to the fate of the four nuclei derived from the division of the megaspore mother cell. The different patterns of nuclear aggregation in the embryo sac may also affect the embryonic development.

As a working hypothesis, the embryo sac may be recognised as a biochemical and biophysical system of considerable complexity. Maheshwari (1950) has illustrated many different conditions in the embryo sac. The supply of nutrients arriving by way of the chalaza will tend to maintain a gradient from the antipodal to the micropylar end. Notwithstanding the variety of detail in embryo sac formation in different species, the eventual organisation is rather alike in all. At maturity, the *Polygonum*, *Allium*, *Fritillaria* and *Adoxa* types, as described by Maheshwari (1950), have all a three-nucleate egg apparatus, an antipodal group, and two central, or polar nuclei (fused); and in the other types the egg apparatus, at least, is of the usual kind. In some genera, e.g. *Peperomia*, *Plumbago*, *Plumbagella*,

Acalypha, etc., the organisation of the embryo sac is radically different. In these genera it will, therefore, be interesting to see if the embryonic development shows any special features, these possibly throwing light on factors involved.

The immediate environment of the egg, or ovum, includes the micropylar passage, by which the pollen-tube enters, the two synergids, the adjacent embryo sac cytoplasm, the nucellar tissue, and, at fertilisation, the contents discharged from the pollen tube. The synergids, which initially have a cellular organisation with a vacuolated cytoplasm, usually degenerate before, at, or soon after, fertilisation of the egg, but they may persist in some species. They do not usually extend beyond the limits of the embryo sac wall, but cases are known in the Compositae where they elongate and penetrate into the micropyle, and even through and beyond it. The egg itself consists of the female nucleus and surrounding cytoplasm, enclosed in a thin wall or pellicle, and attached to the embryo sac wall near the micropyle. A small vacuole may be present near the point of attachment, the nucleus being typically situated at the other end, i.e. away from the micropyle. Though at a distance, the antipodal cells may have an effect on the fertilised egg. The central fusion nucleus (or polar nucleus), from which the endosperm is formed, may have important and, in different species, variable effects in the embryonic development.

Embryo sacs with disturbed polarity have been described: Maheshwari (1950) has summarised the relevant data.

The embryo sac is usually regarded as being devoid of appreciable food reserves, presumably because of its growth to large size and its eventual vacuolation. The considerable enlargement, however, is itself indicative either of rapid growth of the surrounding cells, or of the presence of osmotically active substances in the embryo sac. Starch is commonly present in the embryo sac of some species. The investigation of the storage materials in the embryo sac has been rather neglected by embryologists intent on other details (Dahlgren, 1939). In some species, e.g. *Arachis*, *Tilia*, *Penstemon* and *Acacia*, the embryo sacs are so full of starch as to make cytological observations difficult, while in *Styphelia* the egg tends to be obscured by the starchy accumulations. In most species that have been investigated the starch content becomes maximal about the time of fertilisation, and gradually decreases during the embryonic development. In some species large quantities are still present during endosperm formation. Even the egg apparatus may show evidence of starch accumulation. The nutrition of the embryo, by the general mechanism of the embryo sac tapetum, or by special haustorial structures, is considered later (*see* Maheshwari (1950) for references to the literature).

THE ENDOSPERM

Contemporaneously with the zygotic development, another factor becomes incident, namely, the developing endosperm. The central fusion nucleus forms the endosperm on being stimulated by fusion with a male nucleus. The endosperm is usually a triploid tissue but instances are known of haploid endosperm, while tetraploid and pentaploid endosperms are also known. In albuminous seeds the endosperm typically grows much more quickly than the embryo.

Although the endosperm will, of necessity, be treated rather briefly here, this tissue is very important in the development of the angiosperm embryo. Thus far, a majority of the investigations of endosperm have been undertaken from the anatomical and cytological rather than from the physiological point of view. The endosperm in the Gramineae, especially that of maize, has been extensively investigated from the genetical point of view. Maheshwari (1950) has contributed a full and interesting chapter on endosperm to which the reader is referred. The extensive review by Brink and Cooper (1947) on 'The Endosperm in Seed Development,' with its bibliography of 283 titles, should also be consulted.

The evolutionary origin and morphological nature of the angiosperm endosperm are difficult subjects. It is doubtful if an understanding of angiosperm endosperm can be gained by comparing it with that in gymnosperms. The angiosperm embryo sac, whatever its phyletic origin may have been, is a unique evolutionary specialisation; within it, in the formation of endosperm, we may recognise a further innovation.

Whereas the fertilised ovum becomes activated and forms a polarised embryo, the fertilised polar nucleus, which is usually situated near the centre of the embryo sac, shows no such development. The differences in physiological conditions at the micropylar end and in the centre of the embryo sac may be slight, but they must be considered highly important. Even in the Onagraceae, where the embryo sac has only four nuclei, with three forming the egg apparatus and one the polar nucleus, the latter, though fertilised like the ovum, does not form an embryo but an endosperm. As the ovum and the polar nucleus are genetically identical, as are also the two nuclei from the pollen tube, the zygote and fertilised polar nuclei are also identical. Indeed, irrespective of its chromosomal constitution, the central nucleus typically yields endosperm—a formless mass of cells, bearing no resemblance to a second embryo. The various theories of the endosperm as an anomalous embryo, though interesting notions, do not appear to lead anywhere.

The participation of a male nucleus in the inception of the endosperm is a very general phenomenon. According to investigators such as Němec (1910), the composition of a hybrid endosperm will be such as to be adjusted to, or compatible with, the needs of the developing hybrid embryo, the implication being that the nutrition provided by the nucellus and embryo sac alone might somehow be inadequate. Much could obviously be said both for and against this view. Some young embryos may require a very delicately balanced supply of growth-regulating substances and other metabolites, but it should not be overlooked that the endosperm also draws all its nutrients from the embryo sac and adjacent tissues. Certainly, where no endosperm is formed the embryo soon stops developing and degenerates. By its active nuclear division, cell formation and growth, the endosperm is able to draw, like all actively growing tissues, on the materials in the adjacent cells; and this has the effect of surrounding the embryo with a richly proteinaceous tissue on which it in turn can draw for its further growth. Merely to indicate some of the elements of the problem at once shows what a complex process embryogenesis really is. Moreover, while the embryo is developing, maturation is also proceeding in the tissues surrounding the embryo sac, i.e. there is competition for nutrients between the tissues within and outside the embryo sac (Brink and Cooper, 1940, 1947).

During the development of the embryo and endosperm, the surface of the embryo sac becomes actively absorptive, breaking down and utilising the materials from the adjacent nucellar tissue. In various species, the embryo sac may elongate into haustorial structures of a remarkable kind. In these developments we may perhaps see some of the innovations by which the flowering plants have become the most advanced and highly elaborated members of the Plant Kingdom. In some species, the endosperm forms extensive haustorium-like structures. (For a review of the many and varied embryo sac developments, the reader is referred to Maheshwari, 1950.) How these diverse, post-fertilisation embryo sac developments affect the embryogeny are clearly matters to which plant embryologists might well devote much attention and thought.

Rao (1938) has suggested that in those plants in which the embryo grows rapidly from the outset and is early differentiated, the endosperm tends to be non-cellular, cell formation taking place only at a later stage. But where the embryo grows slowly, and where the seed typically contains an immature and undifferentiated embryo, the endosperm is cellular from the beginning, or quickly becomes so. Various examples are cited of undifferentiated embryos which are surrounded by cellular endosperm, e.g. *Peperomia pellucida*, *Magnolia*, *Linaria vulgaris*, *Sarcodes sanguinea* (Oliver, 1890) and *Striga lutea* (Mitchell, 1915), the last two species being parasites. Many species show early formation and differentiation of the embryo and in these the endosperm is free-cellular at first, only becoming cellular later, Maheshwari (1950) has countered Rao's suggestion by stating that there are many examples which do not support this correlation. Nevertheless, some such correlation is perhaps to be expected, but it might be qualified, in different species, by the nutritional status of the ovule.

FERTILISATION AND EARLY EMBRYOGENY

In such a large systematic group as the flowering plants, with all their diversity of gynoecium, placentation and ovule shape, there is naturally a considerable variety of ways in which the male gamete eventually makes contact with the ovum. The relevant details have been surveyed by Maheshwari (1950). Here our primary concern is with the formation of the zygote and the factors that determine its initial and subsequent conformation, Figs. 53–55.

The actual gametic union seems to be a full and complete one and considerably different from that recorded for many gymnosperms. In some species, cytoplasm has been observed surrounding the male nucleus. Male cytoplasm may also surround the ovum, and about this time there may be disruption or disorganisation of the synergids. The biochemical and biophysical situation at the time of fertilisation is undoubtedly complex: many separate but inter-related events, some at the microscopic level, but almost certainly many more that are quite invisible, follow in rapid succession, e.g. the movement of the male nucleus, and its changing shape as it comes into contact with, and is absorbed into, the female nucleus. Yet it is an ordered complexity, for out of it there regularly comes the characteristic development of the embryo. Whether or not cytoplasm from the male gamete takes part in the formation of the embryo—a matter of genetical importance—is not definitely known.

Syngamy is followed by a period of rest, or, more probably, of reorganisation, during which the large vacuoles at the micropylar end of the ovum gradually disappear, and the cytoplasm round the nucleus becomes densely homogeneous. The primary endosperm nucleus usually divides a little before the zygote. The so-called 'resting period' of the zygote may be only a few hours, e.g. 4–6 hours in the Compositae and Gramineae, or many days, e.g. 14–15 days in *Theobroma cacao*.

It is a reasonable inference that polarity is determined in the un-divided zygote, or even in the unfertilised ovum. The still undivided zygote typically elongates in the axis of the embryo sac and small vacuoles become uniformly distributed through the cytoplasm. With some rare exceptions, the first nuclear division is followed by the formation of a transverse wall; i.e. as in pteridophytes, the first wall is at right-angles to the axis of the developing germ. Free nuclear division, as in the proembryo phase in gymnosperms, has not been reported in the angiosperms. In the two-celled embryo, the cell next to the micropyle is known as the *basal cell*, and that which projects into the embryo sac as

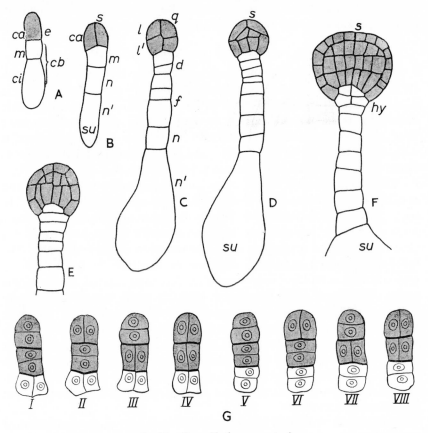

Fig. 53. *Capsella bursa-pastoris*

A classical example of embryogeny in a dicotyledon. Stages in the embryogeny illustrating Souèges' system of analysis and nomenclature (*see also* Fig. 55). The first transverse wall divides the zygote into an apical and a basal cell, *ca* and *cb* respectively. The products of these two cells and their respective contributions to the embryonic development are indicated; *e*, embryonic cell; *su*, suspensor; *hy*, hypophysis; *s*, position of shoot apex (semi-diagrammatic, after Souèges). G, *Chelidonium majus*. Different types of proembryo at the six-cell stage (after Souèges).

the *terminal cell*. The diversity in the early embryogeny of dicotyledons and monocotyledons depends largely on the nature of the further development of these two cells. The *basal cell* (i) may remain undivided with or without subsequent enlargement, or (ii) it may undergo further transverse divisions either (*a*) contributing to the embryo proper, or (*b*) not doing so. The *terminal cell* (i) may divide longitudinally, or (ii) transversely, either (*a*) not contributing to the suspensor or (*b*) contributing to it. The several possible developments of the basal and terminal cells may be combined in various ways. Now, if we begin with an elongating zygote in which the partition walls are laid down in general conformity with Errera's law of cell division by walls of minimal

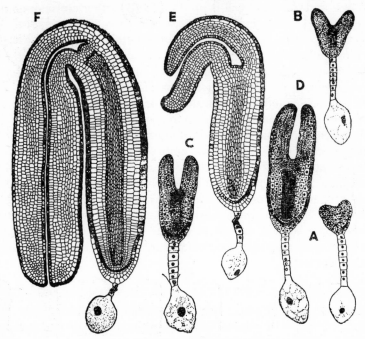

Fig. 54. *Capsella bursa-pastoris*
Later stages in the development of the embryo (after Schaffner).

area (modified in different species in relation to the gene-determined metabolites present), then the several patterns of development indicated above are what we might expect to find in a survey of a varied and considerable assemblage of species.

THE SOUÈGES SYSTEM OF CLASSIFICATION

On the basis of extensive investigations of angiosperm embryos, Souèges has outlined a system of classification of embryonic development based on the mode of segmentation (in particular, *see* Souèges 1937, 1938, 1939, 1949, 1951). In this scheme four *embryonomic types* are recognised: (1) fundamental types or archetypes; (2) secondary or derivative types; (3) superposed types; (4) irregular types. The first three are definable by the laws of embryonomy (*see below*), but the fourth type is not. Souèges considers that the third and fourth types may be the result of hybridisation, the second the result of adaptation by condensation or convergence. He also recognises two major divisions, or *periods*. In the first of these periods, i.e. types 1, 2, and 3 above, the developing embryo obeys the laws of embryonomy: in the second period only the terminal cell of the two celled proembryo obeys the laws, and the basal cell is omitted from further consideration.

The first period comprises three series: in A, the terminal cell of the two-celled embryo is divided by a longitudinal wall and is considered the most primitive: in B, the wall of the terminal cell is longitudinally oblique; in C, the proembryo consists of a linear series of four cells. Three comparable series are also recognised in the second period. Each period includes six megarchtypes, these being based on the behaviour of the basal cell during the embryonic development. Johansen has criticised this system on the grounds that it is based on a too restricted survey of angiosperm embryos, and that the separation of series A and B is debatable. His own scheme is that of types and their variations. Souèges pays most attention to the terminal cell of the two-celled proembryo: Johansen considers that both the terminal and basal cells should be given equal consideration. In this work these matters of embryo classification cannot be treated at length, but it is recognised that their value may increase as our knowledge of the factors in embryogenesis increases.

SOME GENERAL ASPECTS: LAWS OF EMBRYONIC DEVELOPMENT

Johansen (1950) states that angiosperm embryology may be considered in terms of *general embryology* and *special* and *comparative embryology*. General embryology might be further subdivided into *embryonic morphology* (the static aspect, comprising the study of the external form and internal structure), *embryonic physiology* (the dynamic aspect, the emphasis being on growth), and *embryogeny* (defined as the kinematic aspect, and comprising the major part of past and contemporary embryological investigations). Embryogeny may be further subdivided into *embryogenesis* (the origin of the embryo), *embryo-tectonics* (the architecture, i.e. cellular pattern of the embryo), *embryogenergy* (the destinations or functions of the embryo). In the writer's view the several aspects of embryology should not be separated, though, admittedly, it may be convenient to do so for some purposes. At any particular stage, the form and structure of an embryo are the result of antecedent gene-controlled metabolism, together with the physical and other factors which become incident in the enlarging embryo; and the way in which an embryo develops determines its functional activities.

Johansen (1950), following Souèges (1937), speaks of 'fundamental laws of embryogeny' and states that there are 'certain characteristics pertaining to embryos which partake of the nature of laws.'[1] 'Since the embryonomic laws are essentially specific, they provide the explanation for the fundamental organisation of the embryo of a given species. . . .' 'when the laws of embryonomy for a given species have been determined, they serve to define this species from the embryological standpoint.' Souèges (1937) has made it clear that his laws of embryogeny are 'truly specific, proper to the species.' But once the primary, specific laws have been established for a number of species, it becomes possible to state general laws which serve to define embryonic types or groups, thus making possible a classification of embryos—'the supreme objective of all embryological studies.' It would be true to say that Souèges' laws relate to the data of descriptive embryology rather than to the causes of embryonic development.

The laws of embryonomy are as follows: (Souèges 1937; Johansen, 1950).

The Law of Parsimony states that no more cells are produced by the embryo than are absolutely necessary.

The Law of Origin states that in any species the sequences of cell formations are established in a particular way and with such regularity that the origin of any cell can be specified in terms of, or related to, the earlier units of the sequence.

The Law of Numbers states that the number of cells produced by different cell generations varies with the species and depends on the rapidity of the segmentation in the cells of the same generation.

The Law of Disposition states that in the course of normal embryonic development, the cells are constituted by divisions in clearly determined directions and appear to occupy positions in accordance with the rôle which they must play.

The Law of Destination states that, in the normal embryogeny of any species, the cells of the proembryo give rise to clearly determined parts, and always to the same parts of the embryo.

Commentary. If these laws are intended, as Johansen (1950, p. 95) states, to 'provide the explanation for the fundamental organisation of the embryo of a given species,' it may be doubted if they do, in fact, achieve this aim. The progressive organisation manifested in the

---

[1] The essential feature of a law, as generally understood in the natural sciences, is that it has both a particular and a general application, and that it states the truth about related phenomena.

Law: Scientific and philosophic uses: In the sciences of observation, a theoretical principle deduced from particular facts, expressible by the statement that a particular phenomenon always occurs if certain conditions be present.

Laws of Nature: The order and regularity in Nature expressed by laws (1853). The conformity of individual cases to the general rule is that which constitutes a 'Law of Nature.' (*Shorter Oxford English Dictionary.*)

development of an organism is essentially due to gene-determined physiological factors and to various physical and environmental factors. The relevant fundamental laws would relate to the action and interaction of these factors and would attempt to relate the energy involved to the organisation developed. But the laws as stated do contribute to a description of, and afford a formula for, the orderly embryonic development.

Johansen considers that the law of parisimony may be the fundamental law and that all the others are derived from it. In this connection we may note that Haberlandt (1914) laid emphasis on what he described as the *principle of economy of material* and the *principle of efficiency* as pervading all development in plants, the latter principle being tantamount to a natural law. As stated by Johansen, the law of parsimony might be felt to carry some teleological implication. The law of origin calls attention to the fact that the embryogeny of any species is usually characterised by great regularity and orderliness both in the overall growth and in the sequence of cell division. This is, of course, a very striking fact and one which should not just be taken for granted. It is indicative of the very precise control of development by genetical and other factors. The law of numbers takes cognisance of the fact that each species has its own specific pattern of differential growth and that this becomes apparent in the characteristic histological pattern of the embryo. Johansen states that: 'The number of (cellular) elements engendered conditions the rapidity of the segmentation; it is the essential factor of determination.' The writer would rather say that gene-controlled metabolism and differential growth, together with the various factors which become incident in the enlarging embryo, determine the number and size of cells produced in different regions of the embryo.

The law of disposition, as stated by Johansen, appears to have teleological implications. With rare exceptions, the first division of the elongating zygote is by a transverse wall. The next division in the terminal cell may be either transverse or longitudinal. In many embryological works the segmentation of the enlarging embryo is treated purely as a descriptive morphological study. This is an indispensable initial stage: we must know what the growing embryo is like morphologically and histologically before we can begin to explore the underlying processes. The whole study will gain in vitality and value in so far as the visible anatomical developments are regarded as the result of processes of growth, beginning with a zygote of specific constitution. This law, as also the law of destination, once again reminds us of the extraordinary precision and fidelity with which the histological pattern is repeated during the individual embryonic development. There are occasional exceptions which are worthy of note. Thus, in *Chelidonium majus* (Chelidoneae, a tribe of the Papaveraceae,) the wall dividing the

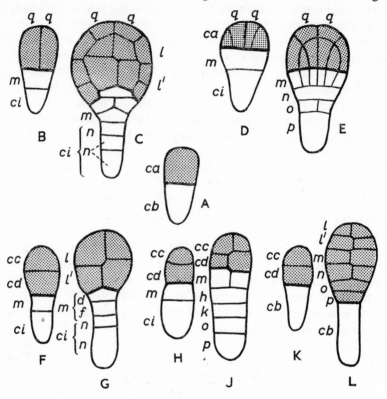

Fig. 55. Embryonomic types

Diagrammatic indication of the five *embryonomic types* and the contributions which the apical and basal cells of the two-celled proembryo make to the further embryonic development; the region of the embryo derived from the distal cell is stippled. A, The elongated zygote has divided by a transverse wall. B, C, Crucifer or Onagrad type as in *Ludwigia*. D, E, Asterad type as in *Lactuca*. F, G, Solanad type as in *Nicotiana*. H, J, Chenopodiad type as in *Chenopodium*. K, L, Caryophyllad type as in *Sagina*. *Souèges' Terminology* (*see also* Fig. 53). When the zygote divides by a transverse wall, the distal cell (*cellule apicale*) is denoted by *ca*, and the proximal or basal cell (*cellule basale*) by *cb*. When the latter cell divides transversely the most basal cell (*cellule inférieure* de la tetrade) is *ci*, and that above it is *m* (*cellule intérmediaire* de la tetrade). When the distal cell *ca* divides by two longitudinal walls, the quadrants are indicated by *q*; and when these divide transversely, the upper and lower cells are indicated by *l* and *l'* respectively. Also when the apical cell *ca* divides by a transverse wall, the distal segment may be indicated by *cc* and the sub-distal segment by *cd*. When *cc* divides by a transverse wall, the distal segment is *l*, and the adjacent segment *l'* (as in Souèges' Second Period Embryos).

basal cell may be orientated in almost any direction; and the sixteen-celled proembryo may show any one of eight segmentation patterns. Of these, four of the patterns can be referred to an inverted T-shaped tetrad, and the other four to a linear tetrad, Fig. 53 (Souèges, 1936, 1937).

To explain the phenomena that underlie the law of destination in terms of the process of growth may be indicated as one of the major tasks in plant embryology. This law is closely related to the preceding one. The determination of the relationships between the initial segmentation pattern and the subsequent organogenesis has been described as *embryogenergy*.

Embryonal Formulae. Souèges' classical demonstrations of embryonic development have led to the general acceptance of his descriptive formulae. These indicate the origin and relationships of individual cells during the early embryogeny. The laws of embryonomy indicated above relate to, and have their inception in, these formulae. The formulae facilitate comparisons between embryos, and reveal at once the essential histological similarities and differences. Fig. 55 illustrates the system of lettering as proposed by Souèges.

EMBRYONOMIC TYPES

The cellular configuration of the embryo at the four-celled stage, Fig. 55, and the part played by each of these cells in the organogenic development, constitute the basis for a classification of embryonomic types. Schnarf (1929), Johansen (1945, 1950) and Maheshwari (1950) have distinguished five principal types of dicotyledon embryo.

I. *The terminal cell of the two-celled proembryo divides by a longitudinal wall:*

(i) The basal cell plays only a minor part or none in the subsequent development of the embryo.

Crucifer (or Onagrad) type, Fig. 55B, C.

(ii) The basal and terminal cells both contribute to the development of the embryo.   *Asterad type*, Fig. 55D, E.

II. *The terminal cell of the two-celled proembryo divides by a transverse wall:*

(*a*) The basal cell plays only a minor part or none in the subsequent development of the embryo:

(i) The basal cell usually forms a suspensor of two or more cells
Solanad type, Fig. 55F, G.

(ii) The basal cell undergoes no further division and the suspensor, if present, is always derived from the terminal cell.

Caryophyllad type, Fig. 55K, L.

(*b*) The basal and terminal cells both contribute to the development of the embryo.   *Chenopodiad type*, Fig. 55H, J.

Johansen (1950) recognises a sixth type—the *Piperad* type—in which the first wall is longitudinal or nearly so. He also substitutes the term *Onagrad* type for *Crucifer* type.

These several types are indicated diagrammatically in Fig. 55. Various embryos from different orders are illustrated in Figs. 56–59.

Thanks to the investigations of Hanstein (1870) and Famintzin (1879) and later of Souèges (1914, 1919), the embryology of *Capsella bursa-pastoris*, though by no means generally representative, has become a classical example of dicotyledonous embryonic development. It also happens to be a useful and convenient 'teaching type' and as such may be briefly described here. The first division of the zygote is by a transverse wall. The terminal or distal cell now divides longitudinally and the basal cell transversely, so that the proembryo consists of four cells. The two terminal cells now divide by a longitudinal wall at right-angles to the first, a quadrant stage being thus constituted. Division of these cells by transverse walls yields the octant stage, the distal region of the embryo now consisting of a small growing sphere, Fig. 53C. The distal four octant cells on further development give rise to the shoot apex and two cotyledons; and the proximal four cells to the hypocotyl. All the eight cells enlarge considerably and divide by periclinal walls, the outer cells forming the dermatogen, the inner ones, after further divisions, giving rise to the periblem and plerome initials, Fig. 53D. Contemporaneously, the two basal cells elongate and undergo a number of transverse divisions, an elongated suspensor of 6–10 cells being formed. The proximal cell, i.e. the cell which is situated close to the micropyle, becomes conspicuously enlarged and is usually considered to have a haustorial function. The most distal of the suspensor cells, which is contiguous with the spherical distal region, continues to develop and functions as the hypophysis. This cell enlarges, projects a little into the spherical distal region, divides by a transverse wall and the two daughter cells by two vertical walls at right-angles to one another, a group of eight cells being thus formed, Fig. 53D, E, F. The most distal group of four cells forms initials of the root cortex, while the proximal group gives rise to the root-cap and the root epidermis, Fig. 54. The spherical embryo continues to enlarge with further divisions of its constituent cells. As the cotyledons begin to develop in the distal region, the spherical embryo becomes transformed into a somewhat flattened cordate body. Both the cotyledons and the hypocotyl now begin to elongate, chiefly by transverse divisions of their cells; the nascent shoot apex consists of a small-celled region, situated in the depression between the cotyledons. The root apex is meanwhile becoming organised, and incipient vascular tissue can be seen in the hypocotyl between the shoot and root apices. The enlarging embryo

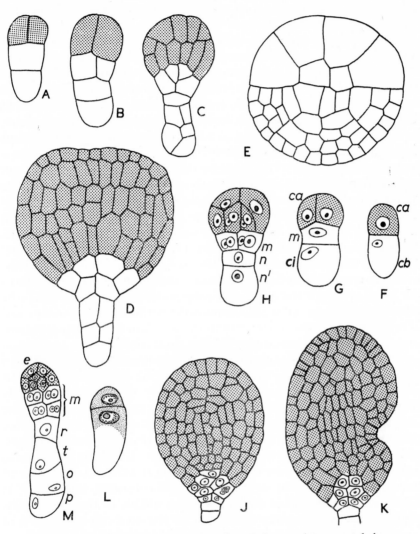

Fig. 56. Embryonic development in dicotyledons and monocotyledons
A–E, *Myosurus minimus*. A–D, The region derived from the apical cell (*ca*) of the
embryo is stippled. E, Embryo in transverse section. F–K, *Luzula forsteri*. L, M,
Geum urbanum. Lettering according to the Souèges system; *e*, epiphysis. (A, B,
× 650; C, D, × 600; semi-diagrammatic, after Souèges.)

begins to bend as it adapts itself to the curved embryo sac, Fig. 54 (*see also* Fig. 83).

In an investigation of the late embryogeny in *Pisum*, Reeve (1948) has shown that the epicotyl apex is initiated by periclinal divisions in surface cells before the cotyledons are formed. During the early cotyledonary development a simple apical dome, with one or two tunica layers and a shallow corpus, can be observed. At first the tunica layers undergo frequent periclinal divisions and the apex enlarges; in the fully developed embryo a well organised apical meristem of two layers is present. In seedling and adult plants this apex becomes more highly arched with three or four tunica layers, but its general organisation is as in the embryo. A rib meristem, which is first apparent in the meristematic tissue of the embryo axis, is important in that it contributes to the early rapid growth of the cotyledons. In the young cotyledons the distal meristem is not a highly organised one, the cell divisions being apparently at random. Root formation lags behind that of the shoot, but the first columella tiers, from which the generative root meristem is formed, can be distinguished about the same time as the epicotyl initials. This kind of study is important because it emphasises the need for a full re-examination of histogenesis in seed plants, beginning with the young embryo. Here the reader may also be referred to a developmental study of the apical meristem in different varieties of *Avena sativa* at different temperatures by Hamilton (1948).

A critical analysis of the several embryonomic types will call for a study of the factors which determine the specific distribution of growth. The histological pattern is probably indicative of differential metabolic activity in the embryo, cell division, according to D'Arcy Thompson (1917), tending to restore equilibrium in the system. In any species it is reasonable to suppose that the particular segmentation pattern is gene-determined, for the different kinds, or intensities, of metabolic activity in different parts of the embryo are ultimately to be referred to factors in the hereditary constitution. But in that different reaction systems may yield closely comparable embryonic cell patterns, the use of embryological data in taxonomy and other comparative studies should be viewed with reserve in the present state of knowledge.

In the early stages there are no essential anatomical differences between the embryos of monocotyledons and dicotyledons. Fig. 56F–K shows the development of a simple monocotyledonous embryo, that of *Luzula*. The terminal cell divides longitudinally, as in *Capsella*, and the basal cell transversely. A further longitudinal division in the terminal cell at right-angles to the first yields a quadrant. The subjacent cell also divides by a longitudinal wall. Later, as Fig. 56J shows, the embryo becomes spherical, the upper cell-products of the basal cell

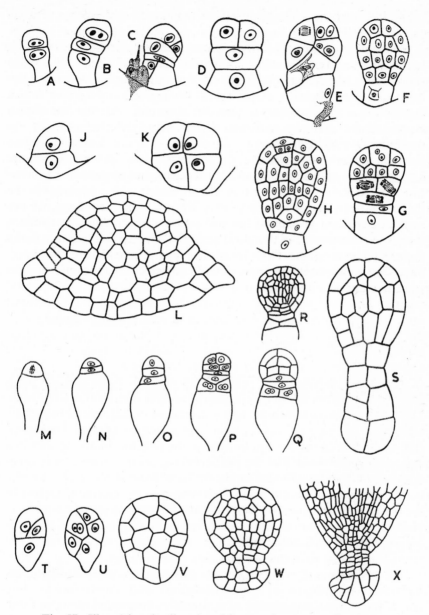

Fig. 57. Illustrating the diversity of form and structure of embryos
A–H, *Ulmus americana* (after Shattuck). J–L, *Eriocaulon septangulare*. J, Two-celled stage. K, Quadrant stage. L, Embryo from mature seed (× 730, redrawn from Smith). M–R, *Sedum acre* (redrawn from Souèges). S, *Chenopodium bonus-henricus* (× 460, diagrammatic after Souèges). T–X, *Trifolium minus* (T–V, × 500; W, × 350; X, × 180; redrawn from Souèges).

contributing to the lower region of the embryo, i.e. the root and root-cap. The embryo now begins to elongate and an indentation appears at the junction of the single cotyledon and the hypocotyl, Fig. 56κ. This is the shoot apex. This series is representative of *Luzula* and other simple monocotyledonous types. In the Liliaceae, e.g. *Muscari*, the basal cell also contributes to the lower region of the embryo. In *Sagittaria* the basal cell does not divide: it becomes distended and takes no part in the formation of the embryo proper. In the formation of the latter the terminal cell undergoes two transverse divisions. The distal cell then divides longitudinally into quadrants and further longitudinal divisions take place in the other tiers in a basipetal sequence. Later the two most distal tiers give rise to the cotyledon, the subjacent tier to the shoot apex, the next two tiers to the root and root-cap, and the tiers below to the suspensor. In such an embryo there is evidently a locus of active growth in the distal region of the embryo. Although the mature embryo in the Gramineae is a complex structure, the early stages are simple and like some already described. These embryos are considered more fully in Chapter XIV.

TAXONOMIC DISTRIBUTION OF THE EMBRYONOMIC TYPES

It is of considerable interest to know to what extent a classification based on embryonomic types is in accord with one based on the usual taxonomic criteria. The following Table gives some indication of the distribution of the several embryonomic types in different orders and families.

1. *Piperad type:*

    Peperomia (Piperales-Piperaceae)
    Balanophora (Santalales-Balanophoraceae)
    Scabiosa (Asterales-Dipsacaceae)
    Euphorbia (Euphorbiales-Euphorbiaceae)

2. *Onagrad or Crucifer type:*

    Godetia, Oenothera, Lythrum
    (Lythrales-Onagraceae and Lythraceae; some Onagraceae, e.g. *Epilobium* are exceptions)
    Capsella, Alyssum
    (Cruciales-Cruciferae)
    Myosurus
    (Ranales-Ranunculaceae)
    Euphorbia (Euphorbiales-Euphorbiaceae)
    Mentha (Lamiales-Labiatae)

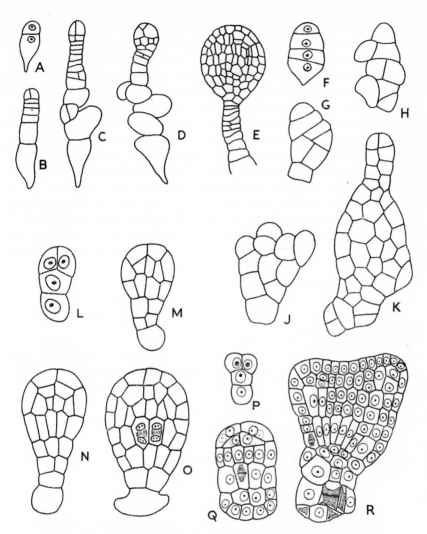

Fig. 58. Illustrating the diversity of form and structure of embryos

A–E, *Sherardia arvensis* (Rubiaceae), showing a curious development of the elongated suspensor ($\times$ 290, redrawn from Souèges). F–J, *Ribes divaricatum* (Saxifragales: Ribesiaceae), showing a curiously irregular initial embryonic development. K, *Ribes aureum*. (F, $\times$ 225; G–J, $\times$ 260; K, $\times$ 225; redrawn from Mauritzon.) L–O, *Urtica pilulifera* (Urticales: Urticaceae) (L, $\times$ 670; M–O, $\times$ 420; redrawn from Souèges). P–R, *Oxyspora paniculata* (Melastomaceae) (P–R, $\times$ 970; after Subramanyan).

Veronica, Catalpa (Personales-Scrophulariaceae; Bignoni-
aceae)
Lotus, Trifolium (Leguminosae-Papilionaceae)
Ruta (Rutales-Rutaceae)
Lilium (Liliales-Liliaceae)
Juncus (Juncales-Juncaceae)

3. *Asterad type*

Senecio (Compositae)
Geum (Rosales-Rosaceae)
Erodium, Oxalis, (Geraniales-Geraniaceae, Oxalidaceae)
Polygonum (Polygonales-Polygonaceae)
Urtica (Urticales-Urticaceae)
Lamium (Lamiales-Labiatae)
Muscari (Liliales-Liliaceae)
Poa (Gramineae)

4. *Solanad type*

Includes genera from the Solanaceae (Gamopetalous Dicoty-
ledons), Papaveraceae, Linaceae (Geraniales), Hydnoraceae
(Aristolochiales)
(All these have been referred by taxonomists to an origin in the
Ranales.)

5. *Chenopodiad type*

Includes *Chenopodium* (Chenopodiales)
Polemonium (Polemoniales)
Myosotis (Boraginales)
(All these are either apetalous or gamopetaleous derivatives of
the Ranales.)

6. *Caryophyllad type*

Includes genera from the Caryophyllales, Fumariaceae
(Rhoeadales), Saxifragales, Lythrales, Sarraceniales, genera
of Leguminosae; and some monocotyledon genera.

While the classification of embryonomic types has no doubt its
place in descriptive studies, and may eventually be seen to possess a
more fundamental value, it appears to bear little relationship to
angiosperm taxonomy. Several embryonomic types and variations
may occur within a single family; and widely separated orders and
families may have embryos of the same type. This is clearly seen in
the Table above. In Hutchinson's phyletic scheme, the basic herbaceous

order of Ranales is considered to have given rise to such orders as the Cruciales, Lythrales, Piperales, to gamopetalous orders such as the Personales and Lamiales, and, in part, to the Monocotyledons. In some

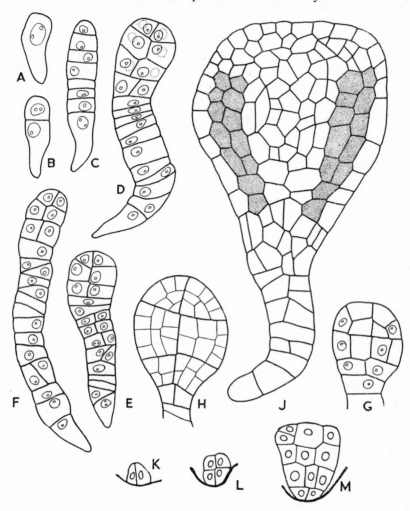

Fig. 59. Contrasted dicotyledon embryos

A–J, *Daucus carota* (Umbelliferae). The young embryo is markedly filamentous. (after Borthwick) K–M, *Sassafras variifolium* (Laurales). The first division of the embryo is by a vertical wall, and the embryo tends to be equidimensional (× 240, after Coy).

genera of these orders embryos of the Onagrad type occur. The other basic order, the Magnoliales, is thought to have given rise to the Leguminosae, Rutales and Euphorbiales, and there also we find genera with embryos of the Onagrad type. This type is also found in two monocotyledonous families, the Juncaceae and Liliaceae. In the Asterad type are included embryos from families of Ranales and Magnoliales and from monocotyledonous genera. In the Lamiales, Gramineae and Liliaceae, both Onagrad and Asterad types have been reported.

In his comprehensive survey of angiosperm embryology, Johansen (1950) has attempted to assign each investigated species to its embryonomic type, or variation of a type. This, indeed, appears to have been the main object in the angiosperm section of his book. But having done this, there is no general discussion of the data in their phylogenetic application. He notes briefly that the data of special and comparative embryology 'follow phylogenetic lines more or less but there exists a certain degree of overlapping since species in very diverse and totally unrelated taxonomic families may follow the identical embryonomy' (p. 93). It may therefore be inferred that if the data of angiosperm embryology have any value in phylesis, that value is obscure and is unlikely to be revealed by morphological studies alone. When Maheshwari (1950) considers the relation between embryology and taxonomy, the development of the embryo is only one of his twelve embryological criteria of comparison, all the others being concerned with the inception of the male and female gametophytes and the details of fertilisation. These other embryological criteria are those which have proved of value in settling problems of taxonomic relationship, the details of the actual embryonic development having been used to a very limited extent only.

Souèges has expressed the view that because of the difficulty of ascertaining the relationships of plants on the basis of their adult form and structure, these being greatly affected by extrinsic factors, an attempt should be made to discover what relationships they show during development. As the early segmentations of the embryo are mainly determined by internal factors, it is reasonable to assume that the comparative study of embryos should be of value in taxonomy. In Souèges view, the unit of classification is no longer the morphological species but the embryonomic type. According to this conception, all the species in a truly related group of plants would have embryos which develop according to identical embryonomic laws. These laws should be restricted to the first four cell generations of the embryo.

EXAMPLE OF A COMPARATIVE EMBRYOLOGICAL INVESTIGATION

Lebègue (1952), has tried to establish, on a strictly embryological basis, the taxonomic relations between the Rosaceae and Saxifragaceae, and between these two and other families, e.g. Cruciferae and Resedaceae. In other words, he has asked: Do the embryological data admit of the two families being placed side by side, as if they were derived from a common ancestral stock? Have they community of origin with the Rhoeadales, all stemming from the Ranales, as Hutchinson (1926) has suggested? Hutchinson regards the Archichlamydeae as diverging in two main lines, the Ranales giving rise to predominantly herbaceous orders and the Magnoliales to predominantly arborescent ones. He considers, however, that these two main phyla 'have often converged on similar lines and are associated in the same family, as is probably the case in Rosaceae' (1926, p. 5). In his phylogenetic scheme, Rosales are derived from Magnoliales, and Rhoeadales and Saxifragales from Ranales. Wettstein (1911), on the other hand, views the Rosales as a comprehensive order, comprising Crassulaceae, Saxifragaceae, Rosaceae and other families. Numerous affinities, in fact, have been suggested for both Rosaceae and Saxifragaceae. Because of the many close similitudes, vegatative as well as floral, the separation of the two families is difficult.

When comparative studies of embryos are undertaken in the interests of taxonomy, it is essential to define criteria of primitiveness and of advancement. Following Milne-Edwards (1867) and Souèges, Lebègue maintains that in a group of related species the most highly evolved is that which shows greatest differentiation and maximal division of labour, i.e. greatest individualisation (Souèges, 1936). At the embryonic level, the most evolved species will be that in which the embryo shows the earliest differentiation; in other words, evolutionary advancement is based on what has been described as the principle of precocity.

Embryologically, the Cruciferae appear to stem from the primitive *Myosurus* type in the Ranunculaceae, Fig. 56. In its possession of a greatly swollen basal cell, *Capsella bursa pastoris* is quite exceptional in the Cruciferae, all other investigated species having elongated filamentous suspensors, Fig. 60A–J. The principle of precocity is illustrated by the fact that the hypophysis is formed in the fifth embryonic cell generation in *Cardamine*, Fig. 60A–C, the fourth in *Sisymbrium* and the third in *Draba verna* (the most evolved type). The systematic grouping based on embryological criteria does not coincide with that based on the usual floral criteria. Lebègue's explanation of this is that floral construction is a considerably less ancient manifestation of evolution than the primary development of organisms as revealed by the embryogeny.

The Resedaceae, Fig. 60K, L, resemble the Cruciferae in their embryology but are more precocious. Indeed, the Cruciferous type of embryology is found in a considerable number of polypetalous and gamopetalous dicotyledons, the relationship thus indicated being in close agreement with Hutchinson's phylogenetic scheme.

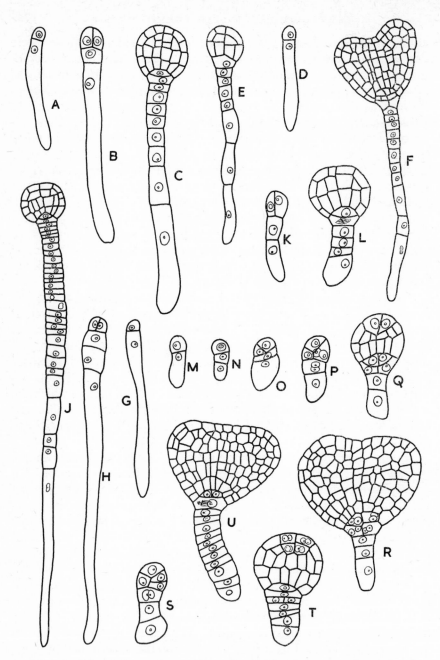

Fig. 60. Dicotyledon embryos, illustrating Lebègue's comparative study of some orders of the Polypetalae (Dialypetalae) (*see also* Fig. 61)

A–C, *Cardamine pratensis* (× 270). D–F, *Nasturtium officinale* (× 270). G–J, *Barbarea vulgaris* (× 340). K, L, *Reseda lutea* (× 340). M–R, *Spiraea ulmaria* (× 450). S–U, *Potentilla aurea*. (S, T, × 450; U, × 340) (after Lebègue).

The herbaceous and woody Rosaceae show considerable differences in their embryological characters. Although the herbaceous Rosaceae show a considerable range in their floral morphology, they exhibit a remarkable similarity in their embryology. That of *Geum urbanum*,

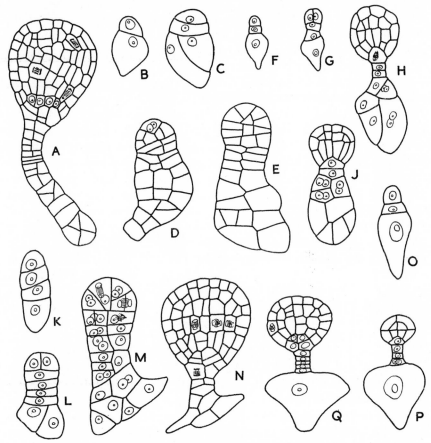

Fig. 61. Dicotyledon embryos as in Fig. 60

A, *Poterium sanguisorba* (× 250). B–D, *Crataegus oxyacantha* (× 340). E, *Malus communis* (× 450). F–H, *Saxifraga caespitosa* (× 235). J, *S. cotyledon* (× 340). K–N, *Peltiphyllum peltatum* (K–M, × 340; N, × 270). O–Q, *Penthorum sedoides* (× 410) (after Lebègue).

Fig. 56L, M, may be taken as typical. The apical, or terminal, cell of the two-celled proembryo gives rise to the cotyledons and epicotyl only, all the rest of the embryo, including the hypocotyl, root, root-cap and suspensor, being products of the basal cell. In these species of Rosaceae, the terminal cell is divided by a first and then a second oblique wall, a distinctive apical cell, apical cell group or epiphysis, being thus formed. This cell persists for some time, but later it is subdivided into small cells which yield the elements of the dermatogen and periblem. On embryological grounds the woody Rosaceae are held to be the more primitive. *Malus*, Fig. 61E, *Pyrus* and *Crataegus*, Fig. 61B, D, are low in the evolutionary scale; *Fragaria*, *Potentilla*, Fig. 60s–U, and *Geum* are high; and *Spiraea*, Fig. 60M–R, is the most advanced of all. *Rosa* and *Rubus* occupy a middle position. In Lebègue's view, the subdivisions of the Rosaceae might well be raised to higher rank, e.g. to familial rank. In embryological comparisons, there is a greater difference between *Spiraea* and *Crataegus* than between the Cruciferae and Resedaceae, or between Saxifragaceae and Crassulaceae. Lebègue's studies do not lead him to suppose that the Polycarpicae, based on the type of *Myosurus*, have any embryological community with the Rosaceae.

In the Saxifragaceae, e.g. in *S. caespitosa*, Fig. 61F–H, both the body of the embryo and the greater part of the suspensor are derived from the terminal cell of the two-celled proembryo. The early embryogeny is characterised by a linear series of cells, and would be assigned to Souèges second period. In this and related species, Fig. 61J, the basal cell of the suspensor becomes enlarged and divided by transverse and longitudinal or obliquely longitudinal walls. *Peltiphyllum peltatum*, at one time included as a species of *Saxifraga*, is characterised by a curiously irregular suspensor, Fig. 61K–N, and *Penthorum sedoides*, Fig. 61O–Q, by a distended basal suspensor cell. The former species is considered by Lebègue to be exceptional among the Saxifragaceae in the matter of its embryogeny, in that both the basal and terminal cells divide by transverse walls; and unlike *Saxifraga*, almost the whole of the suspensor in *Peltiphyllum* is derived from the basal cell. The basal cell, which has first divided transversely, subsequently divides again in a variable manner, yielding a multicellular and somewhat asymmetrical suspensor. Certain irregular embryonic developments in *Peltiphyllum* are like the normal developments found in *Geum*. From these comparative studies Lebègue concludes that *Peltiphyllum peltatum* 'appears to have evolved secondarily from the floral point of view in the direction of the Saxifragaceae,' but, as the embryological investigations show, its origins are profoundly different.

With regard to the possible affinities of Rosaceae and Saxifragaceae, Lebègue points out that although very close anatomical and floral similarities are known (e.g. sections of the petioles of *Saxifraga*, *Spiraea* and *Alchemilla* are practically identical, and *Spiraea* and *Astilbe* show closely comparable floral development), the embryological developments are quite different in the two families. Embryos of Saxifragaceae belong to Souèges second period, those of Rosaceae to the first period. The saxifrage embryonomic type, however, shows many resemblances to the *Myosurus* type, except that in the latter the embryonomic laws apply to the whole of the proembryo, whereas in the former they apply only to the further development of the terminal cell of the two-celled proembryo. Lebègue justifies his (and Souèges') classification of embryo types, as compared with Johansen's classification, by the statement: 'What matters in an embryo is the embryonic body which contains in its cells the future plant and its vital potentialities. The suspensor characters appear to be relatively less important and should be treated as secondary and subordinate characters in a classification.' The present writer does not entirely agree with this view: the embryo grows as a whole and must be analysed as such.

From a comparison of the two series or lines, Cruciferae, Resedaceae, etc., and Saxifragaceae, Crassulaceae, etc., Lebègue concludes that these are parallel evolutionary series that could have evolved from a common stock—the Ranales. These embryological studies, however, do not yet admit of the construction of a phylogenetic classification. Certain groups, e.g. Cruciferae, Resedaceae and Capparidaceae, possessing embryos of the *Myosurus* type, are evidently closely related; but they are very different embryologically from groups considered by taxonomists to be related to them, e.g. Papaveraceae and Fumariaceae.

ANOMALOUS EMBRYOS

Embryos, whether of dicotyledons or monocotyledons, with anomalous segmentation patterns, are important in that they emphasise the fact that the embryo grows as a whole and that this integrated wholeness is the phenomenon of major importance. The cellular pattern, though it exercises an effect, is essentially subordinate to the overall growth development. Thus we may note that, notwithstanding the numerous embryonomic types that have been specified on the basis of the segmentation pattern, all of them at maturity share very much the same organisation of cotyledons, shoot and radicle. Indeed, unless the whole embryogeny had been worked out, it would be impossible to relate the several organs and tissues to the initial segmentation pattern. The constancy of destination of the cells derived from the four-celled proembryo, as emphasised by Souèges, has been challenged by several investigators, e.g. Borthwick (1931) and Bhaduri (1936). They argue that in related species, or even in the same species, each cell of the proembryo does not invariably give rise to the same part of the mature embryo.

GENERAL COMMENTARY

Embryologists have now produced a mass of precise observations on the embryonic development of a large number of species. Their investigations have demonstrated the exactitude and specificity of the processes of embryonic growth, cell division and organogenic development in many species. In these phenomena they perceive the working of embryonomic laws. In each species, every cell division, as it were, is meaningful in a high degree; and this indeed is true can we but discover the meaning. Because of the specificity and regularity of the embryonic segmentation pattern in each species, and, further, the regularity with which cells in certain positions give rise to particular organs or tissues—all visible expressions of the orderly working of the genetical constitution—a classification based on embryology seems reasonable and feasible. It is reasonable to argue that species with the same general hereditary constitution will be closely comparable in their embryonic development; conversely, close similarities in the embryonic development are an indication of taxonomic affinity. These propositions are borne out by the Cruciferae. Closely related families may also be expected to have much in common in their embryonic development, whereas unrelated families may show histological differences. The basic question is: Are these arguments supported by the observed facts?

In different species, because of differences in their genetical constitutions, the distribution of growth, and concomitantly the segmentation pattern, may be different. In some species the zygote is divided transversely into two almost equal cells; in others, the two cells are very unequal in size and very different in their subsequent development, i.e. in their metabolic activity. In general, the basal cell contains substances which are osmotically active, whereas in the terminal cells such substances are probably utilised in the synthesis of protoplasm. Now, as a fact, we still know very little about the constitution of biological reaction systems and the way they work. Differently constituted reaction systems may yield closely comparable segmentation patterns; and, on the other hand, comparatively small metabolic differences may be attended by considerable differences in the early segmentation pattern. Thus quite small genetical differences may cause considerable differences in the reaction system and, consequently, in the cellular pattern. Until much more is known about organismal reaction systems, and the effect on them of genic mutation and other genetical changes, and on the resulting segmentation pattern, conceptions of the kind advanced by Souèges and Lebègue must be viewed with caution and reserve. For all we know, quite small and perhaps relatively unimportant genetical differences may produce considerable differences in the early embryogeny. If the developing zygote is thought of as a specific reaction system, and if it is borne in mind that the embryo grows as a whole, and that physical factors are closely involved in cell division and in the positions in which cell walls are laid down, the morphological facts of embryology will gain in value and this branch of botanical science will move forward into a new and dynamic phase.

In the view of Maheshwari (1950), a knowledge of angiosperm embryology throws little light on the ancestry of the group, though it does indicate their probable monophyletic origin. He considers that there are no fundamental differences between dicotyledons and monocotyledons, features of a transitional or intermediate character being present in both groups. Angiosperm embryology provides little that enables us to relate this group to other subdivisions of the Plant Kingdom, but the primitive families of the Winteraceae, Degeneriaceae and Trochodendraceae, of which the general morphology and anatomy have been studied by Bailey and his colleagues, may yield data of some interest in this connection (*see* Chapter XIV).

THE SEED AND SEEDLING

In flowering plants, as in gymnosperms, the embryogenic process culminates in the formation of the mature seed awaiting dispersal. The form of the embryo within the mature seed, the construction of the seed, the conditions under which it germinates, the establishment of the seedling, and its morphology and anatomy, constitute the logical extension of the work presented here. In this connection the reader may be referred to Netolitzky (1926) and to recent papers by Corner (1951) and Singh (1952). Factors determining the delayed germination in economic seeds have been considered by Rose (1915). Longevity of seeds under natural conditions and in storage has been considered in a classical work by Ewart (1908); more recently it has been reviewed by Crocker (1938) and considered comprehensively by Crocker and Barton (1953). The reader is referred to the latter authors for recent records and bibliographical details.

Chapter XIV

EMBRYOGENESIS IN FLOWERING PLANTS: SPECIAL SECTION

THE embryonic developments in flowering plants may be studied collectively, either by referring them to a number of embryonomic types, or by considering them in the orders and families to which the species belong, as Johansen (1950) has done. In this book no comprehensive systematic treatment of embryos will be attempted: rather, a kind of sampling will be undertaken to see whether or not, in different groups, or categories, there are associated embryogenic phenomena of special or general interest.

EMBRYOGENESIS IN PRIMITIVE ANGIOSPERMS

Contemplation of the angiosperms prompts an inquiry into the nature of the embryonic development in what taxonomists regard as the most primitive orders and families: Do the embryos of the species that have been investigated show any special features which, for example, might be regarded as primitive? Do they afford a clue to the probable ancestry of the flowering plants? Do they yield any evidence that a classification based on embryology is ever likely to be feasible? These and other questions readily suggest themselves.

The whole subject of the phylogeny of the angiosperms bristles with difficulties: the origin of the flowering plants is still a mystery. As to which are the most primitive families of dicotyledons there may still be some differences of opinion. According to Arnold (1947), the evolution of the angiosperms may have begun to take place during the Mesozoic era, and various seed-bearing predecessors have been suggested as possible ancestors. (*See* Arnold (1938) for a short review of Palaeozoic seeds.) But no fossil forms are known by which the flowering plants can with certainty be related to lower groups. The angiosperms of the Lower Cretaceous are very like those of today, some of them having, indeed, been referred to living families, even genera. But the more primitive types, or prototypes, which are of paramount interest to the phylogenist, are still quite unknown. Species intermediate in character between angiosperms and gymnosperms or pteridophytes are also unknown.[1] Walton (1940) has summarised the situation by saying

[1] For a recent discussion of this matter, *see* Walton (1953). In this review he suggests that such evidence as we possess points to the pteridosperms as the most likely progenitors of the angiosperms.

that the fossil angiosperms—of which representatives of Fagaceae, Moraceae, Menispermaceae, Magnoliaceae and Lauraceae have been observed in early Cretaceous strata—yield no information as to the ancestry of the group beyond what is already provided by living representatives. Along similar lines, Bailey and his colleagues (1942, 1949, 1951) have approached the general problem of angiosperm phylogeny on the assumption that very few orders of flowering plants have become completely extinct, and they have turned to the very curious floral characters found in the Degeneriaceae and related families for evidence of the early features of angiosperms. (The Winteraceae, to which the Degeneriaceae are related, are placed by Hutchinson (1926) in the Magnoliales, his first order in the Archichlamydeae.) Here, our special interest lies in the embryogeny in these primitive angiosperm species. At least one set of observations is available from a study by Swamy (1949) of *Degeneria vitiensis*, Fig. 62.

In *D. vitiensis* the ovule is anatropous, with an outer and inner integument, and an embryo sac with the normal organisation of eight nuclei. There is double fertilisation and cellular endosperm formation. The zygote divides only after about 300 endosperm cells have been formed. The embryonic development is illustrated in Fig. 62. The first division of the zygote is a transverse one, but thereafter the development of both the terminal and basal segments does not follow an exact pattern and may be variable and somewhat irregular. On further development, the embryo becomes a bulky, multicellular, club-shaped structure, with no sharp distinction between the distal formative region and the massive basal suspensor. At this stage, there is still no indication of tissue differentiation. The whole development is thus on the massive eusporangiate basis found in primitive ferns and in gymnosperms. Later, the embryo usually forms three cotyledon (87 per cent) and sometimes four (13 per cent); there is a bulky and somewhat bulbous hypocotyl, a root and a root-cap. At this stage a procambial tissue is also differentiated. The embryo is very small relative to the endosperm. The consistently tricotyledonous condition (with occasional tetracotyledonous seedlings) in *Degeneria* is a very remarkable feature: no dicotyledonous embryos were observed in some 310 seeds. In *Magnolia grandiflora* tricotyledons may be found as occasional abnormalities (Earle, 1938). The embryogenies in various genera of Magnoliaceae show a number of points of similarity with *Degeneria*, e.g. the plasticity of the segmentation pattern, the organisation of an ovoid or club-shaped, undifferentiated embryo, the development and persistence of the massive suspensor, the swollen hypocotyl, the nearly triangular shape of the cotyledon, and the relation of the small embryo to the very large endosperm (Maneval, 1914; Earle, 1938; Swamy, 1949).

Swamy notes that tricotyledonous nodes are of not infrequent occurrence in large populations of seedlings of Magnoliaceous plants. Bailey, Nast and Smith (1943) consider that the Degeneriaceae,

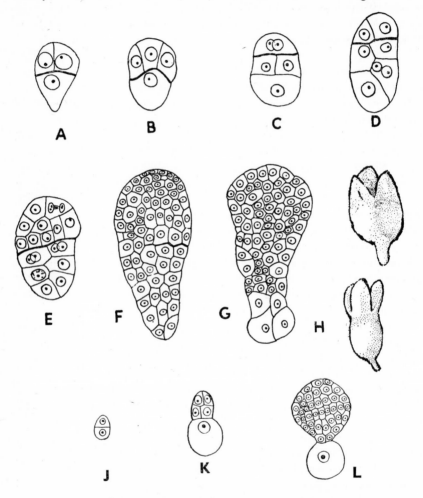

Fig. 62. Embryogeny in primitive dicotyledons
A–H, *Degeneria vitiensis* (A–G, × 283; H, × 90; after Swamy). J, L, *Cercidiphyllum japonicum* (× 560, after Swamy and Bailey).

Himantandraceae and Magnoliaceae should properly be regarded as three distinct but closely related families, all presumably being comprised within the order Magnoliales.

In *Trochodendron* and *Tetracentron*, Nast and Bailey (1945) have noted that the endosperm constitutes the greater part of the seed, the embryos observed being small and undifferentiated, or at the incipient cotyledonary stage. The full details of the embryonic development have yet to be ascertained. A somewhat similar account has been given of the seed of the vesselless dicotyledon *Amborella trichopoda* (Bailey and Swamy, 1948). *Amborella* was originally placed in the Monimiaceae, but Bailey and Swamy consider that this requires much more evidence before it can be accepted. The embryogenies of the nine surviving genera of vesselless dicotyledons merit investigation, (*see* Bailey and Nast (1945) for a discussion of the Winteraceae, etc.)

In *Cercidiphyllum japonicum* the zygote divides transversely and the terminal cell again divides transversely and then longitudinally. The basal cell becomes a swollen suspensor cell, while the terminal cell gives rise to a globular cell mass, Fig. 62J, L (after Swamy and Bailey, 1949). Meanwhile the embryo sac has elongated greatly. The cellular endosperm is characterised initially by dense protoplasm at the chalazal end. This genus was formerly associated with several others (*Trochodendron, Tetracentron*, etc.), but the anatomical evidence, including the embryology, 'provides no cogent arguments for including this genus in any particular family of the dicotyledons.' It should be placed in an independent family on its own. There are no very close resemblances between the embryos of *Cercidiphyllum* and of *Degeneria*. (For a discussion of the taxonomic relationships of primitive dicotyledons, *see* Swamy and Bailey, 1949.)

Sassafras variifolium (Laurales), a primitive dicotyledon, belongs to a genus with as long a fossil history as any angiosperm known in N. America (Coy, 1928). In chronological records it is preceded in time by *Populus, Liriodendron* and *Magnolia*. The embryo sac is of the normal eight-nucleate kind and after fertilisation there is rapid endosperm formation. The zygote may divide either by a transverse or by a longitudinal wall, i.e. the plane of division is not definitely fixed. In its subsequent development the proembryo tends to be massive and flattish, with a somewhat inconspicuous short wide suspensor, Fig. 59K, M. The mature embryo has massive cotyledons with auricles, a plumule bearing small leaf primordia, and a flattish radicle. The development is thus on a massive basis. Johansen (1950) states that this embryo shows close agreement with the *Scabiosa* variation of the *Piperad* type. In *Leitneria floridana* the first wall of the zygote may be transverse or vertical. The embryo develops a massive suspensor and the pear-shaped embryo consists of hundreds of cells before there is any evidence of cotyledon formation (Pfeiffer, 1912). This genus is difficult to associate with any specific group in the Archichlamydeae.

In *Moringa oleifera* (Capparidales) an embryonic development not unlike that in *Degeneria* has been observed (Puri, 1941). There is considerable endosperm formation before any development of the zygote takes place. The segmentation of the embryo is somewhat irregular and results in the formation of an undifferentiated ovoid, bulbous embryo, with a massive suspensor which grades into the embryonic region. On further growth, the ovoid embryo becomes

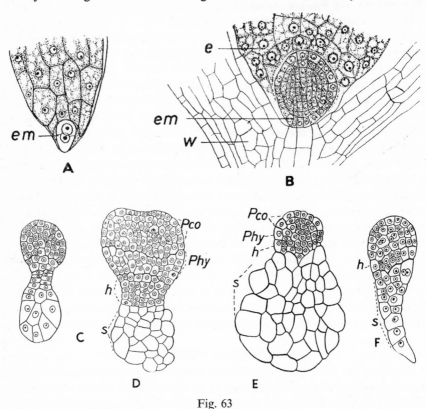

Fig. 63

A, B, *Grevillea robusta* (Proteaceae). A, Two-celled embryo surrounded by endo-sperm. B, A later stage; the embryo is now spherical; there is no suspensor (A, × 300; B, × 225; after Brough). C–F, Embryos of Leguminosae. C, *Rothia tri-foliata*. D, *Sesbania aegyptiaca*. E, *S. grandiflora*. F, *Vigna catjang* (C, D, F, × 187; E, × 133; after Rau).

bilobed distally, the plumule and two cotyledons become organised, and a root primordium is differentiated. The two cotyledons tend to be unequal in size, i.e. in width, the larger one, though single at its point of conjunction with the hypocotyl, becoming two-lobed distally. In fact, there is what appears to be a nascent but unrealised tricotyledonous condition; this may be correlated with the general massive basis of the embryonic development. According to Compton (1913), polycotyle-dony is very rare in angiosperms, many of the reputed examples being instances of schizocotyly: however, tricotyledons are known to occur in species of *Persoonia* (Proteales: Proteaceae), *Nuytsia* and *Loranthus* (Compton, 1913) and in *Eugenia hookeri* (Myrtales: Myrtaceae) (Johnson, 1936).

The Ceratophyllaceae and Nymphaeaceae are similar in their embryogeny: in both the suspensor is absent and the maturing embryo is characteristically many-celled and bulky.

In *Grevillea robusta* (Proteaceae) the division of the zygote begins rather late when the endosperm is well developed. The first division is by a transverse wall, but no suspensor is formed. The next division is at right angles to the first and on further, approximately rectangular, divisions the embryo becomes flattened oval in shape and then disc-like. Periclinal divisions yield a dermatogen and a central tissue mass. Later, two cotyledons, a plumule and a radicle are organised, and incipient vascular tissue is differentiated within, Fig. 63A, B (Brough, 1933). In *Protea lepidocarpon*, the embryo also passes through a globular stage like that of *Grevillea*, and in it also there is no suspensor (Ballantine, 1909). Special interest attaches to the systematic affinity of the Proteaceae. In Engler's arrangement, and also in Rendle's, they are associated with the Santalales; in Hutchinson's with the Thymeliaceae; and in Balfour's with the Rosales. On the embryological and other data for *Grevillea*, Brough considers that the simplicity of the Proteaceae may be primitive and, if so, that affinities with an order lower in the scale than the Thymeliaceae would have to be sought. It may here be noted that some features in the embryogeny are of the kind found in primitive families related to the Magnoliaceae.

MORE ADVANCED DICOTYLEDONS

In Chapter XIII a considerable number of representative embryonic developments among polypetalous dicotyledons have been illustrated. The aim in this Section is to ascertain if those dicotyledons, which are held to be advanced on the criteria of floral morphology, show embryonic developments which support this view, or otherwise have features of special interest.

In some primitive dicotyledons, as indicated in the foregoing Section, the suspensor may be relatively inconspicuous, grading into the embryo proper. In other dicotyledons this organ is liable to undergo various modifications. The large ellipsoidal suspensor of *Capsella*, Fig. 54, has already been noted as being quite exceptional in the Cruciferae; so also is that of *Penthorum*, Fig. 61O–Q, among the Saxifragaceae (Lebègue, 1952). Elongated suspensors are common in certain polypetalous families and may be very striking in some Sympetalae. In *Salvia splendens* the filamentous proembryo elongates both into the endosperm and into the micropylar endosperm haustorium (Carlson and Stuart, 1936). In some species the suspensor cells show remarkable growth and development, sometimes into haustorial structures. Among the Leguminosae, some species of which have greatly reduced or no suspensors, *Pisum*, Fig. 64D, and *Orobus* have greatly elongated pairs of multinucleate, saccate, basal suspensor cells. In *Lupinus* and *Cicer*, Fig. 64B, E, the suspensor is a very long, enlarged, multicellular, filamentous structure. In *L. pilosa* some of the more basal of these cells may become rounded off and lie detached near the micropyle. *Ononis*, Fig. 64G, has a long filamentous suspensor, the cells being full of food reserves. *Phaseolus*, Fig. 64C, has a massive cylindrical embryo, without any sharp distinction between the suspensor and embryo proper. This embryo affords a remarkable illustration of an acropetal gradient of cell size. *Cytisus*, Fig. 64F, has a suspensor consisting of a spherical aggregate of swollen spherical cells. Rau (1953) has illustrated an embryo of *Crotalaria striata* in which the suspensor develops a large number of tubular cells which become associated with the endosperm.

Among the Rubiaceae the remarkable suspensor haustoria have long been known. The suspensor is initially a filament of cells, but later the most basal cells, next the micropyle, grow out as filamentous structures which penetrate into the endosperm and become swollen at their distal ends, Fig. 66. The haustorial function of these cells can scarcely be doubted. Incidentally, they supply evidence of an indirect kind that the embryo probably takes in its nutrients at the basal region and translocates them to the distal formative region. Fagerlind (1937), however, has indicated that these suspensor haustorial tubes may soon become detached from the main body of the embryo, or they may soon degenerate.

In *Myriophyllum* (Halorrhagidaceae) the large basal cell divides by a longitudinal wall and each of the two daughter cells becomes greatly distended, Fig. 65, filling the micropylar end of the embryo sac. A somewhat similar development is found in *Hypecoum* (Fumariaceae) but here the basal cell, and the lower segment of the transversely divided terminal cell, are involved. *Corydalis* has also an enlarged basal cell, in this case with several free nuclei, while in *Fumaria* the basal cell and some of the lower segments of the terminal cell develop into a multicellular foot-like structure, Fig. 65. In *Sedum acre*, and other members of the Crassulaceae, the basal cell becomes greatly enlarged and forms an aggressive haustorium, Fig. 64A, the branches of which penetrate the integuments and even the seed coat.

In *Tropaeolum majus*, the basal cells of the proembryo undergo rapid relative growth, some of them giving rise to a long haustorial

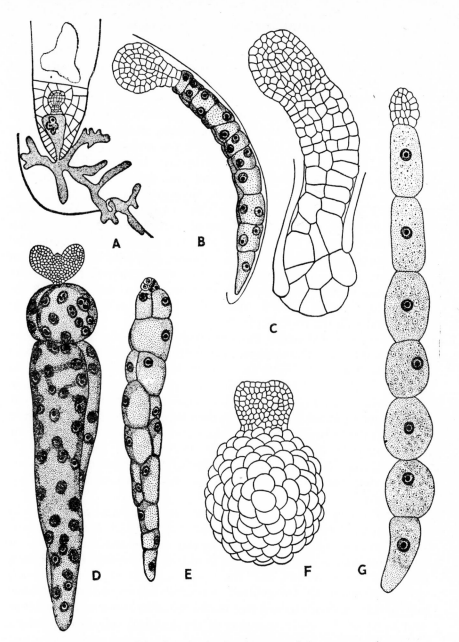

Fig. 64. Modifications in the development of the suspensor in various dicotyledons

A, *Sedum acre*. Apical portion of ovule, showing the embryo and suspensor; the basal region of the latter has grown out into long, branching haustorial processes (after Mauritzon). B–G, The suspensor in various Leguminosae. B, *Lupinus luteus*. C, *Phaseolus multiflorus*. D, *Pisum sativum*. E, *Cicer arietinum*. F, *Cytisus laburnum*. G, *Ononis fruticosus* (after Guignard).

process which pierces the integument in the micropylar region and eventually enters the pericarp. A second haustorial body—the placental haustorium—also arises from the basal cell group, grows through the integument and funiculus, and penetrates to the point of entry of the vascular strand of the raphe (Walker, 1947).

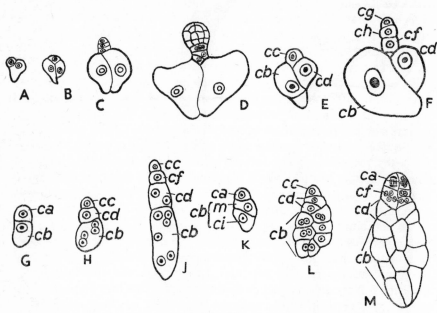

Fig. 65

A–D, Embryogeny in *Myriophyllum alterniflorum*. Note the enlarged synergid-like suspensor cells. E–M, Embryonic development in three genera of the Fumariaceae. E, F, *Hypecoum procumbens*. Extensive development of the suspensor cell which does not divide; when the apical cell divides, the cell next the suspensor also becomes greatly enlarged; together these two haustorial cells have a synergid-like appearance. G, H, J, *Corydalis lutea*. The basal cell undergoes a number of free nuclear divisions, but remains undivided; products of the apical cell contribute to the suspensor. K, L, M, *Fumaria officinalis*. The nuclear divisions in the basal cell (*cb*) are accompanied by wall formation. All the products of this cell, and some from the apical cell (*ca*), contribute to the suspensor (after Souèges).

In general, in the Scrophulariaceae, (which may be selected as an advanced gamopetalous family), the embryo itself does not show any especially unusual features: it is initially filamentous and later consists of a typical multicellular distal region and an elongated suspensor. The post-fertilisation phase is, however, attended by developments of a rather remarkable kind. These have been the cause of some controversy since the days of Hofmeister (1858). In the ovules of *Mimulus tigrinus* and *Torenia fournieri* a single integument surrounds the nucellus which soon breaks down except in the chalazal region (Guilford and

Fisk, 1951). The inner layer of the integument now becomes differentiated as an endothelial layer. A common feature is the presence of chalazal and micropylar endosperm haustoria, Fig. 66. In *Torenia* the apical portion of the embryo sac grows through the micropyle and along the funiculus, from which there may be a loss of cell contents (Balicka Iwanowska, 1899); and in some cases it even reaches the placenta. Starch is present in the developing and mature embryo sac and may still be observed in the early stages of endosperm formation, (*see* Guilford and Fisk (1951) for references to literature).

In *Plantago lanceolata*, Fig. 66C, the endosperm divides to form two cells, of which the chalazal cell becomes binucleate and functions as a haustorium. The micropylar cell divides to form four cells, two of these forming the endosperm proper, while the other two undergo a most remarkable development as micropylar haustoria. They grow out as hypha-like cells with swollen ends, and eventually separate the ovule from the placenta, except for the vascular strands of the funiculus. The developing endosperm is surrounded by a layer of specialised cells that persist even in the mature seed. The zygote does not divide until the endosperm has become multicellular (Cooper, 1942).

In the embryogeney of *Euphorbia rothiana* (Euphorbiaceae), Fig. 66D–G, Srivastava (1952) has illustrated the first division of the zygote by a vertical wall, followed by a transverse wall. During the subsequent development, the embryo becomes pear-shaped, the suspensor being ill-defined, if it could indeed be distinguished. This first division of the zygote by a vertical wall is different from what has been observed in *E. exigua* and *E. esula* by Souèges (1942, 1945), or in *E. presli* and *E. splendens* by Weniger (1927). In *Acalypha indica*, as investigated by Johri and Kapil (1953), the embryogeny is a variant of the Onagrad type. These authors have also given a survey of the embryogeny in all the investigated species of *Euphorbia* and have indicated considerable variability in the details of development in different species.

THE ORIGIN OF THE MONOCOTYLEDONOUS EMBRYO

The origin of the monocotyledonous embryo has long attracted the attention of botanists. Maheshwari has described it as the most difficult problem in angiosperm embryology. In the dicotyledonous embryo the plumule is typically distal and is situated symmetrically between two equivalent cotyledons: in the monocotyledonous embryo the shoot apex occupies a lateral indentation in the somewhat cylindrical embryo and the cotyledon is terminal, Fig. 56F–K. Up to a certain stage in the embryonic development, however, the two types of embryo may be very closely comparable, both being cylindrical, or club-shaped, axial bodies. It has been suggested that the monocotyledonous embryo has resulted from the fusion of the two originally separate cotyledons, or that one cotyledon has been suppressed. In another approach to the problem, investigators have attempted to ascertain whether or not the single cotyledon is a truly terminal organ, or initially a lateral organ which has come to occupy a distal position. The several views have each received some factual support, but although many relevant investigations have been carried out, the problem has not yet been finally resolved.

In *Agapanthus umbellatus* (Liliaceae), a widening, distal 'tubular cotyledonary zone' with two primordia growing at its tip, and surrounding the sunken shoot apex, is to be seen at certain stages in the embryonic development (Coulter and Land, 1914). If both of the primordia develop equally, a dicotyledonous embryo is formed; but, as more frequently happens, one of the primordia soon stops growing while the other, by growing rapidly, becomes a conspicuous terminal organ, leaving the shoot apex in a relatively lateral position. Coulter and Land (1915) have also interpreted the embryo of grasses along similar lines, the scutellum being a functional cotyledon arising from the peripheral cotyledonary ring, while the epiblast is held to be the greatly reduced second cotyledon. They consider that this view is supported by the presence of a conspicuous epiblast in species of *Leersia* and *Zizania* (both Gramineae: Oryzeae). This view will be supported if it can be shown that the dicotyledons afford examples of partial or complete transition to a monocotyledonous condition. In fact, seedlings with a single cotyledon have been found in species of widely separated families, e.g. *Ranunculus ficaria* (*Ranales: Ranunculaceae*), *Corydalis cava* (Rhoeadales; Fumariaceae) *Abronia* (Thymelaeales: Nyctaginaceae), *Carum bulbocastanum* (Umbelliflorae: Umbelliferae), *Blumium elegans, Erigenia bulbosa*, species of Gesneraceae, etc.

The idea that the monocotyledons are an offshoot of some relatively primitive dicotyledon stock has long been entertained, and seemingly receives support from the monocotyledonous embryos of such species as *Ranunculus ficaria* and *Corydalis cava*, Fig. 67. Takhtajan (1945) considers that the monocotyledons must be descended from some

---

Fig. 66. Illustrating various anomalous embryos

A, *Torenia fournieri*. Elongated zygote within the micropylar haustorial endosperm; the embryo sac has also a chalazal haustorium. Note remains of pollen tube, endosperm, and large epithelial cells ($\times$ 250). B, *Mimulus tigrinus*. Endosperm breaking down round embryo, the cotyledons of which are beginning to differentiate; a conspicuous multinucleate micropylar endosperm haustorium can be seen ($\times$ 333). (A and B, after Guilford and Fisk.) C, *Plantago lanceolata*. Longitudinal section of seed, showing embryo and conspicuous endosperm haustoria ($\times$ 180, after Cooper). D–G, *Euphorbia rothiana*. Four stages in the development of the embryo, the first division being vertical ($\times$ 320; after Srivastava). H–L, *Acalypha lanceolata* (H, J, $\times$ 900; K, $\times$ 630; L, $\times$ 450; after Thathacher).

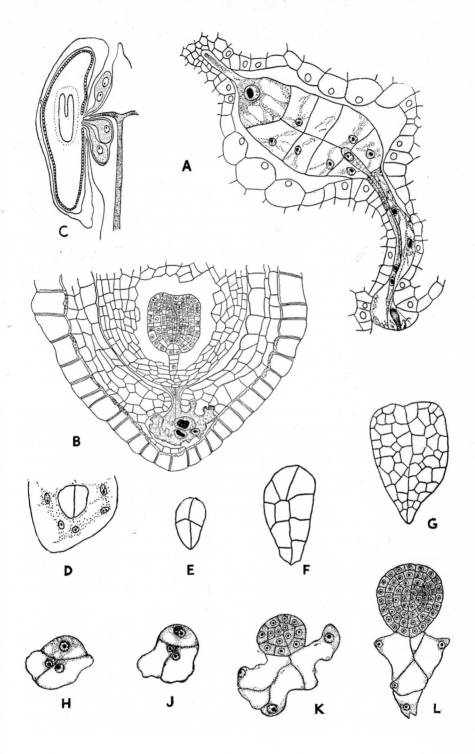

A

C

B

D   E   F   G

H   J   K   L

dicotyledonous or polycotyledonous form and that they afford evidence of deviation from the ancestral form during the early stages of their ontogenetic development; i.e. the process must have involved the substitution of one cotyledon for two during the embryogeny.

Ranunculus ficaria has attracted the attention of both taxonomists and embryologists because of the presence of certain monocotyledonous

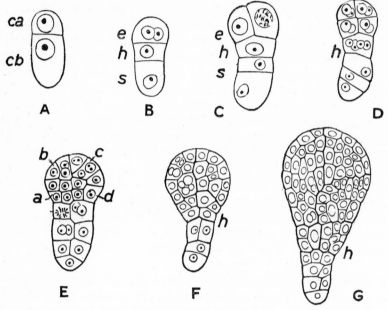

Fig. 67. Embryonic development in *Ranunculus ficaria* up to the time of shedding of seed (after Souèges)

The initial embryogeny, though sometimes irregular, is in general like that of *Myosurus*, Fig. 56.

characters in the morphology and anatomy of the adult plant and of a single cotyledon in the fully developed embryo. As Souèges (1913) and others have shown, the early stages in the embryogeny, though often irregular and frequently abortive, are in general agreement with those for other Ranunculaceae, e.g. *Myosurus*, Fig. 56A–E. At the time of seed dispersal the embryo is still in the proembryo phase, its further development taking place on seed germination. The development of the distal region of the embryo proper is such that it has only one longitudinal plane of symmetry. Johansen's account (1950) is as follows:

'The upper region of the embryo is the first to commence development. This becomes slightly indented at the apex, concave on one side and convex on the other, thus appearing somewhat kidney-shaped when observed in transverse section. The apical concave end of the embryo becomes still further enlarged and gives rise to the two lobes of the cotyledonary lamina, which at first are folded together in such a manner that the tissues which subquently become the upper surface of the two lobes are in contact with one another. The cotyledonary petiole next elongates rapidly; the petiole is grooved on the upper portion at maturity but is only slightly flattened or circular in transverse section throughout the greater part of its length. A second concavity at the basal end of the petiole represents the base of the original lateral concavity present at a younger stage. Certain cells with large nuclei and prominent nucleoli which early develop near the base of the lateral concavity mark the position where the stem apex subsequently arises lateral to the cotyledon and surrounded by its sheathing base. Opposite the cotyledon there is developed a small hump of tissue, occupying the position where the second cotyledon would have arisen if it were actually present (*see* Metcalfe, 1936). Its position and mode of origin indicate that it is the rudiment of a second cotyledon which fails to develop. This hump, like the other cotyledon, is supplied with a provascular strand. As a matter of fact, seedlings with two cotyledons have been observed, hence the rudimentary cotyledon is actually capable of normal development.'

If the embryological evidence indicates that the single cotyledon in monocotyledons is a truly terminal organ, explanations rather different from those outlined above must be sought. Several investigators state emphatically that the cotyledon *does* originate as a terminal structure, the shoot apex being situated in a lateral position near the base of the embryo. Taylor (1921) considers that explanations based on the conception of unequal cotyledonary development, or of the early abortion of one cotyledon, do not accord with the facts as ascertained in *Cyrtanthus parviflorus*; and this appears to be true of the embryos of *Alisma* (Hanstein, 1870), and *Sagittaria* (Schaffner, 1897). In the Alismaceae, as observed by Johri (1935, 1936), the first division by a transverse wall divides the zygote into a large basal and a small terminal segment, as in *Limnophyton obtusifolium*, Fig. 68. The terminal cell gives rise to the whole of the embryo and also contributes to the upper region of the filamentous suspensor. The basal cell, as in *Capsella*, becomes greatly enlarged in *Sagittaria*, *Limnophyton*, *Alisma* and *Butomopsis*.

In *Lilaea subulata* (Juncaginaceae) the initial embryology shows no special features (Agrawal, 1952). Later, however, the embryo consists of a single large suspensor cell and a large ellipsoidal embryo, Fig. 69, the latter continuing to elongate till it fills the embryo sac. This body consists mainly of a massive cotyledon, the cells of which are filled with starch, the shoot apex and root being differentiated relatively late in the lower region of the embryo. These bulky embryos are of interest

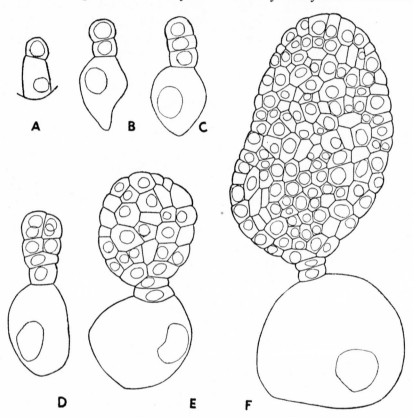

Fig. 68. Embryonic development in a monocotyledon,
Limnophyton obtusifolium
(× 284, after Johri)

in relation to the embryonic developments found in primitive dicoty-ledons (p. 252). They also suggest that the single cotyledon is not likely to be explained in terms of the abortion or suppression of one of the primordia in an initially or potentially dicotyledonous organisation.

If we assume that the ancestors of the monocotyledons had two (or more) cotyledons, and that a critical genetical change, or series of changes, resulted in the monocotyledonous condition, then the ultimate problem is to consider how, at a certain stage in the dicotyledonous embryonic development, the reaction system could have been modified so as to yield this new type of organisation. It has also to be borne in mind that the monocotyledons may be a polyphyletic group, and that

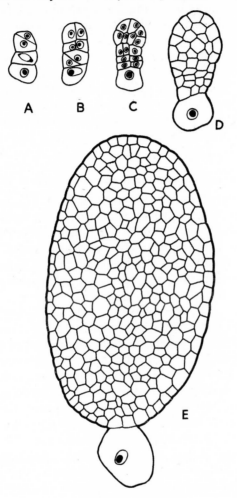

Fig. 69. *Lilaea subulata*

Stages in the development of the embryo; the basal cell enlarges but does not undergo further divisions; the terminal cell divides and gives rise to a large globular to ellipsoidal mass of cells; eventually there is a single massive cotyledon, the lateral shoot apex and the basal root only differentiating at a later stage ($\times$ 330, after Agrawal).

some lines may have diverged from a very primitive dicotyledonous source and others from a more advanced source. It may also be worth pondering whether the kind of mutation that led to the inception of the monocotyledons was one that was liable to happen quite frequently, or only very rarely.

The development of an asymmetrical structure from a symmetrical one, without necessarily involving the abortion of parts, is a very common phenomenon, e.g. the development of zygomorphic flowers. Zygomorphic flowers, e.g. snapdragon, are initially symmetrical and so remain in their peloric or actinomorphic variants. The transition from actinomorphy to zygomorphy is due to changes in the reaction system during growth. Where this takes place as the result of mutation, it may be that a comparatively small genetical change is involved. This may be true of the inception of the monocotyledonous condition. If so, it would follow that the monocotyledons may well be a polyphyletic group.

REDUCED AND ANOMALOUS MONOCOTYLEDON EMBRYOS

The monocotyledons afford some unique examples of greatly reduced embryos, e.g. in the Orchidaceae. The mature seed in the orchids is very small and contains a minute embryo which is almost gemma-like in its simple construction and absence of differentiation, Fig. 70. In the family as a whole, however, the embryogeny shows considerable variation. In some species, e.g. *Epipactis palmatus*, there is very little suspensor development, but in others, e.g. *Orchis latifolia* and *Goodyera*, Fig. 70, a long filamentous suspensor, septate in the former, undivided in the latter, is present.

Even the most ardent disciple of embryonomic types must experience difficulty in assigning the various Orchidaceous embryos to an appropriate group. Johansen (1950) has expounded these difficulties and has classified orchid embryos according to the presence or absence of a suspensor and of embryonal tubes, and whether these tubes arise directly or indirectly from the suspensor initial cell. On this basis, thirteen different developmental patterns can be distinguished. *Herminium monorchis* has a well-developed filamentous suspensor which projects well down into, and through, the micropyle. In *Epidendrum ciliare* there is sustained growth and cell division in the terminal segment, a rather curious, elongated and somewhat bulky embryo being formed, Fig. 70. *Sobralia macrantha* eventually forms a somewhat elongated, bulky embryo. Near the distal end there is an indentation in one side, presumably the site of the shoot apex, the terminal region being probably a primitive or potential cotyledon. *Vanda*, *Cymbidium*, *Phalaenopsis*, *Stanhopea*, and other genera show remarkable growth developments of the basal or other suspensor cells into haustorial embryonal tubes, Fig. 70. These tubes eventually wither about the time of seed dispersal. The mature embryo in *Vanda*

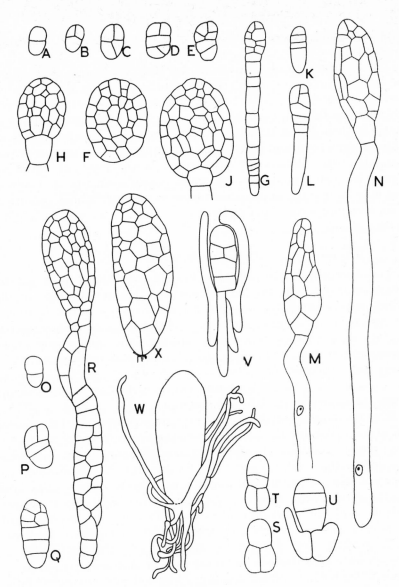

Fig. 70. Orchid embryos

A–F, *Epipactis palustris*. A–E, Early proembryo stages. F, Mature embryo. G, H, J, *Orchis latifolia*. G, Filamentous embryo, with suspensor and four-tiered distal region; the earlier stages are generally comparable with those of *Epipactis*. H, J, Embryos approaching maturity. K–N, *Goodyera discolor*. K, The basal cell is already beginning to elongate. L, Filamentous young embryo. M, N, Nearly mature embryos with greatly elongated suspensor (A–N, × 160). O–R, *Epidendrum ciliare* (O–Q, × 490; R, × 265). S–X, *Phalaenopsis grandiflora*. S, T, Three- and four-celled proembryos. U, V, Early development of embryonal tubes. W, Embryonal tubes at optimum development. X, Mature embryo, with strophiole at base, the latter being all that remains of the embryonal tubes (S–V, × 490; W, × 170; X, × 400). (All from Johansen, redrawn from Treub.)

consists of a spherical, and in *Phalaenopsis* of a club-shaped or ellipsoidal, mass of meristematic cells, showing no evidence of organ or tissue differentiation, and enclosed in, or surrounded by, embryonal tubes.

THE GRAMINEAE

The grasses exemplify the most complex embryonic developments in plants. The embryo, with the scutellum, coleoptile, epiblast and coleorhiza as special developments, and the homologies of these members, have been the subject of investigations and discussions extending over many years, beginning with Malpighi in 1687 (*see* Bennett (1944), Artschwager and McGuire (1949), and Reeder (1953), for indications of the literature).

Coulter and Land (1915) held that the scutellum is a lateral organ, the equivalent of a foliage leaf. Worsdell (1916) thought of it as a terminal laminate cotyledon, the coleoptile being its ligule. Sargant and Arber (1915) favoured the view that the coleoptile is the equivalent of a pair of fused stipules. These are but some of the views to which consideration of the grass embryo has given rise.

The embryogeny of *Poa*, Fig. 71, may be indicated as a fairly regular and representative type for the Gramineae. In other genera the initial cellular pattern may be considerably less regular. At the two-celled stage, the terminal cell, as in maize, may be small, lens-shaped and semilateral in position (Randolph, 1936). It may divide vertically or obliquely, the latter development leading to the formation of an apical cell of temporary duration, Fig. 72. The subsequent divisions are irregular. The embryo becomes club-shaped; it is narrow at the suspensor end and shows a gradient of decreasing cell size into the terminal growing region.

In a comparative study of embryo development in *Zea mays*, *Avena sativa* and *Triticum vulgare*, Avery (1930) has concluded (i) that the

---

Fig. 71. Grass Embryos

Poa annua. A, First division of the zygote. B, C, Later stages in the development of the segmentation pattern. D, The differentiation of the organs is about to begin. E, An older embryo. The lettering is that of Souèges. The distal, or apical, segment of the zygote is *ca*, and the basal segment is *cb*. As the embryo develops

$$ca \to q \to l, l^1$$
$$cb \to m + ci \to m + n + n^1 \to m + n + o + p$$

In E, *cl* is the coleoptile, *eb*, the epiblast, and *pr* the region of the shoot apex.

(from Maheshwari; after Souèges).

F–O, *Hordeum sativum.* F, Fertilised egg. G–K, Development of segmentation pattern. L, M, Beginning of organ formation; *sc*, early stages in the formation of the scutellum; *s*, nascent shoot apex; *c*, nascent coleoptile; *su*, suspensor. N, O, Older embryos showing the aforementioned parts and also the first leaf (*l*), the scutellar vascular trace (*vt*), the root (*r*), the second or seminal root (*sr*), and the coleorhiza (F–K, × 375; L, M, × 165; N, O, × 54; after Merry). P, *Zea mays*. Differentiation of plumule-radicle axis; lettering as above (× 60, after Randolph).

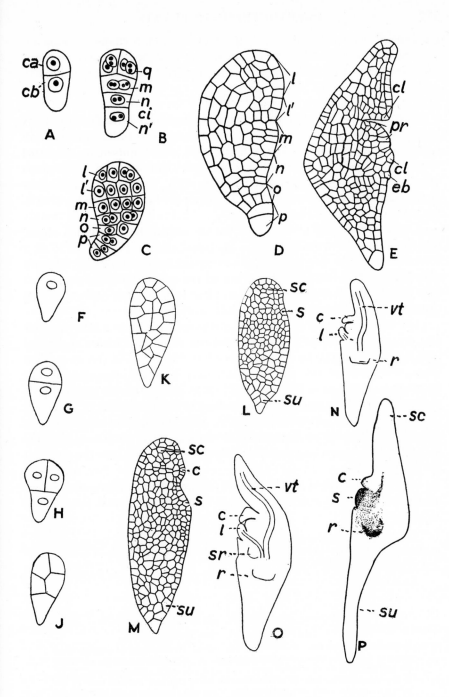

scutellum is the cotyledon, and although it may appear to be terminal at a certain stage in the embryogeny, it is essentially a lateral organ; (ii) that the 'ventral' scale when present is a ligule; (iii) that the epiblast, when present, is not a rudimentary second cotyledon, and probably has little morphological significance; (iv) that the coleoptile is homolgous with a foliage leaf, and is the second foliar member of the embryo; (v) that the elongated structure between the cotyledon and coleoptile in maize and oat seedlings is the first internode of the axis; the same region exists in wheat but is less elongated. In Avery's view the three morphological types which van Tieghem (1872, 1897) distinguished are fundamentally alike; they differ in the location of the meristematic region of the first internode. Avery's illustrations show the mature embryo of *Zea* with at least five leaves within the coleoptile, *Avena* with two, and *Triticum* with three or four, Figs. 72, 73.

In *Triticum vulgare*, McCall (1934) considers that the embryo organs can best be understood by referring to the positional relationships of the organs and tissues of the adult plant, i.e. the assumption is that essentially similar relationships obtain in the embryo and in the adult plant. In the embryo of *Triticum*, the transverse procambial plate which separates the primary root and the shoot is held to be the first node of the young plant. Roots are present at this node. The epiblast which is formed at this level, is interpreted as a vestigial first seedling leaf. The scutellum, which originates at the second node on the opposite side to the epiblast, is held to be the second seedling leaf. The coleoptile, which in *Triticum* has an axillary bud, is difficult to interpret because it arises on the same side as the scutellum. It is recognised as the third leaf, homologous with a bud prophyll.

As to the nature of the epiblast various views have been expressed. In the view of Sargant and Arber (1915), and Avery (1930), it is a mere outgrowth; to Celakovsky (1897) and Worsdell (1916) it is homologous with the auricles of the seed leaves; while to Poiteau (1809), Warming (1879), van Tiegham (1897), Bruns (1892) and Percival (1921), it is a rudimentary leaf. It is not unlike the non-vasculated prophylls and enations in some vascular cryptogams.

Randolph (1936) has shown that the pear-shaped embryo sac of *Zea mays* rapidly encroaches on the large nucellus and integuments, the small linear proembryo lying obliquely at the anterior side, Fig. 72. The initial small, ovoid proembryo enlarges into a club-shaped structure with a well-marked gradation of cell size, the basal cells being large and vacuolated. Apart from the localisation of rapid growth in the small-celled distal tissue, the proembryo is histologically undifferentiated up to the seventh day after fertilisation. Its peripheral cells divide by both anticlinal and periclinal walls, and elsewhere divisions take place in an

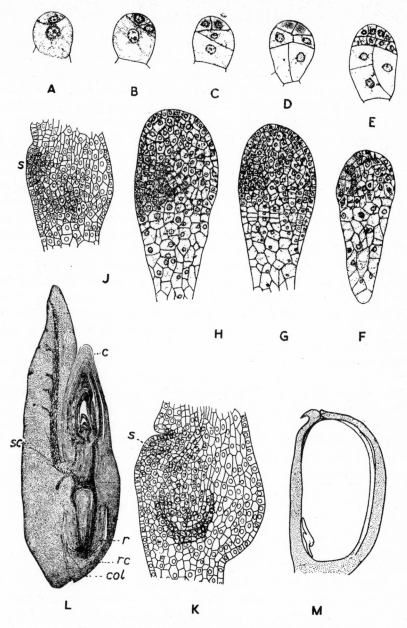

Fig. 72. Development of the embryo in *Zea mays*

A–E, Early stages showing the somewhat irregular segmentation pattern (× 180).
F–H, The enlarging club-shaped embryo shows a gradient of cell size and more
densely protoplasmic cells begin to be apparent in a median-distal lateral position
(× 160). J, K, The shoot apical region (*s*) and root are beginning to be differentiated (× 140). L, A fully developed embryo showing the scutellum (*sc*), the coleoptile (*c*), the coleorhiza (*col*), the root (*r*) and root-cap (*rc*). The scutellar node or
median plate can be seen about the middle of the embryo. M, Longitudinal section
of caryopsis showing the position of the young embryo relative to the endosperm.
(L, after Avery; the others after Randolph.)

entirely irregular manner. About the eighth day a rapid differentiation sets in: an epidermis forms over the distal region and extends down the sides towards the suspensor; in the sub-distal region the cells begin to divide actively by walls at right-angles to the proembryo axis. 'This is obviously a preliminary step in the differentiation of the main axis of the more mature embryo, an axis which does not coincide with the axis of the proembryo' (Randolph, 1936). In the now rapidly enlarging embryo a group of more densely protoplasmic cells is present in a distal lateral position on the anterior side. The rapid growth of the most terminal cells results in the formation of the organ later recognised as the scutellum or cotyledon, and the densely protoplasmic lateral group comes to occupy a position progressively further away from the distal extremity. This lateral meristematic cell mass becomes wedge-shaped, the individual cells grow and divide rapidly, and the region becomes organised as a slightly protruding shoot apex and an endogenous root, this axis being somewhat oblique to the proembryo axis, Fig. 72. About this stage the incipient vascular strand of the posterior-terminal organ, i.e. the scutellum or cotyledon, becomes conjoined with the plumule-radicle axis. Meanwhile the scutellum has enlarged greatly and expanded all round the posterior side of the plumule-radicle axis. These observations suggest that the shoot apex originates distally, but since it develops very slowly as compared with the cotyledon it eventually occupies a lateral position. Like the enlarged foot in lycopod embryos, the greatly enlarged scutellum in the Gramineae is formed adjacent to the endosperm, its strong development being probably related to its proximity to a major source of nutrients. At maturity the plumule-radicle axis is virtually parallel to the scutellum. The suspensor region stops growing soon after the differentiation of the radicle and persists as a vestigial organ. The coleoptile is described as the first ridge of tissue which develops above and later around the shoot meristem. The first plumular leaf arises as a similar ridge on the opposite side of the apical meristem; and eventually three to five additional leaves are formed.

Although Merry (1941) regards the scutellum and coleoptile in *Hordeum sativum* as 'structures morphologically distinct from the foliage leaves and peculiar to the embryo,' he holds that the scutellum is homologous with the cotyledon in other monocotyledonous embryos —a view well supported by his illustrations. In *Paspalum dilatatum*, Bennett (1944) also found that the planes of cell division in the young embryo are irregular, confirming the view that it is the growth of the embryo as a whole that is important. Norner (1881) and Souèges (1924), on the other hand, attempted to refer particular embryonic parts to particular cells in the early embryogeny. The mature embryo in

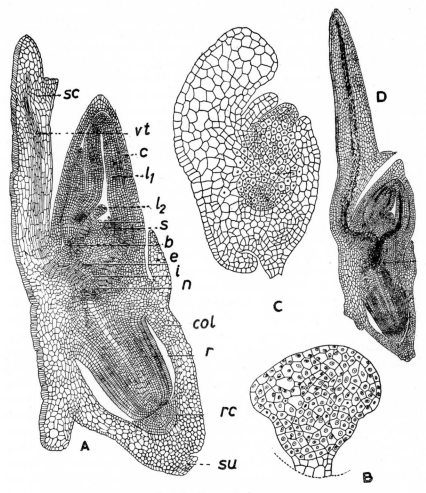

Fig. 73. Grass Embryos

A, *Triticum vulgare*. Embryo in longitudinal median section; *sc*, scutellum, with its vascular trace, *vt*; *c*, coleoptile; *l*, *l₂*, first and second plumular leaves; *s*, shoot apex, with third leaf; *b*, coleoptile axillary bud primordium; *e*, epiblast; *i*, first internode; *n*, first node; *col*, coleorhiza; *r*, root, with root-cap, *rc*; *su*, remains of suspensor (× 53, after McCall). B, C, *Paspalum dilatatum*. B, Young embryo, showing the considerable enlargement of the posterior side. C, Older embryo, showing the scutellum, coleoptile primordium, shoot apex and first root (after Bennett). D, *Avena sativa*. Fully developed embryo. The scutellum has a small ventral scale (on right); the other details are as in A (after Avery).

Paspalum has one foliage leaf but no epiblast. Some of Bennett's illustrations suggest that the scutellum is lateral in origin.

The coleoptile—now a very familiar object because of its extensive use in auxin studies—has been interpreted in several different ways: (i) It is the first leaf of the plumule, and the second leaf of the plant, the scutellum being the first leaf or cotyledon. If the epiblast is regarded as a rudimentary cotyledon, then the coleoptile is the third leaf, but the first plumular leaf. (ii) The scutellum and the coleoptile together form the cotyledon, the coleoptile being variously interpreted as a ligule, as a pair of fused stipules, or as an extension of the cotyledonary sheath. (iii) The coleoptile is the cotyledon, the scutellum being an outgrowth of the radicle or of the axis. (iv) The coleoptile and scutellum are structures peculiar to the embryo and morphologically distinct from the foliage leaves.

Weatherwax (1920), Percival (1927), Avery (1930), Boyd (1931), Randolph (1936), Jakovlev (1937), Yung (1938), and Kiesselbach (1949) have maintained that the coleoptile is homologous with a leaf. Nishmura (1922), Souèges (1924), Howarth (1927), Reznik (1934), and Arber (1934), on the other hand, consider that the scutellum and coleoptile are parts of one structure—the cotyledon. The third suggestion seems to have had no adherents in recent years, while the last, which was proposed by Merry (1941), has obtained little support.

Reeder (1953) has pointed out that investigators of the coleoptile have, to some extent, made their own difficulties, in that they have mainly worked with the somewhat specialised agricultural grasses such as *Zea, Hordeum, Sorghum, Avena, Triticum* and *Oryza*. If the less specialised, or more primitive, genera are investigated, the nature of some of the embryonic parts becomes fairly evident. This in *Streptochaeta spicata*, one of the most primitive of the grasses—taxonomically isolated but probably allied to *Bambusa*—the coleoptile is not a closed conical organ, as in *Zea* or *Triticum*, but is quite evidently a foliar structure, open on the side away from the scutellum and standing in a normal phyllotactic relationship to the first plumular leaf. Its foliar character is confirmed by the details of its vascular system. This consists of five vascular strands, one of which is median. Reeder has thus disposed of the main difficulties of accepting the coleoptile as a foliar organ.

As it seems to the present writer, the grass embryo, though admittedly complex and specialised, is perhaps less difficult to understand than is sometimes thought. In grasses, as in other monocotyledons, the distal region of the pear-shaped proembryo becomes a terminal foliar member and the shoot apex eventually becomes recognisable as an inconspicuous indentation on the side of the embryo facing away from the endosperm. On further growth, a vascular strand is differentiated in the cotyledon and becomes conjoined with the vascular strand differentiated in the first root. Now, this kind of morphological system, comprising a vasculated cotyledon (or prophyll), a root in vascular continuity with it, and a poorly organised shoot apex, is what is found in various eusporangiate ferns, e.g. species of Marattiaceae and Ophioglossaceae. And, as in these ferns, the shoot apex in grasses, however small and inconspicuous it may be initially, is nevertheless the centre of all the ensuing axial development (*see* Chapter IX). Furthermore, we may recall that in ferns, lycopods and *Selaginella*, various parts of the embryo may become greatly swollen and modified in relation to supplies of nutrients. Similarly, in grasses, with their very well developed endosperm, it is not surprising that some parts of the embryo become more or less extensively modified. From Merry's illustrations of the young embryo of *Hordeum*, in which the scutellum is very short and the nascent shoot apex in a relatively distal-lateral position, it is not difficult to suppose that, at an earlier stage, both the incipient scutellum and shoot apex had occupied distal positions. But, in relation to the underlying biochemical pattern, the apical site grows slowly, the foliar site rapidly.

In the grasses, as in other monocotyledons, the cotyledon appears to be truly terminal: there is an even gradation in cell size from the large-celled suspensor to the small-celled distal region. Nevertheless, this club-shaped embryo has in it a characteristic biochemical asymmetry, the shoot apex being always on the side away from the endosperm. If we assume, as we may well do, that the metabolic pattern which underlies the inception of the shoot apex and the first leaf is determined while the embryo is still very small, the difficulties in accepting the apex as the terminal pole of the embryonic axis largely disappear. The cotyledon (scutellum), the coleoptile, and the first foliage leaf will all stand in the normal relation of lateral organs to this axis, though their form and structure may be greatly modified by the nutritional and other factors which are at work during their respective developments. According to Avery: 'The fact that the embryonic stem tip appears to arise from the lateral face of the immature cotyledon need not be construed as meaning that the cotyledon is terminal. A more logical explanation, in view of the position of the suspensor in the mature embryo, would be to consider the origin of the growing point of the stem as having been delayed in development until after the cotyledon has attained considerable size.' Elsewhere, in *Lycopodium* and in eusporangiate ferns, examples of delay in the histological organisation of the shoot apex have been noted, and in them also the position of the axis has been temporarily obscured.

The epiblast in *Avena* and *Triticum* appears as a small, non-vasculated scale-like leaf situated on the opposite side of the embryo from the scutellum and inserted slightly lower down on the embryonic axis. Similar reduced foliar members and semi-abortive embryonic leaves are known among pteridophytes. If the developmental sequence in the formation of the lateral members was as follows (1) scutellum, (2) epiblast, (3) coleoptile, and (4) first plumular leaf, we should have an approximately normal phyllotactic sequence. But, as judged by their positions on the embryo axis, the epiblast lies below the scutellum. However, when we consider that the epiblast is on the side of the axis remote from the endospermous nutrition, and that the cotyledon, which is initially terminal, comes to occupy a lateral position and quickly grows to large size, thereby causing modifications in the general relationship of parts, it is by no means inconceivable, though proof has still to be obtained, that the epiblast is a second foliar member of very limited growth.

PARASITES AND SAPROPHYTES

In view of the differences, sometimes extensive, in the vegetative development of angiospermic parasites and saprophytes, as compared with normal autotrophic species, it is relevant to inquire if these are foreshadowed in the embryogeny. Here it may be noted that although the vegetative development may be greatly modified by an irregular mode of nutrition, the floral morphology is characterised by a certain constancy. Reduced and anomalous embryos are widely scattered through different orders and families. Not all of these pertain to parasites and saprophytes, but some do. The morphological observations will gain in value as the related physiological-genetical processes are more fully investigated. A number of curious and reduced embryos, e.g. of *Rafflesia*, *Scurrula*, *Balanophora*, *Scabiosa*, *Aeginetia* (Oroban-chaceae)*; Voyria*, *Voyriella*, *Cotylanthera* and *Leiphaimos* (Saprophytic Gentianaceae) are illustrated in Figs. 74–78. Some of these have been described briefly by Maheshwari (1950).

Cuscuta reflexa shows much variation in the relative developments of the embryo and suspensor (Johri and Tiagi, 1952). The embryo sac conforms to the bisporic *Allium* type, but abnormal embryo sacs may occur. One of the synergids becomes hypertrophied and persists for a long time, usually associated with the swollen suspensor cells; occasionally a synergid may also be fertilised. The zygote and endosperm develop more or less simultaneously, the latter being at first free nuclear but later cellular and finally gelatinous. The zygote divides transversely; the basal cell gives rise to the suspensor with some contribution from the terminal cell. The suspensor may develop as a series of distended cells, sometimes irregularly disposed, and containing many nuclei. These cells are described as having a haustorial function. The upper region of the suspensor, which is derived from a tier of the embryonic region, consists of two tiers of uninucleate cells. These have

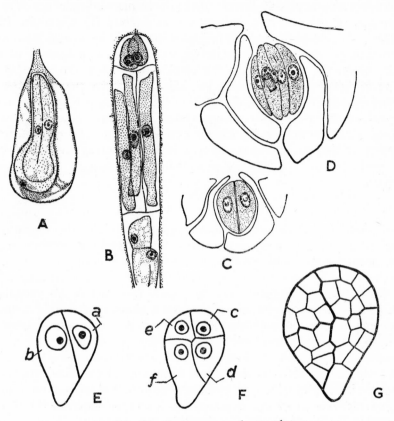

Fig. 74. Various anomalous embryos

A, B, *Scurrula atropurpurea*. A, First division of zygote. B, Enlarged view of distal region of proembryo, showing beginning of elongation of suspensor cells (after Rauch). C, D, *Balanophora abbreviata*. C, Two-celled embryo resulting from longitudinal division of zygote. D, A more advanced stage (after Zweifel). E–G, *Scabiosa succisa*. Stages in the development of the embryo (after Souèges).

a staining reaction similar to the suspensor cells below, but they remain small and uninucleate and project in a foot-like manner into the lower portion of the suspensor, Fig. 75. In some embryos, however, the suspensor remains relatively undeveloped or it may be absent. Both types of suspensor may be observed in the same ovary. The proembryo, at first filamentous, becomes a globular mass, with irregular divisions, and this eventually develops into an elongated, spirally or irregularly coiled embryo, with a distal apex, small plumular scales, and a feebly differentiated central vascular strand. There are no cotyledons. In other species of *Cuscuta* the embryogeny is generally comparable (Fedortshuk, 1931; Tiagi, 1951). Johri and Tiagi disagree with Johansen's placing of the *Cuscuta* embryo in his Caryophyllad type;

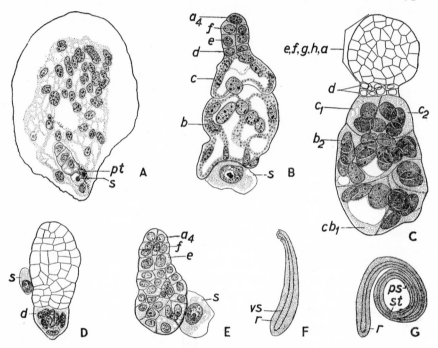

Fig. 75. Embryogeny in *Cuscuta reflexa*

A, Three-celled proembryo, with free endosperm nuclei; *s*, haustorial synergid; *pt*, pollen tube. B, An older embryo; the basal region of the proembryo has developed into two large vesicular, coenocytic suspensor cells, *b* and *c*; the distal region has given rise to four tiers. C, A yet older stage, showing the distal embryonal mass. D, Proembryo with reduced vesicular suspensor; *s*, synergid; E, Proembryo without vesicular suspensor. F, G, Maturation of coiled embryo; *st*, shoot apex; *ps*, plumular scale; *r*, root; *vs*, vascular strand. (A–E, × 165; F, G, × 4; after Johri and Tiagi.)

they consider that it properly belongs to the Solanad type. Tiagi (1951) has compared the embryological development of *Cuscuta* with that in non-parasitic species of Convolvulaceae, and considers that it should be removed to a separate family (i.e. the Cuscutaceae), thus supporting a view already advanced by taxonomists. In the genus *Cuscuta* the genetical changes associated with the transition to the parasitic mode of life can be detected in various anomalous developments of the embryo.

In the Loranthaceae, Balanophoraceae, and Santalaceae (Santalales) the species of the first two families are parasitic, or semi-parasitic, while those of the third include some parasites. Maheshwari (1937) regards these as being among the most difficult angiosperms to investigate embryologically, Fig. 74. Since the Loranthaceae exhibit many curious morphological and anatomical features, some of which are associated with their parasitic habit, it is of interest to ascertain if the embryogeny is characterised by any unusual features and, if so, when these appear. Singh (1952) has described some very remarkable developments of the female gametophyte and embryo in *Dendrophthoe falcata* (*Loranthus longiflorus*), Fig. 76. In this and related genera and species, the whole embryonic environment is a very unusual one. No well-defined nucellus or integument can be distinguished, but there is a considerable mass of megaspore mother cells, each of which gives rise to a linear tetrad of megaspores. Greatly elongated filamentous embryo-sacs, 22–28 mm. long, and with eight nuclei, are formed from the uppermost megaspores. These penetrate upwards into the style with the result that the egg apparatus may eventually be situated close to the stigma. After fertilisation, the several embryo sacs become fused and a composite endosperm is formed. The evidence, sometimes incomplete, of several investigators (Griffith, 1844; Treub, 1881; Rauch, 1936; Schaeppi and Steindl, 1942; and Singh, 1952) is that the first division of the fertilised egg is by a longitudinal wall, this being followed by rapid polar elongation of the embryo and a succession of transverse divisions. The suspensor of the proembryo now undergoes rapid elongation and thereby thrusts the distal embryonic cells down through the style into the endosperm in the ovary region below. If this rapid elongation did not take place, the young embryo would be shed along with the style-like organ which soon falls by abscission. Only one embryo of the initial polyembryonic system reaches maturity. The fully developed embryo has a club-shaped appearance with a single cotyledon and an enclosed sunken plumule. Singh, however, has shown that at an earlier stage there are two distinct and equivalent cotyledons which become fused on further development. A flat, cushion-like radicle constitutes the base of the embryo. The mature fruit is a complex structure consisting of four tissue layers. The seed has no testa. Within the outermost layer of the fruit there is a viscid layer which is responsible for the ejection of the seed and its subsequent adhesion to the host plant. (Fig. 76A–F, from Singh, 1952). *Tupeia antarctica*, Fig. 76G, H, the New Zealand mistletoe (Loranthaceae), which closely resembles *Viscum* and *Loranthus* but belongs to a distinct genus, is also characterised by some quite extraordinary developments of its embryo sac and embryo (Smart, 1952).

In *Striga lutea*, a semiparasitic species of the Rhinantheae-Gerardiae (Scrophulariaceae), the proembryo has large 'tuberous haustoria' at the base of the suspensor, but otherwise it shows no abnormal features, the mature embryo being a typical dicotyledonous one. The chalazal end of the cellular endosperm develops into a long binucleate haustorium which penetrates the integument; the micropylar haustorium is inconspicuous. The question as to whether the parasitic mode of life of the plant affects the embryo sac and embryonic development is one which has often been raised (Bernard, 1903; Mitchell, 1915, etc.). The evidence indicates that there is no direct relationship between the habit of the plant and the haustorial developments of the endosperm. These structures are a general feature in the Scrophulariaceae and are in no way restricted to the parasitic and semi-parasitic genera and species. Thus, in the holoautotrophic genus *Veronica*, the endosperm haustorial development is as in the Rhinantheae. In studies of four total parasites, namely, *Lathraea*, *Orobanche*, *Phelipaea*, and *Cytinus*, Bernard (1903) found all stages of haustorial development. *Lathraea* showed the most extensive haustorial development. Also, in the production of fertile seeds, the parasitic members appear to be just as successful as their autotrophic near-relatives. In other words, the genetical changes which have led to the saprophytic, semi-parasitic, or parasitic modes of life in these organisms have not materially affected the mechanisms of reproduction and embryogenesis. The embryonic development in *Orobanche cernua*, Fig. 77, is characteristic of the group.

In *Aeginetia indica* (Orobanchaceae), a small parasite on grass roots, the ovules are very small, the nucellar epidermis degenerates, and an inconspicuous integumentary tapetum surrounds the mature embryo sac. The early embryogeny is fairly normal, but the mature embryo consists simply of an ellipsoidal cellular mass, with the remains of the suspensor at one end, embedded in a cellular endosperm. The endosperm gives rise to a small chalazal haustorium and to an aggressive micropylar haustorium. The latter develops intercellular hypha-like

---

Fig. 76. Embryogeny in Loranthaceae

A–F, Embryogeny in *Dendropthoe falcata*. A, B, C, Basal, middle and upper regions of a gynoecium in longitudinal section. D, Entire flower; the egg apparatus in the several elongated embryo sacs can be seen in the style; the antipodal cells are in contiguity with the collenchymatous pad (*col*) just above the base of the ovary. E, L.s. of style, showing the biseriate proembryo. F, L.s. of fruit; *ca*, calyculus; *e*, embryo; *end*, endosperm; *pa*, zone of parenchyma; *ps*, perianth scar; *l*, leathery coat of fruit wall; *s*, space through which the embryo sacs pass into the ovary; *ss*, scar of style; *vb*, vascular zone; *vs*, viscid layer (E, × 130; all after Bahadur Singh). G, H, Embryogeny in *Tupeia antarctica*. G, L.s. of female flower, showing elongated embryo sacs with egg apparatus (*E*) in the style, and collenchyma sheath (*c*) at the base. H, L.s. of developing fruit, with viscous tissue (*V*), stylar disc (*D*), collenchyma sheath (*C*), embryo (*E*). (G, × 25; H, × 30; after Smart).

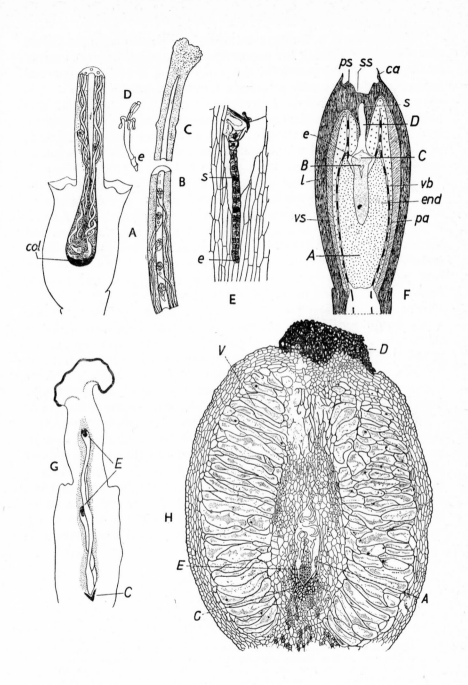

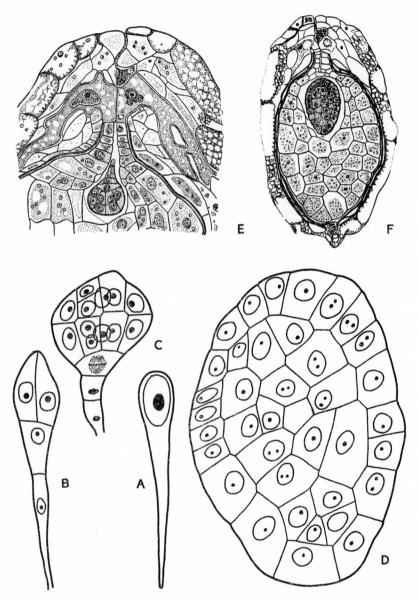

Fig. 77. Embryogeny in *Orobanche cernua*

A, Fertilised ovum. B, Early divisions. C, Older stage, showing formation of
dermatogen and degeneration of suspensor cells. D, Mature ovoid embryo. E,
L.s. of embryo sac, showing aggressive branching micropylar haustorium with
amoeboid nuclei; the embryonic development is as in C. F, L.s. of seed, showing
ovoid embryo and endosperm. (A–D, × 825; E, × 340; F, × 166; after Tiagi.)

branches which penetrate the integument (Tiagi, 1952). In *Cistanche tubulosa* (Orobanchaceae), a leafless total parasite, growing on the roots of *Acacia* and other trees, Tiagi (1952) found that the embryo sac is not characterised by any unusual features, but after fertilisation the embryo remains small and relatively undeveloped. In the small mature seed the embryo is an ovoid structure with tissue differentiation but

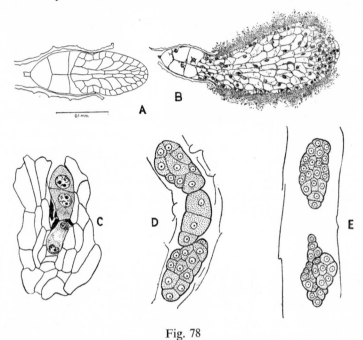

Fig. 78

A, B, Embryogeny in *Monotropa hypopitys*. A, L.s. of seed, showing embryogermling, as yet without mycorrhizic fungus. B, An older germling with fungus (B, × 10; after Francke). C–E, Embryogeny in *Zeuxine sulcata*. C, Binucleate embryo sac and two-celled nucellar embryo. D, E, Formation of several embryos (C, × 490; D, E, × 56; after Swamy).

without differentiation of plumule, cotyledons or radicle. The cellular endosperm forms a rather feeble chalazal haustorium but a very aggressive micropylar one with intercellular hypha-like branches which penetrate the integument. These endosperm developments, however, are general in the autotrophic Scrophulariaceae and are not correlated with the parasitic habit in *Cistanche*.

In *Monotropa hypopitys* (Ericales: Monotropaceae), a saprophytic species well known because of its ectotrophic mycorrhizic nutrition, the mature seed is very small and contains an embryo consisting of three cells only, surrounded by an endosperm of nine cells, Fig. 78A, B. During germination, which apparently only takes place after some inhibiting substance has been dissolved out or removed, the embryo enlarges within the seed and becomes differentiated into a small-celled, embryonic, distal region and a large-celled basal region. At this stage the germ is still uninfected by the symbiotic fungus. On being released from the testa the germ can only continue to grow if it is infected by the appropriate fungus (Francke, 1934). In the saprophytic mycorrhizic species *Sarcodes sanguinea* (Ericales: Monotropaceae), the embryo and the endosperm in the mature seed are also poorly developed (Oliver, 1890).

In *Zeuxine sulcata* (Orchidaceae: Neottinae), a holosaprophytic, rootless species exhibiting an extreme case of absence of chlorophyll and feebly developed vascular tissue, Swamy (1946) has described a very much modified embryogeny, Fig. 78C–E. In the ovule, the megaspore mother-cell begins to degenerate so that few, if any, ovules form a functional embryo sac. Diploid embryos arise adventitiously (apomictically) from the cells of the nucellar epidermis, polyembryony being common. As these embryos are not formed in the normal environment of an embryo sac, it is of some interest to note that while the very young embryo may exhibit some evidence of polarity, older embryos consist of a somewhat irregular mass of quite undifferentiated meristematic cells.

APOMIXIS

By *apomixis* is meant the substitution of the normal sexual reproduction by an asexual process. Apomixis may include the formation of an embryo from an unfertilised ovum (haploid parthenogenesis), or from some other cell of the gametophyte (haploid apogamy); but as the resulting haploid sporophytes are usually sterile, the process is not repeated from one generation to the next. This has been referred to as non-recurrent apomixis. In recurrent apomixis, the nuclei of the embryo sac are usually diploid. Hence we may have diploid parthenogenesis (from a diploid ovum) or diploid apogamy (from some other diploid cell of the gametophyte). Yet other variants are known. In what has been called adventive embryony, or sporophytic budding, the embryo is formed from a cell of the nucellus or the integument and its nuclei are therefore diploid; in these cases, the gametophytic generation has been by-passed. Lastly, in viviparous reproduction, the flowers may be replaced by bulbils or propagules, this being simply an unusual form of vegetative reproduction. (For discussions and data on the cytology of apomixis, the reader is referred to Gustafsson, 1935, 1946, 1947.)

The occurrence of haploid parthenogenesis may be of considerable value in genetical studies in that it enables true-breeding homozygous material to be obtained. Haploid parthenogenesis can be induced in some species by the use of appropriate techniques (*see* Chapter XV), e.g. by stimulating but not fertilising the ovum with pollen of another species, by delayed pollination, etc. Jørgensen (1928) found that when the stigma of *Solanum nigrum* was pollinated with the pollen of *S. luteum*, the male nucleus eventually penetrated the ovum, but there was no effective nuclear fusion and the male nucleus soon began to disintegrate. The ovum, however, was activated as if by normal fertilisation and an embryo was formed. Twin proembryos may sometimes be observed in *Lilium martagon*, Fig. 79A; one of these is formed from the ovum by the normal fertilisation, the other from a stimulated haploid synergid cell. The initial developments of the two embryos are closely comparable but the synergid embryo soon degenerates (Cooper, 1943). Similar observations on synergid embryos have been made by Lebègue (1949) in *Bergenia delavayi* (Saxifragaceae) and by Crété (1949) in *Erythraea centaurium* (Gentianaceae). Maheshwari (1950) has summarised other evidence on parthogenesis, including cases of androgenic haploids in which, as the evidence seems to show, the embryo has developed from the male nucleus alone. In other instances of apomixis the chief interest lies in the cytological rather than in the embryonic vicissitudes. Here we may note that although there may be departures from the normal nuclear arrangements, the embryonic development, presumably in relation to the relatively stable conditions within the ovule, initially follows normal paths. Where there is subsequent degeneration, this is usually attributable to factors in the genetical constitution.

In *Rudbeckia speciosa* (Compositae) a peculiar embryonic innovation, described as semigamy, has been observed, Fig. 79B–D (Battaglia, 1946, 1947). The small male nucleus enters the ovum which is diploid, and activates it but there is no nuclear fusion. On the contrary, it appears that the male and female nuclei divide separately, though often simultaneously during the ensuing embryonic development, with the result that cells containing male nuclei, which are never numerous, come to occupy variable positions in the embryo, a sort of embryonic chimaera being thus formed.

In adventive embryonic development, the embryo has its inception in a diploid cell of the nucellus or integument. This cell becomes densely protoplasmic and divides actively to form a small mass of meristematic cells. This tissue mass grows, or is pushed into the embryo sac, and there it gives rise to what appears to be a normal embryo. In *Citrus trifoliata* (Rutales: Rutaceae), Fig. 79E, F, the normal embryo has a suspensor whereas the nucellar adventive embryos have not, i.e. they resemble the distal region of the normal embryo. From these observations it may perhaps be inferred that there is some delay in the establishment of polarised growth in adventive embryos. In *Citrus*, many viable embryos may sometimes be found in the same seed. Studies of adventive embryos, which may arise in various positions, may prove of value in the causal analysis of morphogenesis.

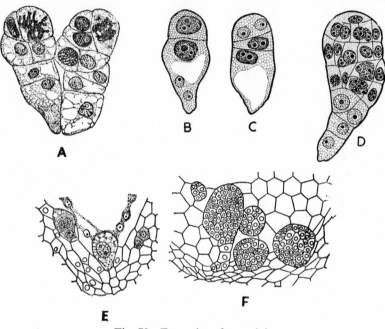

Fig. 79. Examples of apomixis

A, *Lilium martagon*. The proembryo on the left has arisen from a synergid and is haploid; that on the right has developed from the zygote and is diploid (after Cooper). B–D, Semigamy in *Rudbeckia speciosa*. B, Two-celled proembryo with two small nuclei in basal cell. C, Three-celled proembryo showing nuclei derived from sperm in terminal cell. D, More advanced stage; the nuclei derived from the sperm may occupy various positions (after Battaglia). E, F, *Citrus trifoliata*. Zygotic and nucellar embryos; in F, only the zygotic embryo has a suspensor; the embryos are surrounded by endosperm (after Osawa).

Maheshwari states that if the nucellus is intact, the adventive embryos will typically originate from some of its cells; but if the nucellus becomes disorganised, they may originate in the integument. (For other examples, *see* Maheshwari, 1950.) According to the species, adventive embryonic development may take place with or without the stimulus of pollination or fertilisation. The nature of those stimuli is of primary interest to the embryologist. In *Eugenia jambos* (Myrtales: Myrtaceae), adventive embryos originate without pollination, but only if the ovum is fertilised do they attain to their full development (Pijl,

1934). According to Webber and Batchelor (1943), fertilisation is necessary in most varieties of *Citrus* for the maturation of adventitious embryos; and so, too, for the mango (*Mangifera indica*, Sapindales: Anacardiaceae) (Juliano, 1934, 1937). An endosperm is nearly always present in species in which adventive embryos are formed, an exception, according to Archibald (1939), being *Opuntia aurantiaca* (Cactaceae).

Although formed from sporophyte tissue, adventive embryos develop quite differently from normal terminal or axillary shoot buds. The rudiment of a shoot bud is characterised by the early formation of an axis bearing leaves: the adventive embryo, by contrast, passes through the typical embryonic and seedling phases. In *Citrus*, the shoot buds develop into almost thornless shoots, whereas nucellar embryos, like the normal zygotic embryo, yield thorny seedlings. While these morphological differences may be largely due to the nutritional status of the environments of the two kinds of primordium, genetical factors may also be involved. The effect of such factors could perhaps be ascertained by observing the development of young, excised nucellar embryos in suitable artificial media. The ontogenetic 'recapitulation' shown by nucellar embryos is likely to be due to the same factors which determine the normal embryonic development (Swingle, 1927).

POLYEMBRYONY

Polyembryony, or the occurrence of more than one embryo in the seed, first discovered in oranges by Leeuwenhoek in 1719, has been reviewed by Ernst (1918), Schnarf (1929), Webber (1940), Robyns and Louis (1942), Gustafsson (1946), Maheshwari (1950, 1951, 1952), Johansen (1950), and Lebègue (1952), Figs. 80, 81. Cleavage polyembryony results when the zygote or proembryo divides into two or more embryos. This phenomenon, which is common in the gymnosperms, is only of sporadic occurrence in the angiosperms. Examples are afforded by *Erythronium americanum* (Liliaceae) (Jeffrey, 1895; Guerin, 1930); *Tulipa gesneriana* (Liliaceae) (Ernst, 1901); *Limnocharis emarginata* (Butomaceae) (Hall, 1902); *Eulophea epidendraea* (Orchidaceae) (Swamy, 1943). Cleavage polyembryony is of fairly frequent occurrence in the Orchidaceae. In *Eulophea*, the zygote may divide irregularly forming a multicellular mass, the more distal cells of which grow out and form several individual embryos; or the filamentous proembryo may branch and so yield several embryos; or small proembryo buds may develop into separate embryos, Fig. 80D, E. In *Erythronium*, the zygote divides irregularly and forms an embryonic mass, the most distal cells of which grow out separately to form embryos, Fig. 80C.

In addition to the zygotic embryos, other embryos may not infrequently be formed from the synergids (with or without the intervention of a male nucleus), or from the antipodals—a more rare phenomenon.

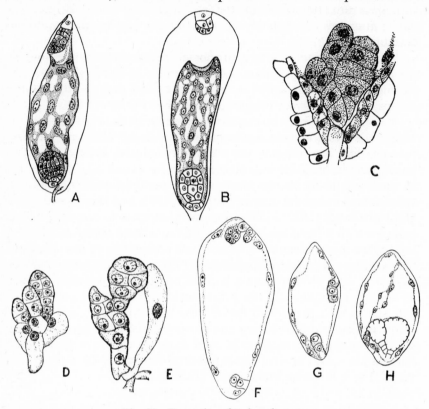

Fig. 80. Examples of polyembryony

A, B, *Ulmus americana*. Normal and antipodal embryos (after Shattuck). C, *Erythronium americanum*. Proliferation of embryonic mass with formation of several embryos (after Jeffrey). D, E, *Eulophea epidendraea*. D, The zygote has formed a group of cells, three of which have given rise to independent embryos. E, A bud has been formed on the right-hand side of the embryo (after Swamy). F, *Elatostema sinuatum eusinuatum*. A zygotic embryo and three antipodal embryos (one undergoing its first division). G, *Elatostema eurhynchum*. Zygotic and lateral embryos. H, *Elatostema acuminatum*. Compound embryo-sac formed by the fusion of two embryo-sacs; that on the right has two well developed embryos; that on the left has two small embryos (F–H, after Fagerlind).

In *Ulmus americana* (Urticales; Ulmaceae), the antipodal nuclei have often an egg-like appearance and embryos are sometimes formed in their vicinity (Shattuck, 1905), Fig. 80A, B. Antipodal embryos have also been found in *Ulmus glabra* (Ekdahl, 1941), *Allium odorum* (Liliaceae) (Modilewski, 1931), *Sedum fabaria* (Saxifragales: Crassulaceae) (Mauritzon, 1933), and *Elatostema sinuatum eusinuatum*

(Urticaceae) (Fagerlind, 1944), Fig. 80F–H. The further development of antipodal embryos, however, has not been determined and it is not known if they are viable. The presence of antipodal embryos, with their inverted orientation, raises interesting questions regarding the relation of the polarity of the embryo sac to the embryonic development.

Adventive embryos afford further examples of polyembryony. In the orchid species *Spiranthes australis*, some of the constituent races yield normal zygotic embryos, but others form two to six adventive embryos from the inner integument (Swamy, 1949).

Polyembryony may be due to the presence of multiple embryo sacs within the ovule (*see* Maheshwari, 1951, for the relevant literature). In some species, polyembryony may be induced simultaneously by several of the methods indicated above. In *Allium odorum* one third to one half of the ovules may contain multiple embryos of ovum, synergid and antipodal origin (Tretjakow, 1895, and Hegelmaier, 1897); and Haberlandt (1923, 1925) has shown that, even in castrated flowers, embryos with diploid nuclei are formed from these nuclei, as also from cells of the inner integument. The innate complexity of this species has been further indicated by Modilewski (1925, 1930, 1931); for it appears that some embryo sacs contain haploid nuclei and some diploid nuclei. In diploid embryo sacs, the polar nuclei are fertilised and yield an endosperm with pentaploid nuclei; the embryos have their inception in the unfertilised diploid egg and antipodal cells. In haploid embryo sacs, the viable embryos are formed from haploid ova after normal fertilisation. The several developmental situations have been summarised as follows by Maheshwari (1950, p. 348):

'(i) In a haploid and normally fertilised embryo sac, embryos may begin to develop from all cells of the embryo sac and even from the adjacent integumentary cells, but only the zygotic embryo survives so that the mature seeds contain a single embryo. (ii) Embryos may also begin to form from one or more cells of the haploid and unfertilised embryo sac, but owing to the lack of an endosperm, which can arise only after triple fusion, their growth is soon arrested and they become non-viable. (iii) In a diploid but unfertilised embryo sac, any of its cells (also the cells of the inner integument) may begin to form an embryo, but eventually they all degenerate owing to the absence of an endosperm. (iv) In diploid embryo sacs, in which the secondary nucleus is fertilised, endosperm formation proceeds actively and all the cells of the sac are capable of giving rise to embryos, but only the egg embryo usually attains maturity.'

Cytological disturbances and somewhat comparable polyembryonic developments have been observed in *Alnus rugosa* (Fagales: Betulaceae) by Woodworth (1930) and in *Atraphaxis frutescens* (Polygonaceae) by Edman (1931). In the latter species, where both micropylar and chalazal embryos were formed, the latter usually degenerated. In

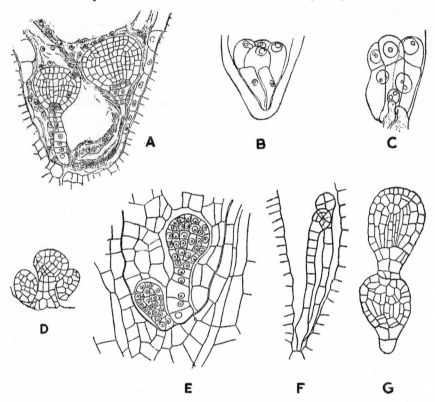

Fig. 81. Further examples of polyembryony

A, *Potentilla aurea* (after Lebègue). B, *Crepis capillaris* (after Gerassimova). C, *Sagittaria graminia* (after Johri). D, *Spathiphyllum patinii* (after Schurhoff). E, *Bergenia delavayi* (after Lebègue). F, *Arabis lyallii* (after Lebègue). G, *Lobelia syphilitica* (after Crété).

Elatostema spp., a multiple-origin polyembryony is also found (Fagerlind, 1944), Fig. 80F, H. Closely contiguous embryos sometimes fuse and form complex tissue masses. As ovum, synergid, antipodal and nucellar embryos tend to become aligned in the embryo sac axis, an ovum and an antipodal embryo may thus have their cotyledons directed towards each other.

The importance of the cytological and genetical aspects of poly-embryony is well illustrated in some species with twin and triplet embryos, the embryos showing the same or multiple chromosome numbers (Webber, 1940). Separate twin embryos, diploid and genetically identical even in heterozygous stocks, and embryos with two plumules but a common radicle, have been observed in *Zea mays* seeds (Randolph, 1936). In *Trifolium pratense*, twin embryos each with a chromosome fragment, and in *Medicago sativa*, twins each with an extra chromosome, have been observed (Skovsted, 1939). All these associated embryos appear to be identical twins, i.e. originating from a single fertilised ovum. Cytologically and genetically identical diploid embryos could also result from the fertilisation of an ovum and one of its synergids. Diploid twins could also arise by nucellar budding and by the inception of an embryo in two separate embryo sacs in an ovule. Haploid-diploid twins have also been reported in a number of species (*see* Maheshwari, 1951). The explanation of this phenomenon is that the ovum is normally fertilised and that another nucleus of the embryo sac is stimulated to develop; or that there are two embryo sacs in the ovule, and that fertilisation in one induces parthogenesis in the other. In the case of diploid-triploid twins, and haploid-triploid twins, several instances of which have been reported (Maheshwari, 1951), the several evident cytological explanations have been advanced. It is often difficult, if not impossible, to determine the cytological events that have led to the formation of twin embryos of different ploidy.

Indications of a useful methodological approach, and of the valuable data that may accrue from critical studies of polyembryony, have been given by Randall and Rick (1945). In cytological investigations of *Asparagus officinalis* they found that of 405 multiple seedlings, 97 per cent were twins, 11 were triplets and there was one set of quadruplets. Diploid twins (with $2n = 20$) were the most frequent, but haploids, triploids, tetraploids and trisomic individuals, with 10, 30, 40 and 21 chromosomes respectively, were also found. In the haploid-diploid twins, the haploid member was always much smaller; with this exception, however, size differences were no guide to the chromosome constitution of the seedlings. The several embryonic conditions are variously attributed to cleavage polyembryony and to the fertilisation or stimulation of two cells in the same or in contiguous embryo sacs. Although there are serious technical difficulties to be overcome, comprehensive investigations combining morphological, cytological and genetical observations, and embryo culture of polyembryonic species, seem likely to advance materially our knowledge of the factors in embryogenesis.

Chapter XV

EMBRYOGENESIS IN FLOWERING PLANTS:
ANALYTICAL AND EXPERIMENTAL INVESTIGATIONS

EXPERIMENTAL studies of angiosperm embryology have been mainly concerned with the compatibilities of the male and female gametes, the inhibition and, not infrequently, destruction of the embryo due to genetical factors, induced parthenogenesis, and factors affecting the embryonic development as ascertained by the methods of aseptic embryo culture. Maheshwari (1951) states that experimental embryology 'is concerned with an imitation and a modification of the course of Nature, with a view to understanding the physics and chemistry of the various processes underlying the development and differentiation of the embryo, so as to bring them under human control to the furthest extent possible.' This definition comes close to the heart of the matter, provided the complexity of organismal phenomena is constantly borne in mind. The experimental embryologist may rightly be concerned with the events leading to the fertilisation of the ovum as well as with its subsequent development. Some of these have been considered by Maheshwari (1950). As our primary interest here lies in the actual embryonic development, our study begins with the activated ovum, or other embryo-yielding cells in or near the embryo sac.

Experimental investigations do not stand alone: they usually have their inception in morphological and anatomical observations, or in the data of growth and metabolic studies. Observational, analytical, and experimental studies should, indeed, go together if an adequate account of the phenomena of development is to be given. In the two preceding Chapters a selection of the descriptive morphological observations has been given: in the present Chapter the data of analytical and experimental investigations are considered.

HORMONES AND SEED DEVELOPMENT

Marrè and Murneek (1953) have shown that one effect of fertilisation in maize is that hormones are produced and that these have a regulating action on the movement of carbohydrates and nitrogen-containing metabolites into the ovule; also, if growth-regulating substances are applied externally, they stimulate the accumulation of sugars and the formation of starch in the young tissues of the flowers and fruits. Ears of an inbred line of sweet corn were treated with water-lanoline emulsions of (i) the ethyl ester of indoleacetic acid and (ii) naphthalene acetic acid at a concentration of 1000 p.p.m., a concentration which is effective in inducing the parthogenetic development of the kernels (Britten, 1950). These were compared with ears in which normal pollination had been effected, and with ears sprayed with a water-lano-line emulsion (as control). In the course of several days no significant changes took place in the carbohydrate content of the kernels used as controls, whereas in both the hormone-treated and pollinated kernels there were marked and qualitatively comparable changes, i.e. an increase in the starch content from its initial low level and in reducing sugar, and a decrease in sucrose. The cob was similarly affected in respect of these changes, indicating that the hormone effect is not restricted to the developing kernels. The pollination and the artificial hormone treatments also resulted in some increase in the hexose phosphates in the kernels, suggesting that the production of these substances was greater than their utilisation, notwithstanding the fact that the ovary was in an active state of growth. In this experiment, Marrè and Murneek have thus been able to show that there is a close similarity between the action of the hormones, or growth-regulating substances, naturally released by the act of fertilisation and those which can be applied artificially. In observations of this kind we get a glimpse of the complex system of biochemical factors and metabolic changes involved in the development of the embryo and endosperm. With the improvement of techniques there can be little doubt that very substantial progress will be made along these lines. Indeed, plant embryologists of the future will almost certainly be largely preoccupied with cellular physiology and, in particular, with the intricate details of the action of hormones and kindred substances. The literature thus far available (reviewed by Murneek (1937), Wittwer (1943) and Britten (1950)) indicates that the developing seed should be viewed as a dynamic system, conspicuous features of which are the localisation and utilisation of the products of assimilation by the embryo. That auxin and other growth-regulating substances play an important part in this process is borne out by an increasing body of experimental data, (see Murneek, 1937; Avery et al., 1942; Wittwer, 1943; Haagen-Smit et al., 1946; Britten, 1947, 1950).

STARCH ACCUMULATION AND UTILISATION IN THE OVULE

The literature of plant embryology contains only scanty information on the translocation, utilisation and accumulations of nutrients. The relation of nutrition to embryonic development has been explored by Buell (1952) for *Dianthus*, a genus in which the suspensor consists of two large basal cells. At the spherical embryo stage, the prevascular cylinder of the hypocotyl is already delimited; and the pattern of the root meristem is apparent in embryos showing cotyledon primordia. The number of cells in the nucellus is still on the increase up to the spherical embryo stage, but thereafter the perisperm starch begins to accumulate, thus affording evidence of active translocation, probably of sugars, into the ovule by way of the funiculus.

The funiculus of the young ovule has only an incipient vascular strand, yet it is able to translocate all the metabolites which are used in

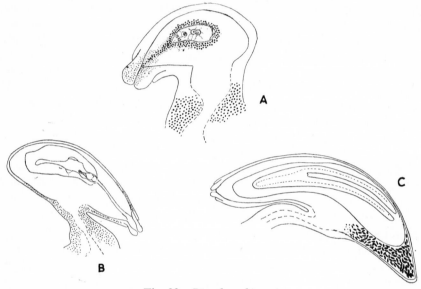

Fig. 82. *Dianthus chinensis*

Starch in ovule and seed. A, Longitudinal section of ovule (diagrammatic) with a seven-nucleate embryo sac and enveloping starch-containing tissue. B, Ovule with young embryo. C, Ovule with maturing embryo. (A, × 102; B, × 29; C, × 21; after Buell.)

the growth of the ovule. Indeed, some starch may actually be stored in the young ovule. By the time the ovum is mature, the funiculus strand has become fully differentiated into xylem and phloem. The synergids, the basal cell of the proembryo, and the endosperm, may all function as absorbing systems and all eventually contribute to the embryonic development. The partial digestion of the nucellus follows a regular pattern, the micropylar region disappearing most rapidly. Indeed, a kind of biochemical pattern is followed during the whole post-fertilisation phase, the central and controlling component being the developing embryo. The large basal suspensor cell has probably an absorptive function. Perotti (1913) found protein granules in it in *Stellaria media*

(Caryophyllaceae), and Rocén (1927) observed starch grains in it in *Basella alba* (Centrospermae: Chenopodiaceae: Basellaceae).

In *Dianthus*, considerable quantities of starch and other reserve foods are present in the placenta, ovary wall and ovule at the time of fertilisation, the most conspicuous starch deposits being in the nucellus prior to fertilisation and during the growth of the embryo from the spherical stage to maturity. Deposits are first present in the funiculus and extend to the micropylar end. Starch is abundant in the embryo sac at fertilisation and is used in the early embryogeny. In ovules containing well developed embryos, starch was still present in the perisperm at the antipodal (i.e. cotyledon) end of the ovule, but not at the micropylar end. This suggests that the mobilisation and uptake of nutrients takes place by way of the basal or radicle end of the embryo, Fig. 82. Dahlgren (1939) has given a list of angiosperms in which starch has been observed in the embryo sac. Reserves of fat and possibly of protein are present in the mature cotyledons and upper hypocotyl, but there is no starch.

AMINO-ACIDS IN DEVELOPING ENDOSPERM

Species with large seeds like *Zea mays* lend themselves to investigations of the metabolites present in the endosperm during the formation of the seed. These observations are of direct or indirect interest in the embryonic development. Widely different types of maize all show the same kinds of free amino-acids and amides, and in about the same proportions, these substances being demonstrable in the endosperm at all stages of development, subject to various fluctuations which have been described. Most of the glutelin complex of proteins are formed during the first half of the grain maturation period, and most of the zein complex during the second half (Duvick, 1952) (*see also* p. 304)

INDUCED PARTHENOGENESIS AND ADVENTIVE EMBRYOGENESIS

Could parthenogenesis be induced in plants, it would be possible to obtain homozygous, true-breeding types for genetical investigations (East, 1930). The problem here is to find some substance, or treatment, which will activate the ovum as the male nucleus does. Already in 1922 Blakeslee and others had shown the possibility of obtaining haploid plants of *Datura*. Methods used to induce parthenogenesis include: (i) exposure of flowering shoots to very high or very low temperatures, or to X-rays; (ii) application of X-ray treated pollen, or of foreign pollen to the stigma; (iii) delayed pollination; and (iv) chemical treatment (Ivanov, 1938; and Kostoff, 1941). Müntzing (1937) obtained a haploid plant of *Secale cereale* by exposing the spikes to low temperatures (0·3°C), and Nordenskiod (1939) got a similar result by exposing them to high temperatures (41°–42°C). Haploids plants of *Triticum monococcum* were found in spikes which had been exposed to X-rays at the time of meiosis (Kihara and Katayama, 1932). When Katayama (1934, 1935) pollinated the stigmas with X-rayed pollen 16 haploids were present among 91 seedlings. Other workers have been less successful: Smith (1946) states categorically that he obtained no increase in the number of haploids by X-ray treatment.

The use of foreign pollen for stimulating parthenogenesis was brought into prominence by Jørgensen (1928) working on *Solanum nigrum*. The formation of haploid embryos following interspecific or intergeneric crossing has also been reported in *Brassica* (Nogouchi, 1928), *Oenothera* (Gates and Goodwin, 1930), and *Triticum* (Nakajima, 1935). In *Triticum monococcum*, the frequency of haploids can be augmented by delaying the time of pollination: when pollen was applied on the sixth day after emasculation, 2 haploids were present in 10 plants; when applied on the seventh day, 4 haploids were present in 44 plants; when applied on the eighth day, 5 haploids were present in 18 plants; and when applied on the ninth day, 3 haploids were present in 8 plants (Kihara, 1940).

Yasuda (1940) found that by injecting aqueous solutions of 'belvitan'[1] into the ovaries of *Petunia violaceae*, some striking changes took place in the course of three days. In some ovules the nucellar cells enlarged as a result of the stimulation; in others, the egg divided once or twice forming a small proembryo; and in yet others the anti-podal cells became enlarged. According to Yasuda the belvitan promotes cell-division in embryonic cells but causes only cell-wall growth in mature cells. It is not known if the small embryos thus induced were haploid or diploid, nor if they were capable of further development.

From his survey of the investigations thus far reported, Maheshwari (1950) concludes that a satisfactory method for inducing partheno-genesis in higher plants has not yet been discovered. Various techniques have yielded some results in special cases, but the number of partheno-genetic plants so far obtained is still small: we cannot yet produce haploid embryos at will with the consistency that polyploids can be induced with colchicine. The difficulty seems to be that although the egg can be made to develop parthenogenetically, no artificial means of inducing endosperm formation is known.

To be able to induce and rear adventive, i.e. nucellar, embryos, possessing a genetical constitution identical with that of the parent, would be of academic interest and practical value. In cultivated fruit trees, such as *Citrus* spp., the method enables uniform root-stocks to

---

[1] Belvitan: presumably a proprietary growth-regulating substance.

be used, while in some strains of *Mangifera indica* (the mango: Anacardiaceae) it affords the readiest means of propagating desirable varieties unchanged; zygotic embryos, on the other hand, yield a wide range of fruiting types. Because of their importance in horticulture, many attempts have been made, thus far with little success, to induce adventive embryos at will. Haberlandt (1921, 1922) tried to achieve this in *Oenothera* by pricking and squeezing the ovules, on the hypothesis that the proliferation of the embryo-forming cells might be due to a necro-hormone proceeding from adjacent degenerating cells. In one ovule he obtained two embryos which he considered to be of nucellar origin, but this is disputed by Beth (1938) who repeated the experiment in *Oenothera* and other plants without success.

Blakeslee (1941) has observed that haploid plants of *Datura stramonium*, which apparently originate from unfertilised eggs, are of frequent occurrence. This suggested that it should be possible to produce such plants by chemical or other treatment, but so far positive results have not been obtained (van Overbeek and Conklin, 1941). It has become apparent, however, that successive chemical stimuli are involved in embryo formation. These include a stimulus from the growing pollen tubes which initiates development in the placentae and integuments, a stimulus for the further growth of the ovary which prevents its abscission, and a stimulus for the development and differentiation of the unfertilised eggs.

Overbeek, Conklin and Blakeslee (1941) have explored the possibility of inducing parthenogenesis in the egg cell of *Datura stramonium* by injecting the ovary with various chemical substances. These attempts were unsuccessful, but when a 0·1 per cent solution or emulsion of the ammonium salt of naphthaleneacetic acid or indolebutyric acid was injected, several curous multicellular warty outgrowths of what appeared to be the integumentary tapetal layer eventually filled the embryo sac. These undifferentiated tissue masses, which had typically diploid nuclei, and which had originated in the same manner that adventive embryos originate from the tapetal layer, are described as 'pseudoembryos.' In experimental studies of *Hosta*, in which it has long been known that fertilisation is essential for the production of adventive embryos, Fagerlind (1946) found (i) that pistils receiving abundant pollen of the same species set seeds normally, the embryos being of nucellar origin; (ii) that pistils receiving an inadequate supply of pollen yield some normal and some small ovules, the latter showing neither pollen tubes nor endosperm formation and only incipient adventive embryogeny; (iii) that various foreign pollens had no inductive effect; and (iv) that pistils treated with 1 per cent indoleacetic acid in lanoline remained attached to the plant and three weeks later the ovules contained young adventive embryos; no endosperm was formed, however, and there was no further embryonic development. From these experiments it could be concluded that growth-regulating substances have some part in the induction of adventive embryos, but that, in the absence of endosperm, the general or special nutrients required for the further embryonic development are not available.

EMBRYO CULTURE

In growth and other studies of embryos, it is desirable, if not essential, to be able to induce ovum development and to culture embryos of all ages in media of known composition. Maheshwari (1950, 1951) has summarised the literature on embryo culture from its inception at the hands of Hannig (1904) to the present day. Hannig showed that crucifer embryos, about 1·2 mm. long and therefore fairly well developed, could be grown to adult plants in nutrient media containing sugars, mineral salts, amino-acids, plant extracts and gelatin. Stingl (1907) found that the embryos of various species of Gramineae could be excised and successfully implanted in the endosperm of other genera. Camara (1943) has recently confirmed these observations: indeed, he observed that embryos of *Triticum vulgare* grew better when implanted in the endosperm of *Secale* than in that of *T. durum* or *T. turgidum*. Dietrich (1924) has recorded the successful culture of immature embryos of a number of species in Knop's solution enriched with 2·5–5·0 per cent cane sugar and 1·5 per cent agar. Growth in such media had the effect of eliminating some of the 'normal stages' of development, the excised embryos growing directly into seedlings. It thus appears that the normal morphological development of an embryo is largely determined by the nutritional status of its environment. Laibach (1925, 1929), while making some interspecific crosses in the genus *Linum*, found that the cross *L. perenne* × *L. austriacum* yielded fruits of approximately normal size; but the seeds were greatly shrunken and only about half as heavy as the normal seeds. By dissecting out the embryos and placing them upon damp blotting paper he was able to induce their germination and the resulting plants flowered and fruited. The reciprocal cross *L. austriacum* × *L. perenne* was more difficult, for here the fruits were shed prematurely, the seeds being then only one-thirteenth of the weight of normal seeds and incapable of germination. However, embryos from this cross, if excised when about a fortnight old and placed on cotton wadding containing 10–15 per cent cane sugar, continued to grow. A couple of weeks later, when the embryos were removed from the sugar solution and placed on moist blotting paper they germinated within a few days and eventually yielded normal vigorous plants. These observations have important implications, among others that crosses between higher plants, which appear to yield non-viable or abortive seed, may yet be made to yield growing embryos and eventually seedlings and mature plants. Thus Tukey (1944) showed that the early-aborting embryos of *Prunus* hybrids could, if dissected out and maintained in culture, be grown to mature and vigorous fruiting trees. Earlier, Jørgensen (1928) had used the method to obtain hybrids between *Solanum nigrum* and *S. luteum*. Other records are those of Bensley (1930) using *Gossypium hirsutum* and *G. herbaceum*; Skirm (1942): species of *Prunus* and of *Lilium*; Brink, Cooper and Ausherman (1944): *Hordeum jubatum* and *Secale cereale*; Smith (1944): *Lycopersicon esculentum* and *L. peruvianum*; Iwanow-skaya (1946): *Triticum durum* and *Elymus arenarius*; and Sanders (1948): several species of *Datura*.

In crosses between *Hordeum jubatum* and *Secale cereale*, fertilisation takes place within four hours of pollination but the hybrid seeds collapse and fail to germinate. If, however, the 9–12 days old hybrid embryos are dissected out and placed in an artificial culture medium, they will grow. One such seedling was maintained into the flowering stage. Although no seeds were set by this plant, the important point had been demonstrated that intergeneric crosses were sometimes possible and that the death of the resulting embryo was not necessarily due to inherent lethal factors but to unknown factors in the environment during development (Brink, Cooper and Ausherman, 1944). It has been a fairly general experience that hybrid embryos tend to abort before the cotyledons are differentiated, i.e. some metabolic factor (or complex of factors) becomes critically important at this stage. The nature of this factor has not yet been ascertained. The older the embryo the more nearly autotrophic it is. The main technical problem in embryo culture, therefore, is to establish the conditions required by very young embryos; for these either die or develop into a mass of callus.

Embryo culture is important economically because it enables potentially valuable hybrids to be reared. It also affords a means of curtailing the time required to obtain plants of species in which the seeds normally have a long dormant period prior to germination. In this connection, Barton and Crocker (1948) have used the method of embryo culture to obtain early information on the viability or germina-tion-capacity of seeds: non-viable germs soon become discoloured, whereas viable ones enlarge and become green and autotrophic.

Embryo culture is also important in that it affords an experimental approach to the action of various nutrients in morphogenetic processes. Thus Doerpinghaus (1947) has examined the differences between species of *Datura* in their capacity to utilise different carbohydrates.

When the growth of excised embryos of ten species of *Datura* was tested in culture media in which sucrose, dextrose, levulose, mannose and glycerol were used as the sources of carbon, it was found that the different species varied considerably in their reactions to these compounds. For example, *D. metel* grew well with mannose but poorly with sucrose and the reducing sugars, and not at all with glycerol; whereas *D. innoxia* could not utilise mannose as well as sucrose or dextrose, and could not use levulose and glycerol. In most species, sucrose is still the best source of carbon thus far tested.

LaRue (1936) succeeded in culturing small embryos, about 0·5 mm. long, of species from a number of different families. Inorganic media alone proved inadequate for the growth of young embryos, sugar and growth-regulating substances, e.g. indoleacetic acid, yeast extract, etc., being essential.

Whereas seedlings increase in size mainly by cell enlargement, embryos do so by continuing in an active state of cell division. The factors controlling the growth of embryos are thus not the same as those which control the enlargement of seedlings. But the embryonic regions of the latter, i.e. their apical growing points, may be affected by those biochemical factors which are active in the embryo.

Impetus was given to the study of embryo culture by van Overbeek, Conklin and Blakeslee (1941, 1942) and van Overbeek (1942) when they showed that whereas mature embryos of *Datura stramonium* are completely self-sufficient in respect of growth factors, and on simple culture media containing minerals and sugar can grow directly into seedlings, very small excised embryos do require growth factors. Such factors occur in coconut milk. *In vitro* cultures of embryos, only slightly beyond the proembryo stage when excised, remained embryonic in the presence of coconut milk for at least ten days when kept in darkness. Root growth was suppressed. Coconut milk contains at least three growth-regulating substances: (i) the *embryo factor*, which makes for cell proliferation or continued meristematic activity; (ii) auxin in concentrations sufficient to cause inhibition of root growth; and (iii) a factor which causes an increase in the growth of the cotyledons, i.e. a leaf-growth factor, the effect of which is particularly marked in the presence of light.

When the embryo factor was added to a culture medium (containing agar, minerals, dextrose, vitamins B1, B6, C, pantothenic acid, nicotinic acid, adenine, glycine and succinic acid), very small embryos increased up to 500 times, and even up to 3,500 times, their original volume in the course of a week. The embryos were quite normal in appearance but all their cells, as ascertained by various means, were apparently involved in the proliferation. In the absence of the embryo factor, using the basic medium given above, most proembryos did not grow, though some developed into undifferentiated callus-like bodies. It is thus possible to induce at will typical or atypical growth. In the embryo factor we have a chemical substance which makes for, or sustains, meristematic activity. Embryos kept for a few days without this factor were unable to respond to subsequent applications and soon lost their viability. Before it can affect the growth of embryos, the embryo factor must apparently reach a certain threshold concentration: the younger the embryo, the higher is this threshold value. In other words, as an embryo becomes older it is increasingly able to synthesise its own growth factor, the mature embryo being entirely autotrophic.

The condition of the plant from which embryos are obtained affects the behaviour of the embryos in culture. Embryos from plants kept in a warm but poorly lighted greenhouse failed to develop on the basic medium, whereas those from plants growing outside at relatively low temperatures in an abundance of light grew on the basic medium alone. Van Overbeek concludes that the latter conditions are probably favourable for the formation of embryo factor in the parent plant, the factor being probably a hormone-like substance.

That the watery endosperm of the coconut contains the growth-promoting 'coconut-milk factor' at all stages of development has been shown by Steward and Caplin (1952). Some activity is also shown by parts of the immature embryo but not by the solid endosperm. Growth-promoting substances of analogous activity have been detected in the immature milky endosperm of maize, in the gelatinous material in immature walnut fruits, and in the young gametophyte of *Ginkgo biloba*. The tissues from which these substances have been obtained appear to grow at the expense of, or to be nourished by, the nucellar tissue. In *Cocos, Zea,* and *Juglans* it is the immature embryo that eventually benefits from the growth factor. The conditions that are conducive to the accumulation of the substance seem to involve, or to be associated with, a delay in the growth of the embryo but a precocious formation of the endosperm.

When immature embryos of *Hordeum vulgare* were excised and cultured in a medium containing 12·5 per cent sucrose, minerals and agar, considerably improved growth was obtained when *Hordeum* endosperms were placed on the medium surrounding the embryos (Ziebur and Brink, 1951). These endosperms also stimulate the growth of immature embryos of other genera. Coconut milk and malt extract, both of which promote the growth of some dicotyledonous embryos in culture, had no favourable effect on *Hordeum* embryos.

Immature sedge embryos (species of *Carex*) can be excised and successfully grown in Whites' standard nutrient solution (Lee, 1952).

The best root and shoot growth was obtained in a medium containing 0·2–6·0 per cent sucrose.

Utilisation of Nitrogen Compounds. A knowledge of the forms in which nitrogen can be utilised by embryos of different ages is of paramount importance. Spoerl (1948) has pointed out that although most embryos *in situ* probably receive and utilise nitrogen in an organic form, comparatively little is known of the effect of such substances on the growth of embryos in culture. Accordingly, he used various amino acids as sources of nitrogen in the culture of orchid embryos, cultures supplied with ammonium nitrate and others with no nitrogen affording a basis for comparison. Orchid seeds, both immature and mature, are useful for such studies since the germ is small and undifferentiated and the seed devoid of storage materials. Of some nineteen aminoacids tested, most were found to act as inhibitors to normal embryo development; and none yielded as good growth as ammonium nitrate. Arginine was the only aminoacid which supported good growth in young embryos, all the others tested having an inhibitive effect under the experimental conditions. With older embryos, aspartic acid proved a good nitrogen source, but glutamic acid neither supported good growth nor inhibited it. Growth in the light was significantly better than in the dark with several of the nitrogen sources and also when no nitrogen was supplied. Cysteine and cystine, however, gave better growth in the dark. These experimental results show that little of the nitrogen of the aminoacids is as effectively utilisable by the growing embryo as is that of ammonium nitrate.

Other studies of aminoacid utilisation by species from different systematic groups show little consistency in the results obtained. Thus Burgeff (1936) and Withner (1942) found no stimulation of growth of orchid embryos on the addition of individual aminoacids, or mixtures of aminoacids, to a medium already supplying inorganic nitrogen. Knudson (1932) found several of these acids to be inadequate nitrogen sources for embryo growth. Brown (1906), however, reported that asparagine, aspartic acid, and glutamic acid gave increases equal to that from potassium nitrate in dry weight of excised barley embryos. Klein (1930) states that aminoacids are absorbed by plants under sterile conditions, but are not equally utilisable; and Virtanen and Linkola (1946) have found that aspartic and glutamic acids are used especially well by pea and clover plants, but these acids cause a loss of dry weight in wheat and barley plants. MacVicar and Burris (1947) have reported that very good growth of clover plants was obtained with asparagine, glutamine, arginine and glycine. Among moderately good sources of nitrogen were alanine, histidine, cystine, glutamic acid and urea, whereas norleucine, methionine, tyrosine, leucine, tryptophane and phenylalanine were poor sources, some producing severe toxic effects.

Sanders and Burkholder (1948) have reported the successful culture of excised *Datura* embryos to healthy seedlings on nutrients containing only inorganic salts and sucrose. Development was slower in culture than in the seed and premature differentiation of roots and shoots occurred. Various organic compounds were found to stimulate embryo growth and retard premature differentiation. When casein hydrolysate with cysteine and tryptophane, mixtures of aminoacids, or single amino-acids, were added to nutrient solutions for embryos ($\pm$ 0·2 mm. in length) of *D. inoxia* and *D. stramonium*, the best growth was obtained with casein hydrolysate *plus* cysteine and tryptophane, and with a mixture of aminoacids approximating to the composition of casein hydrolysate. The experimental results indicate that there are inter-actions of the acids in their effect upon embryo growth. Whereas some aminoacids were stimulatory, others were inhibitory. Moreover, the embryos of the two species responded differently to individual amino-acids. These investigators suggest that aminoacids are probably important in the growth and differentiation of plant embryos and possibly in such phenomena as seed dormancy and the crossability of species.

MODIFIED ONTOGENETIC PATTERNS

When culturing excised immature embryos of deciduous fruits, Tukey (1937) observed that the ontogenetic growth pattern was modified in a definite and characteristic manner. Instead of following the usual path of embryonic development, cultured embryos grew into plantlets which exhibited a definite conformation, or growth pattern, this being apparently related to the age of each embryo when excised. The normal progressive morphological development of the embryo should not, therefore, be regarded as an inevitable recapitulation of ancestral history but as the necessary result of factors in the embryonic environ-ment. Mature, or nearly mature, embryos may also produce unusual types of growth, but these are unlike those obtained from very young embryos. Mature but non-after-ripened seeds of *Rhodotypos kerrioides* yielded plants with a dwarfish appearance, with short stocky hypocotyls and internodes, and small dark green leaves (Flemion, 1933); this investigator also reported a similar type of growth for non-after-ripening embryos of peach, apple and hawthorn. Davidson (1934, 1935) described all plants raised in culture from immature peach embryos as abnormal and dwarfish, with small, wrinkled and peculiarly curled leaves. Von Veh (1936) found that seedlings of apple, pear, quince, plum and cherry, raised from non-after-ripened embryos, developed into dwarf plants. Lammerts (1942) obtained similar results with apricot, peach, cherry, rose and camellia.

In Tukey's experiments, each size of embryo that could be grown in culture yielded a characteristic growth pattern, this being comparable with the 'juvenile' and 'adult' forms known in other plants. This seems to confirm Goebel's view that organisms are constantly changing throughout their ontogenetic development, and that the genetical constitution of a plant alone does not determine morphogenesis and functional activity. Tukey observed that embryos in culture do not pass through the morphological stages characteristic of those within the seed; instead, they enter at once into an independent development characteristic of the age of the embryo when excised. The younger the embryo is on excision, the more abnormal is its growth behaviour; and the older the embryo is on excision, the less easily is it upset by the new environment. Embryos at different stages of development have different requirements: a liquid medium is favourable at one stage of development and not at another; and glucose is favourable at one stage and inhibiting at another. Even mature seeds must be after-ripened before they develop normally. These facts indicate that both internal and external factors must be considered. The failure of embryos to follow the 'normal' pattern of embryonic development outside the embryo sac raises the question as to the nature of the environment which brings about 'normal' development. Hannig (1904) and others have shown that the shape of the embryo is altered by the surrounding tissue.

Using self and hybrid embryos of *Datura discolor*, *D. inoxia*, *D. metel* and *D. stramonium*, the embryos where possible being excised at the heart-shaped stage, Sanders (1950) studied the effects of different concentrations of sucrose, $Na(PO_3)_n$ and $Fe_3(PO_4)_2$ and filtered malt extract in the culture medium. It was observed that the vigour and type of embryonic growth were determined primarily by the size of the embryo at excision, this being especially marked in the response to sucrose. The effect of the genetical constitution was indicated by the fact that the growth of *D. stramonium* with 4·0 per cent sucrose was 42 times that with 0·5 per cent, whereas embryos of the other three species only increased from 1·2 to 1·7 times over the same range. Some other specific differences were also observed in relation to the concentration of $Na(PO_3)_n$ in the medium. With regard to growth values, hybrid embryos resembled one or both parents, were intermediate between them, or, occasionally, were unlike either parent. Reciprocal hybrids were usually similar.

Embryo development in artificial culture media may follow normal or abnormal paths in different circumstances. Among abnormal developments observed by Sanders in *Datura stramonium* were failure to grow, tissue swellings, swollen spreading cotyledons, premature differentiation of roots and/or plumules, multiple and fasciated embryos, and irregular bud-like growths. When the normal embryonic differentiation has been arrested, the renewed growth proceeds from a plurality of growing points. The degree of differentiation at the time of excision appears to be the chief factor determining the type of growth produced in culture. Initially normal embryos tend to continue to develop normally in culture media; initially abnormal embryos, if they grow, tend to develop abnormally.

Normal embryos in culture in due course pass out of the embryonic into the seedling phase, the attendant changes being comparable with those which normally take place on seed germination. In some embryo cultures, however, the growth developments in plumule, hypocotyl and radicle may take place independently of one another. Sanders found that root formation in *Datura* is favoured by medium concentrations of $Na(PO_3)_n$ and the lower concentrations of $Fe_3(PO_4)_2$, and, in particular, by the omission of malt. The elongation of the hypocotyl increased with increased sucrose, with decreased $Fe_3(PO_4)_2$ and with the addition of malt, but was unaffected by the $Na(PO_3)_n$ concentration. The growth of the plumule, on the other hand, occurred more often at the lower sucrose concentrations, at the higher $Na(PO_3)_n$ concentrations, and with the omission of malt. These embryo culture experiments thus demonstrate how different are the nutritional requirements of the several organs, both quantitatively and qualitatively. In liquid culture media, the normal, regulated growth of the embryo may be disturbed, one or other of the organs tending to grow more rapidly or more slowly according to the balance of nutrients provided. Lee (1950) has shown that, in tomato seedlings, the relative growth values of the individual organs are different when the organs are isolated than when they form part of an intact plant, e.g. isolated cotyledons have higher growth values than intact attached ones, but the reverse is true of stems and roots. The factors determining these differences in relative growth are probably the correlative effects of one part on another, the relative availability of the substances required for growth, translocation effects, and the conversion of substances during translocation.

A DEVELOPMENTAL STUDY OF CAPSELLA

Rijven (1952) has investigated the physiology of the embryo and endosperm of *Capsella* during development. The embryogeny of this classical species was described by Hanstein (1870) and Souèges (1916, 1919) Figs. 53, 54. Germination is described by Rijven as beginning 'at the moment that the embryonic tissue—in a state of cell division and plasmatic growth—becomes separated by an intercalated section of incipient cell elongation.' The period before this elongation of tissue sets in includes the pregerminal phases.

The Stages of Development of the Embryo in Ovulo
(after Rijven)

Stage	Length without suspensor	Shape
I	18–50μ	globular
II	50–80μ	reversed trapezium; height and breadth equal; third dimension somewhat smaller.
III	80–150μ	heart.
IV	150–350μ	intermediate between III and V; characterised by longitudinal growth of the cotyledons and of the hypocotyl to a slightly less extent.
V	350–700μ	'torpedo'; the cotyledons are flattened against each other and constitute half the length of the embryo.
VI	700–900μ	'walking-stick'; caused by the cotyledons having turned back in the top of the ovule.
VII	900–1700μ	upturned U; the one leg formed by the hypocotyl, the other by the flattened cotyledons.
VIII	1760μ	full-grown embryo.

When freshly excised, young embryos are green from the heart-shaped stage onwards and contain some starch, though starch is not present before this stage. Mature embryos have an ivory-white appearance; their cells contain no starch but abundant aleurone grains and fats. As from the 'torpedo' stage (*see* Table), the starch grains are large and numerous and are mainly located in the hypocotyl; fats also begin to be present from about this stage (Fig. 83). From the globular to the fully-grown embryo, there is almost a hundred-fold increase in length. Embryo length plotted against time through the embryonic development yields an almost perfect sigmoid growth curve.

Ovules containing immature embryos are highly turgid, the endospermic sap, which contains naked nuclei and their enveloping cytoplasm, exuding freely on puncturing. Sap pH was found to be 6·0, its osmotic value at the torpedo stage being isotonic with $\frac{3}{8}$ mol. mannitol (8·4 atm.). Sugars and starch are present in the sap and aminoacids were also detected. The cells of the embryo may be assumed to be in equilibrium with the embryo sac sap: hence embryos placed in distilled water show a marked initial swelling.

Globular embryos, i.e. less than 100μ, have not been successfully grown in culture, the heart-shaped stage (stages III and IV) being critical in this respect. This is an important stage in the morphogenetic development in that it marks the transition from the initial radial symmetry to the bilateral symmetry that become apparent with the formation of the cotyledons. This change in symmetry is attributed by Rijven to induction by bilaterally disposed gradients in the ovular environment. Certainly some *in vitro* embryos did not lose their radial

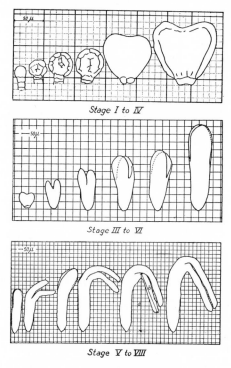

Stage I to IV

Stage III to VI

Stage V to VIII

Fig. 83. *Capsella bursa-pastoris*
Diagrammatic representation of embryo development; *see* Text (after Rijven).

symmetry and developed as many as six cotyledons, a result like that obtained by Overbeek, Conklin and Blakeslee (1942) using *Datura* embryos. Failure to grow very young embryos indicates that certain ingredients are lacking in the synthetic culture medium or that certain refinements have not yet been achieved. Embryos at the torpedo stage grow well in culture. The osmotic value of the culture medium (or embryo sac sap) is an important factor in determining the nature of the embryonic growth.

Sucrose proved to be the best source of carbohydrate for embryo growth in pure culture. Casein-hydrolysate strongly promoted growth. Glutamine was the outstanding aminoacid for use in culture media for

Capsella: it gave better growth results than a nitrogen-equivalent complete aminoacid mixture. Ammonium lactate could not serve as a substitute for aminoacids. In contrast with glutamine, asparagine yielded low growth values, the embryos being characterised by an abnormally rapid and strong production of starch.

It appears that some aminoacids, such as tyrosine and glycine, are unsuitable for the culture of *Capsella* embryos. Although glutamine, mentioned by Street (1949) as the prevailing amide in the seedlings of Brassicaceae (Cruciferae), gave very good growth results, Rijven considers that there may be yet other aminoacids, or related compounds, that promote embryonic growth. Steward and Thompson (1950) have stated that there are still twenty unidentified substances indicated by paper-chromatography which belong to this category. The failure of asparagine, a homologous compound, to promote growth of *Capsella* embryos is the more remarkable when we remember how important it is in protein synthesis in *Pisum*, *Lupinus* and other Leguminosae.

The addition of bios, purine derivatives, and other growth-regulating substances, gave negative results. Indoleacetic acid gave a small but significant effect, stimulating growth at 0·001 p.p.m. and inhibiting it at concentrations greater than 1·0 p.p.m. Other investigators also have found that the addition of various growth-regulating substances has little effect on the growth of embryos *in vitro*. Sanders (1950) obtained negative results with them using *Datura* embryos, and Rappaport, Satina and Blakeslee (1950) have reported that nucleic acid is inhibitory. With *Pisum* on the other hand, growth-regulating substances have been found to have promoting effects, but this was in the post-germinal phase.

Large, post-germinal embryos in culture yielded no evidence of precocious germination. The germination characteristically took place when the osmotic value of the medium was lowered. In fact, there are important differences in the cultural requirements of pre-germinal and post-germinal embryos.

EXPERIMENTS ON OLDER EMBRYOS

The study of older embryos not only carries its own interest but may contribute towards an understanding of the younger and less accessible stages. Contemporary investigators are concerned with the culture of mature embryos, with the conditions required for the germination of the seeds of different species, some of which present difficulties, and with an analysis of the associated physiological process. The information obtained from some of these studies is of practical importance in horticulture.

In a study of the 'hormonising' of seeds, Kruyt (1952) grew excised pea embryos, with or without the attached cotyledons, in sterile culture media. The effects of various pre-soaking treatments, with and without growth-regulating substances, of factors in the medium, and of leaving larger or smaller amounts of cotyledon attached to the growing embryo, were investigated. The ratio of the amount of reserve material in the cotyledons to the size of the embryo has an important effect on the morphogenetic development, root and shoot growth being stronger in proportion to the amount of cotyledon tissue left on the embryo. No development of plumular leaves takes place in the dark, and even in the light embryos deprived of cotyledons scarcely form such leaves. In fact, both leaf and root formation are determined by the presence of cotyledon tissue. The action of various growth substances, administered by pre-soaking the seeds, apparently takes place mainly by way of the cotyledons. (For a survey of the physiology of seeds, *see* Crocker and Barton, 1953.)

NON-VIABLE EMBRYOS AND OVULAR TUMOURS

The production of interspecific crosses affords a convenient way of modifying the immediate environment of the embryo, i.e. the endosperm. Brink and Cooper (1940, 1944, 1947) have noted that in normal seed development there is a balanced or regulated growth of the embryo, the endosperm and the nucellar tissue. The embryonic developments in crosses between *Dianthus chinensis* (with 2n = 60) and *D. plumarius* (with 2n = 90) were studied by Buell (1953), the embryogenesis in the two species being closely comparable. Viable seeds are not produced when *D. chinensis* (♀) is crossed with *D. plumarius* (♂). Young embryos, however, are formed and develop to the spherical stage; but thereafter they cease to grow and degenerate, most of them having disintegrated 9–10 days after pollination. Various histological differences were noted as between the hybrid embryo and that of *D. chinensis* of the same age; there were also characteristic differences in the respective endosperms. The reciprocal cross, *D. plumarius* (♀) and *D. chinensis* (♂) is also incompatible, but the embryonic development shows fewer irregularities than the other. The growth of these embryos is slow as compared with the normal controls (i.e. *D. plumarius*). Disintegration of the hybrid embryos, which again attained to the spherical stage, began about 4 days after pollination, and after 8 days only fragments of the disorganised embryos remained. The basal cells are the first to be affected. Various anomalous endosperm developments were observed at an early stage, e.g. failure to digest the nucellus at the normal rate. The abortion of the embryo is probably to be attributed to a breakdown in chemical regulation, possibly involving growth-regulating substances or enzyme balance (Sachet, 1948). Schneider

(1953) has attributed the abortion of the embryo in an aneuploid apple to genetical factors.

When *Datura stramonium* is crossed with *D. metel*, the embryo degenerates after undergoing only two or three divisions (Satina and Blakeslee, 1935). In the cross *D. prunosa* × *D. metel*, the primary endosperm nucleus undergoes several divisions but the zygote usually remains undivided. In two other crosses, *D. meteloides* × *D. discolor* and *D. ceratocaula* × *D. meteloides* (Sachet, 1948), most of the ovules are fertilised and the endosperm and embryo at first develop normally, though rather slowly. When the embryo has reached the spherical stage, the endosperm begins to disintegrate but there is enlargement and active division of the cells of the integumentary tapetum, or endothelium. The voluminous tissue mass which is formed invades the embryo sac and replaces the endosperm. The embryo survives in this mass for a few days but does not undergo further divisions. Ultimately it degenerates and disappears and hence viable seeds are not produced.

Satina, Rappaport and Blakeslee (1950) have pointed out that if, in attempted interspecific crosses, the pre-fertilisation barriers can be overcome, so that the male nucleus comes into contact with the egg cell, fertilisation will usually take place. In many such crosses, however, the zygote may fail to develop into a viable embryo, and potentially interesting hybrids are thus not obtained. This difficulty can sometimes be overcome by the excision and artificial culture of young embryos. Our information on the factors which cause the arrested growth of hybrid embryos, or bring about their early abortion, is still very inadequate. The tumour-like tissue mentioned above is consistently present in *Datura* ovules showing embryo abortion, i.e. in incompatible crosses. This incompatibility between species, which is of primary importance in evolution, has been the subject of important investigations by Blakeslee *et al.* They consider that fuller investigation of the action of tumoral growth in hybrid ovules may eventually lead to techniques enabling wider species and even generic crosses to be made.

Abnormal histological developments leading to embryo abortion in ovules have been reported in other plants. Intrusive growths into the embryo sac have been reported in *Oenothera* crosses by Renner (1914), in *Epilobium* crosses by Michaelis (1925), in *Medicago* by Brink and Cooper (1940), in *Nicotiana* × *Petunia* crosses by Kostoff (1930), in reciprocal diploid and tetraploid *Lycopersicon* crosses by Cooper (1945), and in various *Nicotiana* species crosses by Kostoff (1930) and by Brink and Cooper (1940). The cell proliferations observed in these materials are generally comparable with those in *Datura*. The arrest of embryo growth and the collapse of seeds have been reviewed in detail by Brink and Cooper (1947). Different views have been advanced to explain the latter phenomenon. According to Laibach (1925, 1929, 1931), the maternal ovular tissue exercises a fatal influence on the growth of the embryo, but in *Linum*, as in *Datura*, the embryo can be kept alive if it is removed in time from its surroundings. Hiorth (1926) suggested that these anomalous developments are to be understood as disturbances in the physiological relation between the embryo and the maternal tissue. Fagerlind (1944) and Blakeslee *et. al.*, have referred to the possible stimulatory effect by the male parent in this connection. But, as Satina, Rappaport and Blakeslee (1950) point out, the growth processes in ovules from incompatible crosses still require elucidation. In particular, the cause of the abnormal growth of the endothelial layer in *Datura* is highly enigmatic; for, in compatible fertilisations, this layer acts as a source of nutriment to the embryo while in incompatible crosses it eventually has a destructive action on it. The growth of the tumour stops when the cell contents of the endosperm and of the embryo have been absorbed. No outward growth of the tumour has been observed. The speed and intensity of tumour growth depend on several factors such as the species and races used in the crosses. Large swollen seeds, with a jelly-like substance but without tumours, may also be found. In such seeds the endothelium as well as the contents of the embryo sac is destroyed.

Various attempts were made by Satina *et al* (1950) to prevent the abortion of embryos in ovules in interspecific *Datura* crosses, but all proved unsuccessful. These included the treatment of ovaries with pollen extracts, the treatment of the pollen with vapours and solutions of auxins, the treatment of ovaries with extracts of styles and ovaries of selfed *Daturas*, the injection of different hormones, vitamin mixtures, enzymes and nutrient media into the ovaries, spraying leaves with sugar solutions containing enzymes, and the injection and spraying of malt extracts. Tumoral tissues and embryo-sac contents from incompatible *Datura* crosses were added to semi-synthetic cultures of normal *D. stramonium* embryos and were found to have an inhibiting effect on embryo growth; the inhibition varied from 52–100 per cent, the latter causing the death of embryo. Extracts of ovular tumours have now been prepared by Rappaport, Satina and Blakeslee (1950) and their effects observed when they were injected into the embryo sacs of incompatible crosses and selfed strains, Fig. 84. It has been ascertained that, in tumours associated with embryo abortion in incompatible crosses of *Datura*, a water-soluble thermostable substance, unrelated to auxin, is present. This substance can inhibit the growth of selfed *D. stramonium* embryos both *in vitro* and *in vivo*. The embryo-sac contents of inhibited ovules contain a substance capable of inhibiting another set of capsules. This substance is reported as having been effective

in three successive passages, and this may be indicative of a self-dupli-
cation, or autocatalytic reaction, such as occurs in viruses, or of a new
formation of inhibitor stimulated by the originally injected tumour
extracts. Such tests as have been made of this substance indicate the
presence of nucleic acids. It has also been found that the embryo-sac

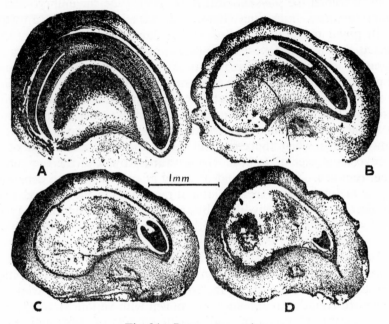

Fig. 84. *Datura stramonium*

Transverse section of *D. stramonium* 2_n-ovules from injected capsules. A, Ovule
from untreated locule with normal embryo at the stage of 'bent torpedo.' B, Ovule
from locule injected with solution of 1·0 p.p.m. RNA; slightly retarded embryo at
the 'advanced torpedo' stage. C, Ovule from locule injected with solution of RNA
100 p.p.m.; embryo retarded at the 'young torpedo' stage. D, Ovule from locule
injected with RNA 250 p.p.m.; embryo retarded at the 'heart' stage and endosperm
partly digested. A and D are ovules from different locules but from the *same*
capsule (all × 30; after Rappaport, Satina and Blakeslee).

contents of ovules of selfed *Datura* capsules contain (±) 6 times as
much of the same substance as is present in the ovules of an incompatible cross. Extracts of embryo-sac contents of selfed *Datura* ovules
with high nucleic acid content, as well as commercial desoxyribonucleic and ribonucleic acids, were injected into ovules of incompatible
crosses, but embryo abortion still took place. Ribonucleic and
desoxyribonucleic acids inhibited embryo growth in selfed *D. stramonium* capsules: the former also inhibited embryo growth in cultures,
but the latter did not. The embryo-sac contents of *D. stramonium* and
D. meteloides both contain nucleic acids; but extracts of the embryo-sac

contents of their incompatible hybrids did not show the presence of nucleic acids, although they strongly inhibited embryo growth. Although nucleic acids may have an inhibitory effect on embryo growth similar to that of ovular tumour extract, it is considered that they are probably not truly alike in their action.

In a comparison of the effects of nucleic acids and extracts of ovular tumours on the development of *Datura* embryos, Rappaport (1950) found that both ribonucleic and desoxyribonucleic acid, when injected into young selfed *D. stramonium* capsules, produced an inhibitory effect apparently similar to that caused by injections of extracts of ovular tumours. The endosperm disintegrated and the embryonic development was strongly retarded or completely inhibited. Higher concentrations of these substances usually caused the death of the ovules, ribonucleic acid showing greater effects at lower concentrations than desoxyribonucleic acid. When ribonucleic acid was added to embryo cultures of *D. stramonium*, it caused an inhibition of about 70 per cent at a concentration of 10 p.p.m. but no significant inhibition was observed by additions of the same concentration of desoxyribonucleic acid. These investigations are being continued.

SUGAR REQUIREMENTS AT DIFFERENT STAGES

Rietsema *et al.* (1953), in a study of the sucrose requirements of *Datura stramonium* embryos *in vitro*, incubated during 8 days, have recorded the following observations. Different stages of development require different minimal sucrose concentrations for growth: pre-heart stages, 8–12 per cent; late heart stage, 4 per cent; and nearly mature embryos grow even without sucrose. The optimal concentration for hypocotyls is ($\pm$) 8 per cent in the pre-heart stage and decreases to 1·0–0·5 per cent in the torpedo stage. Cotyledons and hypocotyls have the same growth rate up to 5–8 mm.; thereafter hypocotyls alone continue growth. Roots develop when hypocotyls are 2·5–4 mm. long. Their optimal sucrose concentration is ($\pm$) 2 per cent. Higher concentrations than 4 per cent decrease root formation. Different embryo stages require different osmotic values of the medium. The optimal osmotic value decreases as the embryo stage advances. If the osmotic value is kept constant, all embryo stages respond in the same way to changes in the sucrose concentration.

CYTOGENETICAL AND PHYSIOLOGICAL STUDIES OF ENDOSPERM AND EMBRYO

In that the endosperm provides the medium in which the growth of the zygote through to the fully organised embryo in the mature seed takes place, and that the inception of both the embryo and endosperm is normally determined by the entry of the male nuclei into the embryo sac and their fusion with the egg and polar nuclei, physiological investigations of the relevant cytogenetical phenomena seem likely to make for important advances in our knowledge. If the gametophyte is of the normal type, the zygote and primary endosperm nuclei, with 2x and 3x chromosomes respectively, are alike qualitatively, except that the endosperm nucleus has two gene complexes of megaspore origin. In the *Oenothera* (Onagraceae) type of development, the zygote and primary endosperm nuclei are identical. But in gametophytes of bisporic and tetrasporic origin, the gene complexes of the polar nuclei are unlike and, on fertilisation, the zygote and primary endosperm nuclei will differ qualitatively. These nuclei will also differ from those of the adjacent nucellar tissue. Different chemical reactions may thus result from the development of the endosperm in different instances, and these may affect the embryonic development. Brink and Cooper (1947), to whom the reader is referred for a valuable review of these matters, have pointed out that the genetical constitution of the endosperm, e.g. in the Gramineae, can be varied in known ways by controlling the kind of pollen used in fertilisation, and that this approach has proved of great value in investigating the properties of endosperm and its effects on the developing embryo. They have also indicated, by reference to the relevant literature, that several kinds of hereditary modification of the balance between the embryo, endosperm, and maternal tissues may lead to seed abortion. These cytogenetic and physiological phenomena, including that of hybrid vigour, seem likely to occupy an important place in future studies of embryogenesis.

In concluding this Chapter on the experimental investigation of angiosperm embryology, it may be noted that the most promising field of work appears to lie in physiological genetics; for the basic phenomenon of the normal embryonic development of any particular species is that there is a regulated specific growth development of the zygote into a progressively larger, more complex and highly differentiated entity. This growth development is the result of the characteristic metabolism of the germ itself and of its environment, both of which are gene-determined. As we have seen, modern biochemical techniques and experimental ingenuity have enabled a beginning to be made in the study of these very important and interesting embryological phenomena.

Chapter XVI

GENERAL CONCLUSIONS

GENERAL FEATURES OF EMBRYOS

SPECIES from the major systematic groups—Algae, Bryophyta, Pteridophyta and Spermatophyta—show marked differences in their size, form, structure and reproduction, i.e. they exemplify different levels of organisation. And while there is general agreement that these levels of organisation afford evidence of the progressive and continuous evolution of plants, more or less wide 'phyletic gaps' separate not only the major systematic groups but even groups of closer affinity. Having now before us the data of a general survey of plant embryology, we may therefore inquire if there are any organisational features which are common to all embryos. In other words, does the relative simplicity of embryos enable us to perceive essential similarities, and possibly relationships, between organisms which become obscured during their subsequent development to the adult state under the impact of genetical and environmental factors? Such homologies of organisation as embryos may show are, of course, of the greatest interest from the causal point of view, quite apart from their value in taxonomy.

In the zygotic development of all plants, from algae to angiosperms, the following phenomena are of general occurrence:

(i) In the mature or newly fertilised ovum, the distribution of metabolites is, or quickly becomes, markedly heterogeneous; and with or without an attendant elongation of the zygote, an accumulation of different metabolites takes place in two diametrically opposite regions, the polarity of the new organism being thereby established. These observations have also a general application to the germination of spores.

(ii) Where the ovum is enclosed, the physiological activity of the surrounding tissue is probably important in determining its polarity. In the free-floating zygotes of algae, factors in the environment may induce the reactions which lead to the establishment of polarity.

(iii) In the polarised zygote, the apical or distal pole becomes the principle locus of protein synthesis, growth and morphogenesis; whereas the basal or proximal pole is characterised by the accumulation of osmotically active substances, its cells becoming vacuolated and distended.

(iv) The first division of the zygote is typically by a wall at right angles to the axis, cell division being probably stimulated by the increase in size and the instability associated with the drift to cytoplasmic or metabolic heterogeneity. As cell division tends to restore equilibrium in the system, the position of the partition wall will be such that the forces present in the two daughter cells will be balanced. According to the nature and distribution of these forces, the zygote may be more or less equally divided, or it may be divided into a small, densely proto-plasmic distal cell and a larger basal cell. The nature of this division is thus ultimately determined by the specific constitution and meta-bolism of the zygote.

(v) During the further growth of the embryo, the positions of the successive partition walls are in general conformity with Errera's law of cell division by walls of minimal area.

(vi) As the embryonic development proceeds, factors in the genetical constitution and in the environment become effective; growth is specifically allometric or differential; and the embryo begins to assume a distinctive form. An immense diversity of form is thus possible, but, with some exceptions, e.g. colonial algae, axial development is a general concomitant of the establishment of polarity.

(vii) While the embryo is still small, it shows an acropetal gradient of decreasing cell size. With the exception of those algae which grow by means of an intercalary meristem, the distal region of the axis, which may remain perennially embryonic, becomes organised histologically as an apical growing point.

(viii) Nutrients are taken up from the environment by the more basal tissues of the embryo and translocated to the apex. Primary growth is in the nature of an accretionary process, the older tissues becoming firm and rigid and showing various characteristic concentric and radiate differentiation patterns.

It is thus possible to specify a number of developments that are typical of the embryogeny of all classes of autotrophic plants. This homology of organisation could be ascribed to (a) the origin of all classes of plants from a common ancestor; (b) the morphogenetic action of the same physical and chemical factors and developmental relationships; or (c) the evolution of parallel or convergent genetical systems. The differences between the embryos of related species, or between those of species in the larger taxonomic units, are due primarily to genetical factors. Thus, in many monocotyledons, the segmentation pattern of the young embryo is practically identical with that of many dicotyledons; but later, the distribution of growth in the embryos becomes notably different, one forming two cotyledons with a terminal shoot apex, the other a single terminal cotyledon with a lateral apex. The unavoidable conclusion is that the different distributions of growth in the two embryos are gene-determined, as is also the distinctive growth pattern throughout the ontogenetic development. But environmental and other factors are also active in determining the nature of the embryonic development and hence, to arrive at any comprehensive understanding, all the factors which may be involved must be duly considered.

FACTORS AND RELATIONSHIPS IN EMBRYOGENY

It is assumed that *all* the factors in the embryonic development work in accordance with the laws of physics and chemistry. The factors and relationships involved may be indicated as follows.

Genetical Factors. If, as is generally accepted, these determine both the general and specific metabolism of plant cells and tissues, then substances such as growth-regulating substances, enzymes, etc., are ultimately gene-determined. Since a gene is essentially a large organic molecule, the reactions which it stimulates and controls must proceed in conformity with the laws of physical chemistry as applied to organic reaction systems. As a working hypothesis, a fertilised ovum may be regarded as a complex, gene-determined, reaction system. According to the components of the system and the sustaining environmental conditions, characteristic chains of reactions will be set in motion, and the resulting biochemical pattern, or patternised distribution of metabolites, will constitute the basis for the visible morphological and histological developments.

Physiological and Physical Factors. Important aspects of the embryonic development are referable to physical factors and to physiological processes and relationships that are common to all green plants. Diffusion gradients, the action of gravity, light, surface tension and other forces, the tendency towards a state of equilibrium in a dynamic system, various factors in the environment, and organismal phenomena such as correlation, the reciprocal relationships of parts, the inception of growth centres, and functional activities, may all be involved in the embryonic process. Here it is important to note that differently constituted reaction systems may yield closely comparable organismal patterns (Turing, 1952; Wardlaw, 1953). The characteristic development of an embryo, then, is due to a whole nexus of factors and relationships; and while genetical factors are primary, other, essentially extrinsic, factors are among the proximate causes of the observed developments.

Protoplasmic Organisation. The direct action of genes and of various physical and environmental factors does not, however, afford the basis for an adequate account of embryogenesis. The zygote of a particular species is not simply a complex diffusion reaction system: it is an organismal system, with a *specific organisation*, perhaps with a definite micro-structure of some kind, in which complex reactions not only take place, but take place in an orderly manner. At some future time it may be that this specific protoplasmic organisation will be partially defined in terms of physical chemistry; meanwhile, as Needham (1942) and Woodger (1945) have emphasised, there is need for a theory of zygote structure, in addition to the theory of the gene, to explain embryological data. In the view of Needham and others, the way in which a young embryo develops is determined by the protoplasmic organisation of the fertilised ovum. That such organisation exists is indicated by experimental and other evidence, but its nature cannot yet be defined. Studies of centrifuged eggs have suggested that the ovum contains a framework of a viscid protoplasmic substance which can recover its normal form after distortion; and it is known that the eggs of some species may develop normally after their movable ingredients have been stratified. In some eggs, however, the cytoplasm may apparently flow like a liquid. Needham envisages the protein chains of the protoplasmic lattice as being 'connected at many points by residual valencies and relatively loose attachments' and as being capable of springing back into position after disarrangement. This he refers to as *dynamic structure* in protoplasm. Schleip (1929) has pointed out that in every attempt to explain the polarity and symmetry of eggs 'some as yet unknown property of the protoplasm has to be introduced.' He refers to this property as the *intimate structure* of the protoplasm. Needham has indicated the kinds of theories and facts that may contribute towards an understanding of the intimate structure. Liquid crystals, i.e. substances in the paracrystalline state, may be important, because (he says) 'living systems actually *are* liquid crystals, or, it would be more correct to say, the paracrystalline state undoubtedly exists in living cells' (1942, p. 661). Paracrystalline substances have elongated molecules which can be distributed or arranged in different ways, regular and irregular, according to the conditions in which they exist: the molecules may be completely at random, as in the true isotropic liquid state, or they may be disposed in different patterns with a high degree of regularity in the crystalline solid state. The protoplasmic organisation at any particular time is also of the greatest importance in determining the competence of cells to react to morphogenetic and other stimuli.

Child (1941, p. 694) agrees that living protoplasts and the skeletal materials (cell walls) do yield remarkable evidence of a definite molecular or micellar structure and orientation (*see also* Frey Wyssling, 1948). Change of pattern of proteins in relation to tension can also be demonstrated and there is evidence of molecular orientation to surfaces and interfaces. But, in Child's view: 'Protoplasms in general have not yet been shown to possess any such structure that might serve as a basis for developmental pattern. Evidence of the presence in eggs or other reproductive cells of a space lattice related to developmental pattern is at present lacking' (*see also* Weiss, 1950). According to Seifriz (1935, 1936, 1938), there is, in protoplasm, a continuity of structure consisting of elongated molecules (as in carbohydrates and proteins) to which the polarity and symmetry of organisms can be attributed. Harrison (1936), too, has advanced a molecular hypothesis to account for specific regional localisations: the embryonic developmental pattern is to be ascribed to the protein pattern. Because of the bipolar character of protein molecules, Harrison considers that they may become orientated in the cell possibly in relation to the point of attachment in the ovary; and, in relation to the different chemical properties at the poles, two material gradients will be initiated. Local reactions will also take place at points along these gradients and the complications of development will ensue. In all these theories, Child sees the need for introducing metabolic factors without which the structure must remain static, if it can indeed come into existence. Molecular orientation, in short, 'must result secondarily from the metabolic differential pattern.' The diffusion reaction theory of morphogenesis advanced by Turing (p. 34) would account for the differentiation of the zygote and for many aspects of the embryonic development without the need for invoking a specific protoplasmic structural organisation.

Zoological studies indicate that some differential distribution and segregation of materials are present in all eggs (Weiss, 1939). Most animal zygotes show axial differentiation, the reserve materials being aggregated at the basal pole and those needed for meristematic activity at the apical pole. The interior of the egg is typically in a semi-liquid condition. Although the organisation in the animal egg has often been considered to be based on some kind of framework, no such structure can be detected, the network of fibrils seen in cytological material being considered to be artefacts produced by coagulation. In Weiss' view this, however, 'does not preclude the possibility of a *dynamic* structure, that is, a definite pattern into which the diverse molecular groups would force one another by mutual specific repulsions, attractions and other interactions.' But he admits that this assumption is wholly hypothetical. Microscopical studies justify the view that the surface cytoplasm of eggs has some organisation, but this 'is simple beyond comparison, when contrasted with the enormous diversity of local characters appearing in the later course of development.' The progressive development of heterogeneity in the germ, and the specific localisation of organ primordia are not determined by the segmentation pattern, the cleavage pattern being a result of the organisation of the egg cytoplasm.

Cellular Potentiality. As an embryo develops, its cells and parts, or regions, become differentiated in characteristic ways. On this subject many views have been expressed. Driesch (1908) thought of the different protoplasmic potentialities of the zygote as being very early distributed among the cells of the embryo, cells in certain positions inheriting the particular properties or qualities of specific regions of the ovum: this is the conception of the Cellular Mosaic. But other workers, such as Dalcq (1938, 1941), consider that all meristematic cells may retain their totipotency for a long time and that their specialisation in a particular direction is due to the action of hormones emanating from special centres of growth activity. A majority of botanists would no doubt subscribe to the latter rather than the former view.

NUTRITION, GROWTH AND ORGANISATION

A developing zygote is a specific dynamic system, operating in a particular environment. Under normal conditions for the species, this environment—prothallus or embryo sac and nucellus—provides the nutrients used by the embryo during its growth. While the specific constitution and organisation of the zygote will determine, or limit, the kind (or kinds) of pattern that may be developed from it, the particular pattern actually developed may be more or less directly due to factors in the environment, e.g. physiological gradients, the balance of nutrients supplied, and so on. In general, in the matter of its nutrition, the young embryo behaves like a shoot in miniature.

In a number of lycopods, *Selaginellas* and ferns, the early embryogeny is characterised by conspicuous carbohydrate metabolism and by a delay in the organisation of the shoot apex and the axial vascular system. The considerable phase of suspensor development in gymnosperms may perhaps be ascribed to somewhat comparable nutritional relationships; and instances of extensive suspensor or parenchyma development, with delayed organisation of the shoot apex, are also known in the embryology of flowering plants. These observations suggest that in the early embryogeny the supply of nitrogen-containing metabolites, or of substances essential to protein synthesis and the maintenance of meristematic activity, may be limiting. Overbeek, Conklin and Blakeslee (1941, 1942) and Overbeek (1942) have shown that whereas mature embryos of *Datura stramonium* are completely self-sufficient in respect of growth factors, and, on simple culture media containing minerals and sugar can grow directly into seedlings, very small embryos must have growth factors added to the medium if growth is to continue.

EMBRYOLOGICAL SIMILITUDE

Not only are the major phyletic lines or subdivisions of the Plant Kingdom separated by wide 'phyletic gaps,' but gaps may also separate taxonomic groups of apparently close affinity. It may therefore be asked if the present survey indicates that the basic structural plans, or organisational patterns, of species in the major groups are perhaps less different than their adult conformations lead one to suppose. The answer to this very difficult question appears to be in the affirmative: in an earlier Section (p. 317) it has been seen that certain features are common to the embryological development of all plants except the simplest filamentous algae, colonial algae, fungi and lichens. To use Woodger's terminology, the constructional plans (or *Bauplans*), as manifested in *the early embryogeny*, in *Oedogonium, Fucus, Marchantia, Funaria, Lycopodium, Angiopteris, Pinus, Capsella* and *Lilium* are more alike than they are unlike; they have, in fact, a great deal in common. In their initial development, the zygotes of these representative genera react as if they shared a common basic substance; but later, when various specific genetical factors begin to act, very divergent morphological developments become evident. In the alternative interpretation —that the living substance is rather different in them all—the comparable embryonic developments might be attributed either to parallel or convergent evolution, or to the impact of the same extrinsic factors. There is general acceptance of the view that bryophytes, pteridophytes and seed plants all evolved from green algal ancestors, and therefore it may be assumed that all have some protoplasmic organisation and constituents in common. For example, the photosynthetic, respiratory and osmotic mechanisms appear to be common to all autotrophic plants. It is therefore understandable why some developmental features are common to species in different major groups. It is a considerably more exacting task, however, to decide whether or not the data of embryogeny enable us to discern affinities between major divisions such as algae, bryophytes and pteridophytes, or ferns, gymnosperms and flowering plants.

In comparing early embryonic developments, it would be helpful to know how mutations may affect the immediate post-zygotic development. What, for example, is the nature and magnitude of the genetical change that determines the loss of the suspensor in a group, or genus, in which that organ is normally present? In the zygote, envisaged as a reaction system, it may be that a comparatively small constitutional change determines the presence or absence of a suspensor; e.g. in the Marattiaceae and Ophioglossaceae there are species with a suspensor and related species without one; and among flowering plants we can find practically every gradation between species with a well developed suspensor and those in which it is inconspicuous or virtually absent. Sooner or later the angiosperms may be expected to yield evidence as to the kinds of genetical change that determine differences in the early embryogeny; for some of these early differences prepare the way for the very considerable differences between the adult organisms.

EMBRYOGENESIS AND PHYLOGENY

In the post-Darwinian or so-called Phyletic Period, botanists were confident that it would be possible to devise a satisfactory, and even fairly complete, phylogenetic classification. It was held that algae, bryophytes, pteridophytes, gymnosperms and angiosperms constituted a continuous evolutionary sequence, i.e. one long-sustained line of descent, protrayed as a genealogical tree consisting of a major stem and lateral branches. Later, however, it was realised that closely comparable morphological and anatomical features might be due to parallel or convergent evolution, and that there might have been evolution along several comparable but quite distinct phyletic lines. Indeed, it is now apparent that many major trends of special interest to biologists, e.g. from isogamy to oogamy in algae and fungi, or from actinomorphy to zygomorphy in floral structure, have taken place independently in unrelated phyletic lines.

In the Phyletic Period, it was thought that bryophytes and pterido-phytes, both amphibious archegoniate plants, formed part of a con-tinuous line of descent from a filamentous green algal ancestor, the pteridophytes being more progressive offshoots from a bryophyte ancestry. To-day it is agreed that both subdivisions had probably algal ancestors, but it is no longer held, at least with conviction, that pteridophytes were derived from bryophytes: and even if they were, the gap between the two seems unbridgeable on existing criteria of comparison. Some authors have tried to get over this difficulty by saying that the bryophytes have remained at a level of organisation through which the pteridophytes must have passed, the conception of a lineal relationship being thus retained without the necessity of specifying linking organisms. It was also formerly held that the pteridophytes are a coherent group, members of the several classes being vascular cryptogams with the same general reproductive organisa-tion and life history. In contemporary taxonomy the concept of Pteridophyta has been replaced by four major phyletic lines or sub-divisions, i.e. Psilopsida, Sphenopsida, Lycopsida and Filicopsida (or Pteropsida),[1] each stemming from some green algal stock, or from a leafless and rootless archetype of vascular plants which was perhaps

[1] For a review of the designation of the vascular plants *see* Just (1945).

not unlike the fossil *Rhynia*. Here, too, it has been suggested that if the more complex vascular plants were not derived from a Psilopsid ancestral type, they probably passed through that level of organisation in the course of their evolution.

Although wide phyletic gaps admittedly separate algae, bryophytes, pteridophytes, gymnosperms and angiosperms, the fossil evidence is, nevertheless, generally consistent with the view that these groups appeared in that sequence during the process of evolution. The existence of some kind of linking relationship is thus a reasonable inference. In the present context we may ask if the embryological data either enable us to bridge the phyletic gaps or to apprehend more adequately their nature.

In his Theory of Transformation, D'Arcy Thompson (1917, 1942) has shown that in a related group of organisms it is possible to indicate homologies, or identities, which were not evident before, by the use of deformed Cartesian coordinates. By this method, morphological differences in organisms of the same affinity can be analysed and, in many instances, can be shown to be more or less simple deformations of an original type. In the view of Richards and Riley (1937) the true field for the use of D'Arcy Thompson's Method of Transformation lies in development and not in evolution, or, as Medawar (1945) says, 'in the process of transforming, and not in the *fait accompli*.' The real transformations that underlie the evolutionary transformations are zygotic transformations and these do not lend themselves to treatment by this method. (For recent discussion of this aspect, *see* Medawar, 1945; Richards and Riley, 1937; Richards and Kavanagh, 1943, 1945; Needham, 1942; Woodger, 1945; Wardlaw, 1952.) Woodger has pointed out that although the 'structural plans' (*Bauplans*) of the adults of two species may be very different, the two may have a Bauplan in common at the unicellular zygote stage; and if we had an adequate theory of cell-organisation we might be surprised to find how little the Bauplan determining the zygote of one species differs from that of another.

The green algae may be regarded as organisms with constitutional limitations on their capacity for growth to any considerable size and they have remained at a low level of organisation—the simple or branched filament. *Nitella*, *Chara*, and some members of the Chaetophorales, may be indicated as green algae in which a considerably higher level of organisation has been attained; but they still remain limited in their size development and differentiation. Indeed, it seems reasonable to accept the view of Fritsch (1945) that those green algae which were capable of developing to larger size, and of becoming more highly differentiated, became the progressive and successful plants of the land. The brown algae, and in particular the Fucales and Laminariales, afford examples of organisms which are not closely restricted in their size development: they have attained to a considerable level of somatic organisation and in their embryogeny are not unlike plants considerably higher in the evolutionary scale.

In their sporophyte and gametophyte generations the bryophytes also show genetically-limited growth development. In the development of a moss zygote, the cell divisions are such as to define an apical cell and this cell grows and divides as if a vegetative axis was about to be formed. After a few divisions, however, apical growth virtually ceases, the further developments resulting in the organisation and maturation of the capsule. This is the general pattern of bryophyte development. An interesting exception is provided by *Anthoceros*. In this genus (*see* Chapter V), although the vegetative growth of the distal region of the sporophyte soon stops, the sporophyte continues to elongate by intercalary growth just above the haustorial base. Comparisons have been made between the sporophytes of *Anthoceros* and of some vascular plants, and it has been suggested that this genus affords common ground between bryophytes and pteridophytes. It is very doubtful if this view can be upheld. The kind of bryophyte which could have been a forerunner of the Pteridophyta, if we assume the real existence of such a relationship, would have been one with a thalloid gametophyte and a robust embryogeny in which the apical growth persisted for some considerable time, i.e. before the sporogenous phase supervened. No bryophyte possessing this organisation is known; indeed, such an organism would have been a nascent pteridophyte, probably resembling *Rhynia major*. It may thus be suggested that during the Early Palaeozoic period there was a group of advanced and actively evolving green algae which possessed a nascent archegoniate organisation—this common organisation being subsequently retained, though modified in various ways, in all plants above the algal level. The Bryophyta would include those organisms in which there was a constitutional restriction of apical growth in the sporophytic development, while the vascular plants would include all those in which there was no such restriction. From the foregoing considerations it will be seen that the embryological evidence is not contrary to the conception of a common ancestry for archegoniate plants.

We may now consider how embryological study affects the old conception of Pteridophyta. While the embryos in the several constituent classes have some general features in common, they also show characteristic differences. The embryogenies of *Lycopodium* and *Selaginella* are closely comparable and so also are those of eusporangiate and leptosporangiate ferns. But, on the embryological evidence,

Psilotineae, Lycopodineae, Equisetineae and Filicineae are sufficiently different as to be regarded as distinct phyletic lines, though the possibility of their having sprung from a common ancestor, or ancestral group, is not necessarily precluded. Similarly, a study of gymnosperm and angiosperm embryos affords no clue as to how the latter should be related phylogenetically to the former.

Investigations of numerous dicotyledon embryos have shown with what a high degree of precision and constancy the successive developments take place in any particular species. Particular genetical factors apparently become effective early in the ontogenetic development. If, now, in a species which is in an active state of evolution, there are mutant genes which affect the *early embryogeny* as well as the later stages of development, it is conceivable that the embryonic development could become so modified that the older embryos of parental and mutant types would no longer closely resemble each other. Considerations such as these enable us to envisage, if only in a very general and speculative way, how major systematic groups could have originated from a common source. In some such way the divergence of the bryophytes and the several lines of vascular plants from a common protoarchegoniate ancestral stock could perhaps be explained. Such views must, of course, be treated with caution: the prevalence of parallel evolution must always be borne in mind and accorded due consideration.

The embryos of related organisms tend to be more alike than the adults, and this Haldane (1932) has explained by saying that the genes which determine the interspecific differences exercise their chief effects rather late in the individual development. But if, as a result of mutational change, certain genes became active at an early stage in the embryogeny, far-reaching morphological and structural changes might follow; and it might be difficult to realise that the mutant and the parental forms were really closely allied. And if we further suppose that changes of this kind, which have been described as *acceleration*, together with other changes, have taken place cumulatively over a long period of time, the eventual morphological differences, which are the bases for separating the larger systematic units, may well mask the original community of origin. The several effects on the embryogeny and adult structure produced by changes in the time of action of genes have been discussed in some detail for animal embryos by de Beer (1930, 1940, 1951). The same process may simultaneously accelerate or retard the action of a large number of genes. Thus a change in permeability, perhaps due to a single gene, would affect the action of many gene-determined metabolites, with important consequential effects on the morphological development. Until we gain a better understanding of the processes involved in embryogenesis and of the nature and magnitude of the factors producing particular morphological results, we are in no position to say how wide the differences are between the configurations which morphologists and taxonomists use as criteria of comparison. Woodger (1945) has summarised the position by saying that when we are able to replace a classification based on adult configurations by one of zygote types, 'phylogenetic speculation will be transferred from the plane of taxonomic transformations between adults to the plane of actual or possible genetic transformations between zygotes.' If we ever reach this position, the seemingly impassable or unbridgeable gaps in the phylogenetic system may be found to have no real existence.

In concluding this Section, the question may perhaps be asked if it is reasonable to expect to find similarities in embryos of distantly related phyletic lines. If the hypothetical common ancestral group is of great antiquity, as it seems to be in the case of the vascular plants, it is hardly to be expected that the embryos of the living forms will be closely comparable. But it is reasonable to suppose that some general basic features may be common to them all, and this, in fact, is what we find. In short, while there may have been more or less close embryological similitude at an early stage in the divergence of the several major phyletic lines from the common ancestral stock, it is scarcely to be expected that this would still be found in the contemporary correlatives.

EXOSCOPIC AND ENDOSCOPIC EMBRYOGENY

When a suspensor is present the embryogeny is typically endoscopic, the suspensor and foot being formed adjacent to the neck of the archegonium and the shoot apex being directed inwards. In exoscopic embryos the sporophyte apex is directed towards the neck of the archegonium. The embryos of bryophytes, Psilotales, Equisetales and of *Isoetes* are exoscopic; those of the Lycopodiales, Marattiales, gymnosperms and flowering plants are endoscopic; those of the leptosporangiate ferns are lateral. The presence or absence of a suspensor has been accorded an important place in comparative embryology. We may, nevertheless, ask if the difference is truly one of fundamental importance. Relatively minor, though consistent, differences in zygotic reaction systems, or zygotic environments, may account for the presence or absence of a suspensor, i.e. may determine the inception of more active protein metabolism at one pole. As we have seen, the fact that the apical region of an endoscopic embryo is thrust into the prothallial tissue makes no important difference to its axial development and organisation, as compared with an exoscopic embryo. In Whitaker's experimental studies of *Fucus* eggs, it was found that small differences in pH, or in the intensity of illumination, on opposite sides of the zygote, may set in motion the reactions which determine the conspicuously polarised morphological development of the young plant. So, too, in the enclosed zygotes of bryophytes, pteridophytes, and seed plants, the orientation of the embryo may be attributable to relatively minor factors, though these become incident with a very high degree of constancy during the development of each particular species. In this connection the eusporangiate ferns are of special interest. In the genus *Botrychium*, some species, e.g. *B. lunaria*, have no suspensor, whereas others, e.g. *B. obliquum*, have a conspicuous and well developed one. In *B. lunaria*, Fig. 31F, the zygote is still spherical or subspherical when it divides to yield an epibasal segment contiguous with the archegonial neck; but in *B. obliquum*, Fig. 31G, H, the zygote undergoes considerable elongation and divides unequally by a transverse wall so that a large suspensor cell lies next to the neck while the small embryonic cell is thrust into the gametophyte tissue. Now here we have two species of the same genus (or, at any rate, indisputably related species, should *Botrychium* be split into two genera), in which the initial embryonic developments are very different. But we cannot regard the genetical differences between the species as being of great magnitude. Similar evidence is afforded by the Marattiales. In *Angiopteris evecta* (Fig. 32) in particular, the embryo is sometimes observed with a suspensor and sometimes without one. There are thus grounds for the view that the presence or absence of a suspensor is a phenomenon which may have been rated above its true genetical or physiological importance. If this conclusion is valid, we begin to see that, in the matter of their early embryogeny, the phyletic gaps between bryophytes, pteridophytes and seed plants may be less considerable than has been supposed.

TOWARDS A STATEMENT OF THE PRINCIPLES OF EMBRYOGENESIS

The factors which determine the embryonic development must be much more fully explored before embryological data can be used with safety in taxonomy and phylogeny. In so far as formal and structural features can be shown to be largely due to extrinsic factors, to that extent they lose their value in phylesis. What seems to be most needed at the present time are working hypotheses relating to embryogenesis and a statement of the principles of embryonic development.

In plants, with their 'continued embryogeny,' hypotheses relating to morphogenesis and embryogenesis will largely, though not completely, overlap. General features in the development of embryos in all classes of plants have already been considered (p. 317) and the factors which may be involved have been discussed (p. 319). In this section an attempt is made to prepare the way for a statement of the principles of embryogenesis. The basic assumption is that the zygote of any species is a highly complex and specific organic reaction system.

If the initial distribution of metabolites in the ovum or zygote is homogeneous, a drift towards heterogeneity soon begins, physiological gradients in the surrounding tissue being probably causally involved. These may determine the polarised distribution of particular metabolites in the egg. In algae, the ova, if initially homogeneous, soon become heterogeneous under the impact of factors in the environment. This polarised distribution of metabolites, which underlies the filamentous or axial development of the zygote, is of profound importance in the ensuing embryonic development. Whether or not a zygote has a specific cytoplasmic organisation of some kind must remain an open question. The polarity of the young embryo, and all the morphological and histological features by which its development is characterised, are primarily referable to an antecedent patternised distribution of metabolites. The inception of a biochemical pattern in the zygote, and the successive changes in it during the embryonic development, are held to be due to the reactions of the gene-determined components of the system, to the impact of physical and environmental factors, and to various organismal relationships which develop during growth. The visible, specific organisation, in short, is due to the hereditary constitution and to the inception and elaboration of a specific biochemical pattern. The basic problem in embryogenesis and morphogenesis is thus to discover how patternised distributions of metabolites, and, in particular, of morphogenetic substances, are brought about. Turing (1952) has indicated how an initially homogeneous diffusion reaction system, of the kind that may be present in a developing zygote, may become heterogeneous and give rise to a patternised distribution of metabolites, thus affording a basis for a morphological or histological pattern.

Since the main physiological processes are common to all classes of autotrophic plants, we may assume that their ova contain (a) metabolites, or reacting substances, which are common to all, e.g. inorganic nutrients, carbohydrates, organic acids, amino-acids, enzymes, etc., and (b) substances, or combinations of substances, which are characteristic of the species. A zygotic reaction system may therefore be expected to develop some morphological and structural features which are common to all embryos and others which are particular to the species, genus or family. In these reaction systems, also, particular genes, or gene-determined substances, will enter actively into the reactions at particular times, this being determined by a number of circumstances (Mather, 1948; Darlington and Mather, 1949) and they will therefore have a greater or less importance at different phases of development.

A biochemical theory would thus afford the basis for both the general and the specific aspects of embryogenesis.

In attempting to refer embryogenesis to physical and chemical factors, it has always to be borne in mind that even the simplest cell is a very complex system, the product of a long hereditary process. Each species, in fact, is a unique physical system.

As an embryo enlarges, the underlying reaction system apparently changes in a characteristic manner. The epigenetic development, which is recognised as being characteristic of plant growth (each stage of development being affected by the stages preceding it), could be referred to the regulated metabolic changes in the morphogenetic regions; and the progressive organisation which becomes evident during development could be ascribed to changes in the initial reaction system under the impact of genetical and environmental factors. Changes in the reaction system during development would also account for another important phenomenon, namely, the competence of cells to react to morphogenetic and other stimuli. Any contemporary biochemical theory of embryogenesis will unavoidably be a vast over-simplification of the processes actually involved in it. To know how different metabolites may react and become distributed so as to constitute a particular pattern is to describe only a part of the morphogenetic process: the energy relations within the system, and the physical properties of the reacting substances and of the final products, must also be known. The evidence thus far available is consistent with the view that, in the actual determination of form and structure, physical factors, such as the forces of cohesion, surface tension, gravity and so on, are of primary importance. The segmentation pattern in many embryos, for example, is in close agreement with Errera's law, the position and orientation of the new walls being largely determined by the forces developed in the enlarging cells.

It is difficult to be specific about a phenomenon such as organisation, but, from the considerations now before us, we begin to see that an activated organismal diffusion reaction system will behave in characteristic ways, yielding a patternised distribution of substances; and that in relation to the biophysical properties of these substances, to various physical factors which become incident, to factors in the environment, and to mathematical relationships, the specific form and structure of the organism will begin to become manifest and will change in a regulated and harmonious manner during growth to the adult state. These regulated and specific developments are what we mean when we speak of organisation. The writer's conception of the morphogenetic process, culminating in the organisation of the adult, is indicated diagrammatically and in a condensed form in the table on p. 332. From a

GENERALISED SCHEME OF MORPHOGENESIS

Growth with Tendency to Maintain Equilibrium

Successive Evocation and Action of Genes

Elaboration of Metabolic and Physiological Processes

Effect of Factors in the Environment

Reciprocal Relationships: Cells and Organs; The Whole and its Parts

Effects of Function on Organs and Tissues

A. Zygote or spore with sub-microscopic organisation and a specific genetical constitution (comprising nuclear and cytoplasmic genes) which control metabolic processes in the cytoplasmic substrate.

B. Under suitable environmental conditions, gene-controlled enzymes, auxins, etc., become available and active; nutrients are taken up, or mobilised from reserves in the zygote; growth begins.

C. The polarity of the enlarging embryo is determined by inherent factors and factors in the environment, the initial partition wall being at right angles to the axis.

D. On further growth, the dispositions of the succeeding partition walls are in general conformity with the principle of cell division by walls of minimal area.

C^1D^1. Concomitantly with C and D, a differential utilisation of metabolites at the apical and basal poles is established, the former becoming the locus of active protein metabolism and meristematic activity.

E. Increase in size brings changes in spatial relationships: there is a decrease in the ratio of surface to volume, a separation of parts and the distinction of superficial and inner tissues; the specific diffusion reaction system in the apical meristem determines the patternised distribution of metabolites and this constitutes the basis for the inception of organs and tissues.

E^1. Concomitantly with C, D and E, biophysical and physical factors become incident and have a large share in determining form and structure; also, growth centres and their physiological fields are established and diffusion gradients set up; and these are important in determining the integrated, regulated or harmonious development of the organism.

F. The distal apex continues as a self-determining morphogenetic region, the tissues to which it gives rise becoming the mature, rigid tissues of the axis.

The *Organisation*—the regulated inception and development of form and structure—characteristic of the species becomes manifest as development proceeds.

consideration of this scheme, it will be seen that vitalistic hypotheses such as that of Driesch (1908) are unnecessary. Equally it seems improbable that there can be any simple theory of embryogenesis and morphogenesis. J. T. Bonner (1952) regards morphogenesis, or the emergence of an organismal pattern, as being referable essentially to the progressive, constructive processes of growth, morphogenetic movement and differentiation: and to the limiting of these processes in various ways by intrinsic and extrinsic factors which check, guide and canalise them. He also advances the thesis that a sustaining aim should be a search for a micro-theory which would explain in a satisfying manner the general phenomena of development, such a theory being more likely to afford an insight into the inner mechanism of the relevant phenomena than any other kind of theory. By a micro-theory he does not imply that all the phenomena of biology are to be brought down to physics and chemistry: some kind of intermediate micro-theory may prove quite satisfactory. Bonner does not advance any micro-theory, but he indicates that the kind that would be satisfying would be one in which, as in crystal structure, the organism could be envisaged as being essentially constructed of small repetitive units. Having in mind the complex nexus of factors involved in embryogenesis, it seems improbable to the present writer that this kind of theory will prove adequate. The diffusion reaction theory of morphogenesis (Turing, 1952; Wardlaw, 1953) could be regarded as contributing to a micro-theory. But, during the individual development the reaction system will change constantly, each successive biochemical pattern being partly determined by, and based on, the preceding ones, and in turn helping to determine those which follow.

THEORY OF RECAPITULATION

The theory of recapitulation, or the biogenetic law—that the ontogeny of the individual organism is a recapitulation of the phylogeny of the race—as proposed by Haeckel (1866, 1875), has not been generally accepted by botanists or zoologists, though it retains a certain historical interest. According to this theory, phylogeny determines ontogeny, the development of an individual organism affording a kind of history of its race, the *adult* states of the ancestors being repeated in a condensed form during the early development of the descendants. There is some evidence which, at first sight, seems to support Haeckel's view; but on closer analysis the theory has not been found valid; in fact, much evidence has been urged against it. Haeckel's theory is closely comparable with that of Müller (1864) who held that, in its development from the egg, an animal might either pass through and beyond the ontogenetic stages of its ancestor, i.e. eventually overstepping the latter's adult state, or show a progressive deviation from the ancestral ontogeny. The first is a theory of parallelism; the second is like one of von Baer's laws (*see* below). In contrast to Haeckel, Müller based phylogeny on ontogeny; for it is by modifications during the process of development that descendants, in their adult state, come to differ from their adult ancestors. The contemporary view is that phylogeny is the result of ontogeny (Garstang, 1922; de Beer, 1951): no case is known in which the evolutionary modification has taken the form of an addition of a new terminal phase to the final phases of some alleged ancestral form. Where a critical attempt has been made to prove the theory of recapitulation, as has been done in zoology, the theory has been found to be invalid. As de Beer (1951, p. 51) says, there 'is embryonic similarity and repetition of characters in *corresponding* stages of the ontogenies of ancestor and descendant, which reveals the affinity between different animals, but supplies no evidence of what the adult ancestral form was like.' As early as 1828 von Baer, from a study of animal development, had reached the following important conclusions—known as the laws of von Baer (*after* de Beer, 1951, p. 3).

1. In development from the egg, the general characters appear before the special characters.

2. From the more general characters the less general and finally the special characters are developed.

3. During its development an animal departs more and more from the form of other animals.

4. The young stages in the development of an animal are not like the adult stages of other animals lower down on the scale, but are like the young stages of those animals.

Some points from de Beer's discussion of this field of research may be briefly indicated here. Since modifications in ontogeny are due to changes in hereditary factors, a phylogenetic sequence is the result of a sequence of modified ontogenies. Evolution is brought about by significant qualitative and quantitative genetical changes. Factors determining new characters, which may appear at all stages in the ontogeny, may, during further changes, be accelerated or retarded in their time of action, sometimes with momentous morphological consequences. Characters which are present in the early ontogeny, and provided they are not too specialised, may through *paedomorphosis* be important in the evolutionary process in that large structural changes are produced without loss of plasticity. (*Paedomorphosis* connotes the production of phylogenetic effects by the introduction of youthful characters into the line of adults; *paedogenesis* is the process by which the appearance of embryonic or early ontogenetic characters is retarded until the adult stage.) The conception and evidence of paedomorphosis afford a means of explaining, or bridging, some of the gaps in the fossil record. De Beer (1951, p. 140) also points out that a character which appears in the early embryogeny is not necessarily primitive or early in the phylogenetic sequence. In short, a knowledge of phylogeny does not enable us to explain the events in the embryonic development. 'Even if we had a *complete* phylogenetic series of adults ancestral to any given descendant, it would not help us to understand the processes of fertilisation, cleavage, induction, differentiation, organogeny, etc., which take place in the ontogeny of that descendant. The historical descriptive study of evolution has no bearing on the causal analytic study of embryology' (de Beer, p. 142). And conversely, even the most adequate knowledge of ontogeny would not of itself explain the essentially historic facts of phylogeny. 'But since phylogeny is but the result of modified ontogeny, there is the possibility of a causal analytic study of present evolution in an experimental study of the variability and genetics of ontogenetic processes.'

THE PLACE OF EMBRYOLOGY IN BOTANICAL SCIENCE

One of the more general aims in contemporary botanical science is to explain how specific organisation is brought about. The relevant studies properly begin with investigations of zygotic constitution and development and the assumption of form and structure in the growing individual plant under the influence of genetical, physiological, physical and environmental factors. The knowledge so gained will make for a more adequate understanding of the conformation of the adult plant and it may well lead to a new or modified outlook on the taxonomic and phylogenetic significance of various morphological and structural features.

In recent years a number of concepts have gained ground as affording at least partial explanations of formative processes in plants, e.g. that the shoot apex is a self-determining primary morphogenetic region, that leaf formation and phyllotaxis may be due to the inception of growth centres or morphogenetic fields at the apex, that the inception or initial differentiation of vascular tissue is due to basipetal effects proceeding from the apices of shoot and leaf primordia, that physiological gradients and the nutritional status of the apex are important in morphogenesis, and so on. These conceptions, largely based on morphological and experimental studies of the apex, do not appear to be in any way invalidated by the present survey of embryonic development. On the contrary, they are supported; and, indeed, it may be claimed that our conception of factors which may determine the inception of pattern and the progressive organisation during the individual development, has been enhanced and deepened.

The descriptive and pictorial aspect of plant embryology, though by no means complete, is well advanced. On the other hand, with some notable exceptions, little has been achieved in the field of experimental and chemical embryology—certainly nothing that is comparable with the achievements of zoologists. Botanical workers in these fields have been few, possibly because of the technical difficulties in handling the small and usually rather inaccessible embryos. It may be that these difficulties have been over-rated. A determined effort to make new discoveries in experimental embryology is just as likely to succeed as experimental work of apices which, not so long ago, was viewed in much the same way. That pure culture technique can be adapted to embryo culture has been shown by various investigators, while surgical techniques have been successfully attempted, though only to a limited extent. Whitaker and his colleagues have shown what can be achieved in the experimental manipulation of *Fucus* eggs. D'Arcy Thompson and others have been impressed by the probable importance of physical factors in morphogenetic processes, including those in embryos. It is very desirable that the hypotheses which have been proposed should be tested experimentally. In contemporary studies of physiological genetics, one of the aims is to discover how and when particular genes act to produce their specific growth and morphogenetic effects. The constancy and specificity of the embryonic developmental pattern in flowering plants, and the occurrence of characteristic anomalous developments in certain hybrids, make it probable that embryological investigations of related plants of known genetic constitution may yield information of particular interest. The activation of the ovum at fertilisation, and the nutrition, growth and development of the embryo, undoubtedly afford a wide field for study.

The foregoing points give some indication of the ways in which botanical science can be advanced by the study of embryos. But it may well be that the really important problems will only be uncovered or envisaged when substantial progress has been made in the experimental work. Lastly, since in embryos we are dealing with cells and tissues, either in the primary embryonic condition, or in the process of becoming differentiated, comprehensive studies of the relevant protein chemistry must be given first place in all investigations that claim to be of a fundamental character.

BIBLIOGRAPHY

AFZELIUS, K., 1928: Die Embryobildung bei *Nigritella nigra*. *Svensk Bot. Tidskr.*, 22, 82.

AGRAWAL, J. S., 1952: The embryology of *Lilaea subulata* H.K.B., with a discussion on its systematic position. *Phytomorph.*, 2, 15.

ALBAUM, H. G., 1938: Inhibitions due to growth hormones in fern prothallia and sporophytes. *Amer. Jour. Bot.*, 25, 124.

ALLSOPP, A., 1949: Experimental and analytical studies of pteridophytes. 15. Further observations on the effect of different concentrations of oxygen on meristems of certain ferns. *Ann. Bot.*, N.S., 13, 355.

ALLSOPP, A., 1951: *Marsilea* spp.: materials for experimental study of morphogenesis. *Nature*, 168, 301.

ALLSOPP, A., 1952: Experimental and analytical studies of pteridophytes. 17. The effect of various physiologically active substances on the development of *Marsilea* in sterile culture. *Ann. Bot.*, N.S., 16, 165.

ALLSOPP, A., 1952: Experimental and analytical studies of pteridophytes. 19. Investigations on *Marsilea*. 2. Induced inversion to juvenile stages. *Ann. Bot.*, N.S., 17, 37.

ALLSOPP, A., 1953: Experimental and analytical studies of pteridophytes. 20. Investigations on *Marsilea*. 3. The effect of various sugars on development and morphology. *Ann. Bot.*, N.S., 17, 447.

ANDERSON, E. N., 1929: Morphology of sporophyte of *Marchantia domingensis*. *Bot. Gaz.*, 88, 150.

ARBER, A., 1934: *The gramineae, a study of cereal, bamboo, and grass*. Macmillan Co., New York; Cambr. Univ. Press.

ARCHIBALD, E. E. A., 1939: The development of the ovule and seed of jointed cactus (*Opuntia aurantiacea* Lindley). *South Africa Jour. Sci.*, 36, 195.

ARNOLD, C. A., 1938: Paleozoic seeds. *Bot. Rev.*, 4, 205.

ARNOLD, C. A., 1947: *An introduction to paleobotany*. McGraw-Hill, New York.

ARTSCHWAGER, E. and McGUIRE, R. C., 1949: Cytology of reproduction in *Sorghum vulgare*. *Jour. Agr. Res.*, 78, 659.

ATKINSON, G. F., 1894: *The biology of ferns*. Macmillan, London and New York.

AVERY, G. S., Jr., 1928: Coleoptile of *Zea mays* and other grasses. *Bot. Gaz.*, 86, 107.

AVERY, G. S., Jr., 1930: Comparative anatomy and morphology of embryos and seedlings of maize, oats, and wheat. *Bot. Gaz.*, 89, 1.

AVERY, G. S., Jr., BERGER, J. and SHALUCHA, B., 1942: Auxin content of maize kernels during ontogeny from plants of varying heterotic vigor. *Amer. Jour. Bot.*, 29, 765.

BACCHI, O., 1943: Cytological observations in *Citrus*. III Megasporogenesis, fertilisation and polyembryony. *Bot. Gaz.*, 105, 221.

BAER, K. E., 1828: Ueber Entwicklungsgeschichte der Thiere. *Beobachtung und Reflexion*. Königsberg.

BALICKA-IWANOWSKA, G., 1899: Contribution à l'étude du sac embryonnaire chez certaines gamopetals. *Flora*, 86, 47.

BAILEY, I. W., 1949: Origin of the angiosperms: need for a broadened outlook. *Jour. Arnold Arb.*, 30, 64.

BAILEY, I. W., and NAST, C. G., 1943: The comparative morphology of the Winteraceae. II. Carpels. *Jour. Arnold Arb.*, 24, 472.

337

BAILEY, I. W., NAST, C. G. and SMITH, A. C., 1943: The family Himantandraceae. *Jour. Arnold Arb.*, 24, 190.

BAILEY, I. W. and NAST, C. G., 1945: Morphology and relationships of *Trochodendron* and *Tetracentron*. I. Stem, root, and leaf. *Jour. Arnold Arb.*, 26, 143.

BAILEY, I. W. and NAST, C. G., 1945: The comparative morphology of the Winteraceae. VII. Summary and conclusions. *Jour. Arnold Arb.*, 26, 37.

BAILEY, I. W. and SMITH, A. C., 1942: Degeneriaceae, a new family of flowering plants from Fiji. *Jour. Arnold Arb.*, 23, 356.

BAILEY, I. W. and SWAMY, B. G. L., 1948: *Amborella trichopoda* Bail., a new morphological type of vesselless dicotyledon. *Jour. Arnold Arb.*, 29, 245.

BAIRD, A. M., 1953: The life history of *Callitris*. *Phytomorph.*, 3, 258.

BALLANTINE, A. J., 1909: Preliminary note on the embryo sac of *Protea lepidocarpon*. *Ann. Bot.*, 22, 161.

BARNARD, C., 1903: Sur l'embryogénie de quelques plantes parasites. *Jour. Botanique*, 17, 23.

BARTON, L. V. and CROCKER, W., 1948: *Twenty years of seed research at Boyce Thompson Institute for plant research.* London.

BATTAGLIA, E., 1946: Ricerche cariologiche e embriologiche sul genere *Rudbeckia* (*Asteraceae*). VIII. Semigamia in *Rudbeckia laciniata* L. *Nuovo Gior. Bot. Ital.*, N.S. 53, 483.

BATTAGLIA, E., 1947: Ricerche cariologiche e embriologiche sul genere *Rudbeckia* (*Asteraceae*). XI. Semigamia in *Rudbeckia speciosa* Wender. *Nuovo Gior. Bot. Ital.*, N.S. 54, 1.

BATTAGLIA, E., 1951: The male and female gametophytes of angiosperms—an interpretation. *Phytomorph.*, 1, 87.

BEAMS, H. W., 1937: The air turbine ultracentrifuge, together with some results upon ultracentrifuging the eggs of *Fucus serratus*. *Jour. Mar. Biol. Assoc. United Kingdom*, 21, 571.

BEAMS, H. W. and KING, R. L., 1939: The effect of centrifugation on plant cells. *Bot. Rev.*, 5, 132.

BECQUEREL, P., 1931: Développement de la fougère mâle en culture pure septique à partir de la spore. *C.R. Acad. Sci.*, 192, 1265.

DE BEER, G. R., 1930: *Embryology and evolution.* Oxford Univ. Press.

DE BEER, G. R., 1950: *Embryos and ancestors* (second edn.; first edn., 1940). Oxford Univ. Press.

BENNETT, H. W., 1944: Embryology of *Paspalum dilatatum*. *Bot. Gaz.*, 106, 40.

BENSLEY, J. C., 1940: Hybridization of American 26-chromosome and Asiatic 13-chromosome species of *Gossypoum*. *Jour. Agric. Res.*, 60, 175.

BERTHOLD, G., 1886: *Protoplasma-mechanik.*

BERRIDGE, E. M., 1909: Fertilisation in *Ephedra altissima*. *Ann. Bot.*, 23, 509.

BERRIDGE, E. M. and SANDAY, E., 1907: Oogenesis and embryogeny in *Ephedra distachya*. *New Phytol.*, 6, 127–134; 167–174.

BETH, K., 1938: Untersuchungen über die Auslösung von Adventivembryonie durch Wundreiz. *Planta*, 28, 296.

BEYERLE, R., 1932: Untersuchungen über Regeneration von Farneprimärblättern. *Planta*, 16, 622.

BHADURI, P. N., 1936: Studies in the embryology of the Solanaceae. I. *Bot. Gaz.*, 98, 283.

BISHOP, M. K., 1929–30: On the occurrence of filamentous embryos in the Bryales. *Mem. and Proc. Manchester Lit. Phil. Soc.*, 74, 97.

BLAKESLEE, A. F., 1945: Removing some barriers to crossability in plants. *Proc. Amer. Phil. Soc.*, 89, 561.

BLAKESLEE, A. F., BELLING, J., FRANHAM, M. E. AND BERGNER, A. D., 1922: A haploid mutant in the Jimson weed, *Datura stramonium*. *Science*, 55, 646.

BLAKESLEE, A. F. and SATINA, S., 1944: New hybrids from incompatible crosses in *Datura* through culture of excised embryos on malt media. *Science*, 99, 331.

BLOMQUIST, H. L., 1944: Development of reproductive structures in the brown alga *Turbinaria turbinata*. *Bot. Gaz.*, 106, 290.

BÖCHER, T. W., 1951: Studies on morphological progression and evolution in the vegetable kingdom. *Kongel. Danske Videnskab. Selskab Biol. Med.*, 18, 13, 1.

BOLD, H. C., 1938: The nutrition of the sporophyte in the Hepaticae. *Amer. Jour. Bot.*, 25, 551.

BOLD, H. C., 1940: The nutrition of the sporophyte in the Musci. *Amer. Jour. Bot.*, 27, 318.

BOLD, H. C., 1948: The occurrence of chlorophyll in the sporophyte of *Ricciocarpus natans*. *Amer. Jour. Bot.*, 35, 440.

BONNER, D. and AXTMANN, G., 1937: The growth of plant embryos in vitro. Preliminary experiments on the rôle of accessory substances. *Proc. Nat. Acad. Sci.*, Wash., 23, 453.

BONNER, J., 1938: Nicotinic acid and the growth of isolated pea embryos. *Plant Physiol.*, 13, 865.

BONNER, J. and BONNER, D., 1938: Ascorbic acid and the growth of plant embryos. *Proc. Nat. Acad. Sci.*, Wash., 24, 70.

BONNER, J. T., 1952: *Morphogenesis: An essay on development.* Princeton University Press.

BORTHWICK, H. A., 1931: Development of the macrogametophyte and embryo of *Daucus carota*. *Bot. Gaz.*, 92, 23.

BOWER, F. O., 1882: The germination and embryogeny of *Gnetum gnemon*. *Quart. Jour. Micr. Sci.*, 22, 278.

BOWER, F. O., 1889: The comparative examination of the meristem of ferns as a phylogenetic study. *Ann. Bot.*, 3, 305.

BOWER, F. O., 1890: Is the eusporangiate or the leptosporangiate the more primitive type in the ferns? *Ann. Bot.*, 5, 109.

BOWER, F. O., 1908: *The origin of a land flora. A theory based upon the facts of alternation.* Macmillan, London.

BOWER, F. O., 1921: Size, a neglected factor in stelar morphology. *Proc. Roy. Soc. Edin.*, 41, 1.

BOWER, F. O., 1922: The primitive spindle as a fundamental feature in the embryology of plants. *Proc. Roy. Soc. Edin.*, 43, 1.

BOWER, F. O., 1923: *The ferns.* Vol. 1. Cambr. Univ. Press.

BOWER, F. O., 1924: Remarks on the present outlook on descent. *Proc. Roy. Soc. Edin.*, 44, 1.

BOWER, F. O., 1926: *The ferns.* Vol. 2. Cambr. Univ. Press.

BOWER, F. O., 1928: *The ferns.* Vol. 3. Cambr. Univ. Press.

BOWER, F. O., 1930: *Size and form in plants.* Macmillan, London.

BOWER, F. O., 1935: *Primitive land plants.* Macmillan, London.

BOWER, F. O., 1948: *Botany of the living plant* (4th edn.). Macmillan, London.

BOYD, L., 1931: Evolution of the monocotyledonous seedling: a new interpretation of the morphology of the grass embryo. *Trans. and Proc. Bot. Soc. Edin.*, 30, 286.

BRACHET, J., 1950: *Chemical embryology.* Interscience Publishers, New York. (First edn. in French, 1944.)

BREBNER, G., 1896: On the prothallus and embryo of *Danaea simplicifolia* Rudge. *Ann. Bot.*, 10, 109.

BREBNER, G., 1902: On the anatomy of *Danaea* and other Marattiaceae. *Ann. Bot.*, 16, 517.

BRINK, R. A. and COOPER, D. C., 1940: Double fertilization and development of the seed in angiosperms. *Bot. Gaz.*, 102, 1.

BRINK, R. A. and COOPER, D. C., 1947: The endosperm in seed development. *Bot. Rev.*, 13, 423.

BRINK, R. A., COOPER, D. C. and AUSHERMAN, L. E., 1944: A hybrid between *Hordeum jubatum and Secale cereale* reared from an artificially cultivated embryo. *Jour. Hered.*, 35, 67.

BRITTEN, E. J., 1947: The effect of naphthaleneacetic acid on the developing maize caryopsis. *Amer. Jour. Bot.*, 34, 211.

BRITTEN, E. J., 1950: Natural and induced parthenocarpy in maize and its relation to hormone production by the developing seed. *Amer. Jour. Bot.*, 37, 345.

BROUGH, P., 1933: The life-history of *Grevillea robusta* (Cunn). *Proc. Linn. Soc. N.S. Wales*, 58, 33.

BROUGH, P. and TAYLOR, M. H., 1940: An investigation of the life cycle of *Macrozamia spiralis* Miq. *Proc. Linn. Soc. N.S. Wales*, 65, 494.

BROWN, H. T., 1906: On the culture of excised embryos of barley on nutrient solutions containing nitrogen in different forms. *Trans. Guinness Research Lab.*, 1, 288.

BROWNE, I., 1913: Review: a colonial contribution to our knowledge of the genus *Lycopodium*. *New Phytol.*, 12, 222.

BROWNLIE, G., 1953: Embryogeny of the New Zealand species of the genus *Podocarpus*, section *Eupodocarpus*. *Phytomorph.*, 3, 293.

BRUCHMANN, H., 1897: *Selaginella spinulosa*. Gotha.

BRUCHMANN, H., 1904: Über das Prothallium und die Keimpflanze von *Ophioglossum vulgatum* L. *Bot. Zeit.*, 227.

BRUCHMANN, H., 1906: Über das Prothallium und Sporenpflanze von *Botrychium lunaria* L. *Flora*, 96, 203.

BRUCHMANN, H., 1909: Vom Prothallium der groszen Spore und von der Keimesentwicklung einiger *Selaginella*-Arten. *Flora*, 99, 12.

BRUCHMANN, H., 1909: Von den Vegetationsorganen der *Selaginella Lyallii* Spring. *Flora*, 99, 436.

BRUCHMANN, H., 1910: Über *Selaginella Preissiana* Spring. *Flora*, 100, 288.

BRUCHMANN, H., 1910: Die Keimung der Sporen und die Entwicklung der Prothallien von *Lycopodium clavatum* L., *L. annotinum* L. und *L. Selago* L. *Flora*, 101, 202.

BRUCHMANN, H., 1912: Zur Embryologie der Selaginellaceen. *Flora*, 104, 180.

BRUCHMANN, H., 1913: Zur Reduktion des Embryoträgers bei *Selaginellen*. *Flora*, 105, 337.

BRUNS, E., 1892: Der Grasembryo. *Flora*, 76, 1.

BRYAN, G. S., 1952: The cellular proembryo of *Zamia* and its cap cells. *Amer. Jour. Bot.*, 39, 433.

BUCHHOLZ, J. T., 1918: Suspensor and early embryo of *Pinus*. *Bot. Gaz.*, 66, 185.

BUCHHOLZ, J. T., 1920: Embryo development and polyembryony in relation to the phylogeny of conifers. *Amer. Jour. Bot.*, 7, 125.

BUCHHOLZ, J. T., 1925: The embryogeny of *Cephalotaxus fortunei*. *Bull. Torrey Bot. Club*, 52, 311.

BUCHHOLZ, J. T., 1926: Origin of cleavage polyembryony in conifers. *Bot. Gaz.*, 81, 55.

BUCHHOLZ, J. T., 1931: The suspensor of *Sciadopitys*. *Bot. Gaz.*, 92, 243.

BUCHHOLZ, J. T., 1932: The embryogeny of *Chamaecyparis obtusa*. *Amer. Jour. Bot.*, 19, 230.

BUCHHOLZ, J. T., 1933: Determinate cleavage polyembryony with special reference to *Dacrydium*. *Bot. Gaz.*, 94, 579.

BUCHHOLZ, J. T., 1937: Seed-cone development in *Sequoia gigantea*. *Science*, 85, 59.

BUCHHOLZ, J. T., 1938: Dissection, staining, and mounting of the embryos of conifers. *Stain Tech.*, 13, 53.

BUCHHOLZ, J. T., 1939: The morphology and embryogeny of *Sequoia sempervirens*. *Amer. Jour. Bot.*, 26, 93.

BUCHHOLZ, J. T., 1939: The embryogeny of *Sequoia sempervirens* with a comparison of the *Sequoias*. *Amer. Jour. Bot.*, 26, 248.

BUCHHOLZ, J. T., 1939: The generic segregation of the *Sequoias*. *Amer. Jour. Bot.*, 26, 535.

BUCHHOLZ, J. T., 1940: The embryogeny of *Torreya*, with a note on *Austrotaxus*. *Bull. Torrey Bot. Club*, 67, 731.

BUCHHOLZ, J. T., 1941: Embryogeny of the *Podocarpaceae*. *Bot. Gaz.*, 103, 1.

BUCHHOLZ, J. T., 1946: Gymnosperms. Taxonomy of Coniferales. *Encyclopaedia Britannica*, 11, 22.

BUCHHOLZ, J. T., 1946: Volumetric studies of seeds, endosperms, and embryos in *Pinus ponderosa* during embryonic differentiation. *Bot. Gaz.*, 108, 232.

BUCHHOLZ, J. T., 1950: Embryology of gymnosperms (précis). *Proc. and Trans. 7th Intern. Bot. Congr.*, Stockholm.

BUCHHOLZ, J. T. and KAEISER, M., 1940: A statistical study of two variables in the *Sequoias*—pollen grain size and cotyledon number. *Amer. Nat.*, 74, 279.

BUCHHOLZ, J. T. and OLD, E. M., 1933: The anatomy of the embryo of *Cedrus*, in the dormant stage. *Amer. Jour. Bot.*, 20, 35.

BUCHHOLZ, J. T. and STIEMERT, M. L., 1945: Development of seeds and embryos in *Pinus ponderosa*, with special reference to seed size. *Trans. Illinois Acad. Sci.*, 38, 27.

BUCHTIEN, O., 1887: Entwickelungsgeschichte des Prothallium von *Equisetum*. *Bibl. Bot.*, 8.

BUELL, K. M., 1952: Developmental morphology in *Dianthus*. I. Structure of the pistil and seed development. *Amer. Jour. Bot.*, 39, 194.

BUELL, K. M., 1952: Developmental morphology in *Dianthus*. II. Starch accumulation in ovule and seed. *Amer. Jour. Bot.*, 39, 458.

BUELL, K. M., 1953: Developmental morphology in *Dianthus*. III. Seed failure following interspecific crosses. *Amer. Jour. Bot.*, 40, 116.

BUGNON, P., 1921: Quelques critiques à la théorie de la phyllorhize. *Bull. Soc. Bot., France*, 68, 495.

BUGNON, P., 1924: Nouvelles rémarques sur la théorie de la phyllorhize. *Bull. Soc. Linn. Norm.*, 7th Ser., 7.

BÜNNING, E., 1948: *Entwicklungs- und Bewegungsphysiologie der Pflanze*. Springer, Berlin.

BÜNNING, E. and WETTSTEIN, D., 1953: Polarität und Differenzierung an Mooskeimen. *Naturwiss.*, 4, 147.

BURGEFF, H., 1936: Samenkeimung der Orchideen. Jena.

BURLINGHAME, L. L., 1915: The morphology of *Araucaria braziliensis*. III. Fertilisation, the embryo and the seed. *Bot. Gaz.*, 59, 1.

BUTTS, D. and BUCHHOLZ, J. T., 1940: Cotyledon numbers in conifers. *Trans. III Acad. Sci.*, 33, 58.

BUY, H. G. DU and OLSON, R. A., 1937: The presence of growth regulators during the early development of *Fucus*. *Amer. Jour. Bot.*, 24, 609.

CAMARA, A., 1943: Transplantacao de embrioes. *Agron. Lusitana*, 5, 375.

CAMPBELL, D. H., 1890: On the affinities of the Filicineae. *Bot. Gaz.*, 15, 1.

CAMPBELL, D. H., 1911: *The Eusporangiatae. Carnegie Inst. Washington Publ.*, 140, 1–229.

CAMPBELL, D. H., 1895, 1918: *Mosses and ferns* (1st and 3rd Edns.). Macmillan, London and New York.

CAMPBELL, D. H., 1921: The eusporangiate ferns and the stelar theory. *Amer. Jour. Bot.*, 8, 303.

CAMPBELL, D. H., 1924: A remarkable development of the sporophyte in *Anthoceros fusiformis. Ann. Bot.*, 38.

CAMPBELL, D. H., 1928: The embryo of *Equisetum debile* Roxb. *Ann. Bot.*, 42, 717.

CAMPBELL, D. H., 1940: *The evolution of land plants.* Stanford Univ. Press, California.

CARLSON, E. M. and STUART, B. C., 1936: Development of spores and gametophytes in certain New World species of *Salvia. New Phytol.*, 35, 65.

CAVERS, F., 1904: On the structure and biology of *Fegatella conica. Ann. Bot.*, 18, 85.

CAVERS, F., 1911: The interrelationships of the Bryophyta. *New Phytol. Reprint*, 4.

CELAKOVSKY, L. J., 1897: Ueber die Homologien des Grasembryo. *Bot. Zeit.*, 55, 141.

CELAKOVSKY, L. J., 1901: Die Gliederung der Kaulome. *Bot. Zeit.*, 59, 79.

CHAMBERLAIN, C. J., 1935: *Gymnosperms.* Univ. Chicago Press.

CHAUVEAUD, G., 1921: *La constitution des plantes vasculaires révélée par leur ontogénie.* Payot et Cie, Paris.

CHEESMAN, E. E., 1927: Fertilisation and embryogeny in *Theobroma cacao* L. *Ann. Bot.*, 41, 107.

CHEMIN, E., 1937: Le développement des spores chez les Rhodophycées. *Rév. Gén. Bot.*, 49, 205.

CHIARUGI, A. and FRANCINI, E., 1930: Apomissia in *Ochna serratula. Nuovo Gior. Bot. Ital.*, N.S. 37, 1.

CHILD, C. M., 1915: *Individuality in organisms.* Chicago.

CHILD, C. M., 1929: Physiological dominance and physiological isolation in development and reconstitution. *Roux. Arch. Entw. Mech. Organ.*, 117, 21.

CHILD, C. M., 1941: *Patterns and problems of development.* Chicago Univ. Press.

CHRISTENSEN, H. M. and BAMFORD, R., 1943: Haploids in twin seedlings of pepper. *Jour. Hered.*, 34, 99.

CHURCH, A. H., 1919: Thalassiophyta and the subaerial transmigration. *Oxford Bot. Mem.*, 3.

CLAUSEN, R. E. and LAMMERTS, W. E., 1929: Interspecific hybridization in *Nicotiana.* X. Haploid and diploid merogony. *Amer. Nat.*, 63, 279.

COKER, W. C., 1907: Fertilisation and embryogeny of *Cephalotaxus fortunei. Bot. Gaz.*, 43, 1.

COMPTON, R. H., 1913: An anatomical study of syncotyly and schizocotyly. *Ann. Bot.*, 27, 793.

CONKLIN, E. G., 1931: The development of centrifuged eggs of ascidians. *Jour. Exper. Zool.*, 60, 1.

COOK, P., 1939: A new type of embryogeny in the conifers. *Amer. Jour. Bot.*, 26, 138.

COOPER, D. C., 1943: Haploid-diploid twin embryos in *Lilium and Nicotiana. Amer. Jour. Bot.*, 30, 408.

COOPER, G. O., 1942: Development of the ovule and formation of the seed in *Plantago lanceolata. Amer. Jour. Bot.*, 29, 597.

CORNER, E. J. H., 1951: The leguminous seed. *Phytomorph.*, 1, 117.

COULTER, J. M., 1908: The embryo sac and embryo of *Gnetum gnemon*. *Bot. Gaz.*, 46, 43.

COULTER, J. M. and CHAMBERLAIN, C. J., 1903: *Morphology of angiosperms.* New York.

COULTER, J. M. and CHAMBERLAIN, C. J., 1910: *Morphology of gymnosperms.* New York.

COULTER, J. M. and LAND, W. J. G., 1905: Gametophytes and embryo of *Torreya taxifolia*. *Bot. Gaz.*, 39, 161.

COULTER, J. M. and LAND, W. J. G., 1914: The origin of monocotyledons. *Bot. Gaz.*, 57, 509.

COULTER, J. M. and LAND, W. J. G., 1915: The origin of monocotyledons: II. Monocotyledony in grasses. *Ann. Mo. Bot. Gard.*, 2, 175.

COY, G. V., 1928: Morphology of *Sassafras* in relation to phylogeny of angiosperms. *Bot. Gaz.*, 86, 1928.

CRÉTÉ, P., 1938: La polyembryonie chez le *Lobelia syphilitica*. L. *Bull. Soc. Bot. France*, 85, 580.

CRÉTÉ, P., 1949: Un cas de polyembryonie chez une Gentianacée, *l'Erythraea centaurium* Pers. *Bull. Soc. Bot. France*, 96, 113.

CROCKER, W., 1938: Life-span of seeds. *Bot. Rev.*, 4, 235.

CROCKER, W. and BARTON, L. V., 1953: *The physiology of seeds.* Chronica Botanica Co., Waltham, Mass.

CUMMINGS, J. M., 1945: Preliminary report on meiotic chromosomes in new *Datura* hybrids from embryos excised from incompatible crosses. *Genetics*, 30, 3.

CURTIS, J. T., 1947: Undifferentiated growth of orchid embryos on media containing barbiturates. *Science*, 105, 128.

CZAJA, A. TH., 1953: Polaritat und Wuchsstoff. *Ber. deutsch. bot. Ges.*, 53, 197.

DAHLGREN, K. V. O., 1939: Sur la présence d'amidon dans le sac embryonnaire ches les angiosperms. *Bot. Notiser*, 221–231.

DALCQ, A., 1938: *Form and causality in early development.* Cambr. Univ. Press.

DALCQ, A., 1941: *L'oeuf et son dynamisme organisateur.* Albin Michel.

DANIELLI, J. F., 1945: Some reflections on the forms of simpler cells. *Essays on growth and form.* Oxford Univ. Press.

DARLINGTON, C. D. and MATHER, K., 1949: *The elements of genetics.* Allen and Unwin, London.

DAVIDSON, O. W., 1934: The germination of 'non-viable' peach seeds. *Proc. Amer. Soc. Hort. Sci.*, 30, 129.

DAVIDSON, O. W., 1935: Growing trees from 'non-viable' peach seeds. *Proc. Amer. Soc. Hort. Sci.*, 32, 308.

DEECKE, T., 1855: Nouvelles recherches sur le développement du *Pedicularis sylvatica*. *Ann. Sci. Nat. Bot.*, 4, 58; also *Bot. Zeit.*, 13.

DIETRICH, K., 1924: Über Kultur von Embryonen ausserhalb das Samens. *Flora*, 17, 379.

DOAK, C. C., 1937: Morphology of *Cupressus arizonica*: gametophytes and embryogeny. *Bot. Gaz.*, 98, 808.

DOERPINGHAUS, S. L., 1947: Differences between species of *Datura* in utilization of five carbohydrates. *Amer. Jour. Bot.*, 34, 583.

DORETY, H. A., 1908: The embryo of *Ceratozamia*; a physiological study. *Bot. Gaz.*, 45, 412.

DORETY, H. A., 1909: Vascular anatomy of the seedling of *Microcycas calocoma*. *Bot. Gaz.*, 47, 139.

DORETY, H. A., 1917: Diagrams in Coulter and Chamberlain's *Morphology of gymnosperms*.

DOYLE, J., 1953: Gynospore or megaspore—a restatement. *Ann. Bot.*, N.S., 17, 465.

DOYLE, J. and LOOBY, W. J., 1939: Embryogeny in *Saxegothaea* and its relation to other podocarps. *Sci. Proc. Roy. Dublin Soc.*, 22, 127.

DREW, K. M., 1952: Studies in the Bangioideae. *Phytomorph.*, 2, 38.

DRIESCH, H., 1908: *The science and philosophy of the organism*. Gifford Lectures, London.

DUPLER, A. W., 1917: The gametophytes of *Taxus canadensis* Marsh. *Bot. Gaz.*, 64, 115.

DURAND, E. J., 1908: The development of the sex organs and sporogonium of *Marchantia polymorpha*. *Bull. Torrey Bot. Club*, 35, 321.

DUVICK, D. N., 1952: Free amino acids in the developing endosperm of maize. *Amer. Jour. Bot.*, 39, 656.

EAMES, A. J., 1913: The morphology of *Agathis australis*. *Ann. Bot.*, 27, 1.

EAMES, A. J., 1936: *Morphology of vascular plants* (*lower groups*). McGraw-Hill, New York.

EAMES, A. J., 1952: Relationships of the Ephedrales. *Phytomorph.*, 2, 79.

EARLE, T. T., 1938: Embryology of certain Ranales. *Bot. Gaz.*, 100, 257.

EAST, E. M., 1930: The production of homozygotes through reduced parthenogenesis. *Science*, 72, 148.

EDMAN, G., 1931: Apomeiosis und Apomixis bei *Atraphaxis frutescens* Koch. *Acta Horti Bergiani*, 11, 13.

EKDAHL, I., 1941: Die Entwicklung von Embryosack und Embryo bei *Ulmus glabra* Huds. *Svenck Bot. Tidskr.*, 35, 143.

ERNST, A., 1901: Beiträge zur Kenntnis der Entwicklung des Embryosackes und des Embryos (Polyembryonie) von *Tulipa gesneriana* L. *Flora*, 88, 37.

ERNST, A., 1913: Zur Kenntnis von Parthenogenesis und Apogamie bei Angiospermen. *Verh. schweiz. naturf. Jahresv. Ges.*, 11, 96, 1.

ERNST, A., 1918: *Bastardierung als Ursache der Apogamie im Pflanzenreiche*. Jena.

ERRERA, L., 1886: Sur une condition fondamentale d'équilibre des cellules vivantes. *C.R. Acad. Sci.*, 103, 822; *Bull. Soc. Belge Microscopie*, 13.

EVANS, A. W., 1939: The classification of the Hepaticae. *Bot. Rev.*, 5, 49.

EWART, A. J., 1908: On the longevity of seeds. *Proc. Roy. Soc. Victoria*, 21, 1.

FAGERLIND, F., 1937: Embryologische, zytologische und bestäubungs experimentelle Studien in der Familie Rubiaceae nebst Bemerkungen über einige Polyploiditatsprobleme. *Acta Horti Bergiani*, 11, 195.

FAGERLIND, F., 1944: Die Samenbildung und die Zytologie bei agamospermischen und sexuellen Arten von *Elatostema* und einigen nahestehenden Gattungen nebst Beleuchtung einiger damit zusammenhangender Probleme. *K. Svenska Vet-Akad. Handl.*, 3, 21, 1.

FAGERLIND, F., 1946: Hormonale Substanzen als Ursache der Frucht- und Embryobildung bei pseudogamen *Hosta*-biotypen. *Svensk Bot. Tidskr.*, 40, 230.

FAGERLIND, F., 1946: Sporogenesis, Embryosackentwicklung und pseudogame Samenbildung bei *Rudbeckia laciniata* L. *Acta Horti Bergiani*, 14, 39.

FAMINTZIN, A., 1879: Embryologische Studien. *Mém. Akad. Impér. Sci. St. Petersburg*, 7, 26 (10).

FARMER, J. B., 1891: On *Isoetes lacustris* L. *Ann. Bot.*, 5, 37.

FARMER, J. B. and WILLIAMS, J. L., 1896: On fertilisation and the segmentation of the spore in *Fucus*. *Ann. Bot.*, 10, 479: also *Proc. Roy. Soc. Lond.*, 60, 188 (1897).

FARMER, J. B. and WILLIAMS, J. L., 1898: Contributions to our knowledge of the Fucaceae. *Phil. Trans. Roy. Soc.*, B, 190, 123.

FEDORTSHUK, W., 1931: Embryologische Untersuchung von *Cuscuta monogyna.* Vahl., und *C. epithymum* L. *Planta,* 14, 94.

FITTING, H., 1900: Bau und Entwickelungsgeschichte der Macrosporen von *Isoetes* und *Selaginella. Bot. Zeit.,* 58.

FLEMION, F., 1933: Dwarf seedlings from non-after-ripened embryos of *Rhodotypos kerrioides. Contrib. Boyce Thompson Inst.,* 5, 161.

FLORIN, R., 1939: The morphology of the female fructifications in *Cordaites* and conifers of Palaeozoic age. *Bot. Not.,* 1939, 547.

FLORIN, R., 1949: The morphology of *Trichopitys heteromorpha* Saporta, a seed of Palaeozoic age, and the evolution of the female flowers in the Ginkgoinae. *Acta Horti Bergiani,* 15, 5, 79.

FLORIN, R., 1951: Evolution in *Cordaites* and conifers. *Acta Horti Bergiani,* 15, 11, 285.

FRANCKE, H. L., 1934: Beiträge zur Kenntnis der Mykorrhiza von *Monotropa hypopitys* L. Analyse und Synthese der Symbiose. *Flora.,* 129, 1.

FREY-WYSSLING, A., 1948: *Submicroscopic morphology of protoplasm and its derivatives.* Elsevier Publ. Co., New York.

FRITSCH, F. E., 1916: The algal ancestry of the higher plants. *New Phytol.,* 15, 233.

FRITSCH, F. E., 1935, 1945: *The structure and reproduction of the algae.* Vols. I and II. Cambr. Univ. Press.

FRITSCH, F. E., 1939: The heterotrichous habit. *Botaniska Notiser,* Lund.

FRITSCH, F. E., 1945: Studies in the comparative morphology of the algae. IV. Algae and archegoniate plants. *Ann. Bot.,* N.S., 9, 1.

FRITSCH, F. E., 1945: Observations on the anatomical structure of the Fucales. *New Phytol.,* 44, 1.

FROST, H. B., 1938: Nucellar embryony and juvenile characters in clonal varieties of Citrus. *Jour. Hered.,* 29, 423.

GANONG, W. F., 1898: Upon polyembryony and its morphology in *Opuntua vulgaris. Bot. Gaz.,* 25, 221.

GARSTANG, W., 1922: The theory of recapitulation. A critical restatement of the biogenetic law. *Jour. Linn. Soc. Zoo.,* 35, 81.

GATES, R. R. and GOODWIN, K. M., 1930: A new haploid *Oenothera,* with some observations on haploidy in plants and animals. *Jour. Genetics,* 23, 123.

GAUTHERET, R., 1945: *La culture des tissues.* Librairie Gallimard, Paris.

GOEBEL, K., 1880: Beiträge zur vergleichenden Entwickelungsgeschichte der Sporangien. *Bot. Zeit.,* 38, 39.

GOEBEL, K., 1897, 1918, 1928, 1930: *Organographie der Pflanzen.* 1st Edn., 2 vols.; 2nd and 3rd Ends., 1918, 1928–1930. Jena. (Engl. edn. by I. B. Balfour as *Organography of plants, especially of the Archegoniatae and Spermaphyta.* Oxford Univ. Press, 1900.)

GOEBEL, K., 1902: Über Regeneration im Pflanzenreich. *Biol. Zentralb.,* 22, 493.

GOEBEL, K., 1908: *Einleitung in die experimentelle Morphologie der Pflanzen.* Leipzig.

GOEBEL, K., 1915: *Selaginella anocardia,* eine weitere apogame Art. *Flora,* 108, 324.

GOEBEL, K., 1922: Gesetzmassigkeiten in Blattaufbau. *Bot. Abhandl.,* I. Jena.

GOEBEL, K., 1926: *Wilhelm Hofmeister.* (Engl. Trans. by H. M. Bower.) *Ray. Soc.,* London.

GOLDSCHMIDT, R., 1927: *Physiologische Theorie der Vererbung.* Springer, Berlin.

GOLDSCHMIDT, R., 1938: *Physiological genetics.* McGraw-Hill, New York.

GRIFFITH, W., 1844: On the ovulum of *Santalum, Osyris, Loranthus* and *Viscum. Trans. Linn. Soc.,* London, 19, 171.

GUÉRIN, P., 1930: Le développement de l'oeuf et la polyembryonie chez l'*Erythronium deus canis* L. *C.R. Acad. Sci.*, Paris, 191, 1369.

GUILFORD, V. B. and FISK, E. L., 1951: Megasporogenesis and seed development in *Mimulus trigrinus* and *Torenia fournieri*. *Bull. Torrey Bot. Club*, 79, 6.

GUSTAFSSON, A., 1935: Studies on the mechanism of parthenogenesis. *Hereditas*, 21, 1.

GUSTAFSSON, A., 1946: Apomixis in higher plants. I. The mechanism of apomixis. *Lunds. Univ. Arsskr. N.F. Avd.*, II, 42 (3), I.

GUSTAFSSON, A., 1947: Apomixis in higher plants. II. The causal aspect of apomixis. *Lunds. Univ. Arsskr. N.F. Avd.*, II, 43 (2), 71.

GUSTAFSSON, A., 1947: Apomixis in higher plants. III. Biotype and species formation. *Lunds. Univ. Arsskr. N.F. Avd.*, II, 43 (12), 183.

HAAGEN-SMIT, A. J., DANDLIKER, W. B., WITTWEB, S. H. and MURNEEK, A. E., 1946: Isolation of 3-indoleacetic acid from immature corn kernels. *Amer. Jour. Bot.*, 33, 118.

HAAGEN-SMIT, A. J., SIU, R. and WILSON, G., 1945: A method for the culturing of excised, immature corn embryos in vitro. *Science*, 101, 234.

HABERLANDT, G., 1914: *Physiological plant anatomy*. (Engl. trans. by J. M. F. Drummond.) Macmillan, London.

HABERLANDT, G., 1921: Über experimentelle Erzeugung von Adventivembryonen bei *Oenothera lamarckiana*. *Sitzber. Preuss. Akad. Wiss.*, Berlin, 40, 695.

HABERLANDT, G., 1922: Über Zellteilungshormone und ihre Beziehungen zur Wundheilung, Befruchtung, Parthenogenesis und Adventivembryonie. *Biol. Zentralbl.*, 42, 145.

HABERLANDT, G., 1923: Zur Embryologie von *Allium odorum*. *Ber. deutsch. bot. Gesell.*, 41, 174.

HABERLANDT, G., 1925: Zur Embryologie und Cytologie von *Allium odorum*. *Ber. deutsch. bot. Gesell.*, 43, 559.

HAECKEL, E., 1866: *Generelle Morphologie*. Berlin. (Partly reprinted as *Prinzipien der Generellen Morphologie der Organismen*. Berlin, 1906.)

HAECKEL, E., 1868: *Natürliche Schöpfungsgeschichte*. Berlin. (Engl. trans. by Ray Lankester, of 8th edn., 1892, as *The History of Creation* (6th edn.), London.)

HAGERUP, O., 1933: Zur Organogenie und Phylogenie der Koniferen-Zapfen. *Kgl. Danske. Vidensk. Selsk. Biol. Meddel.*, 10, 1.

HAGERUP, O., 1947: The spontaneous formation of haploid, polyploid and aneuploid embryos in some orchids. *Kgl. Danske Vidensk. Selsk. Biol. Meddel.*, 20, 1.

HAINING, H. L., 1920: Development of embryo of *Gnetum*. *Bot. Gaz.*, 70, 436.

HALDANE, J. B. S., 1932: The time of action of genes, and its bearing on some evolutionary problems. *Amer. Nat.*, 66, 5.

HALL, J. G., 1902: An embryological study of *Limnocharis emarginata*. *Bot. Gaz.*, 33, 214.

HAMILTON, H. H., 1948: A developmental study of the apical meristem in four varieties of *Avena sativa* grown at two temperatures. *Amer. Jour. Bot.*, 35, 656.

HANNIG, E., 1904: Über die Kultur von Cruciferen Embryonen ausserhalb des Embryosacks. *Bot. Zeit.*, 62, 45.

HANSTEIN, J., 1870: Die Entwickelungsgeschichte der Monocotylen und Dicotylen. *Bot. Abhandl.*, Bonn, 1, 1–112.

HARLAND, S. C., 1936: Haploids in polyembryonic seeds of Sea Island cotton. *Jour. Hered.*, 27, 229.

HARRISON, R. G., 1936: Relations of symmetry in the developing embryo. *Collecting Net*, 2.

HARVEY-GIBSON, R. J., 1894: Contributions towards a knowledge of the genus *Selaginella*. *Ann. Bot.*, 8.

HAUPT, A. W., 1926: Morphology of *Preissia quadrata*. *Bot. Gaz.*, 82, 30.

HEBERLEIN, E. A., 1929: Morphological studies on a new species of *Marchantia*. *Bot. Gaz.*, 88, 415.

HEDEMANN, E., 1931: Über experimentelle Erzeugung von Adventivembryonen bei *Mirabilis uniflora* und *Mirabilis fröebelii*. *Biol. Zentralb.*, 51, 647.

HEGELMAIER, F., 1872: Zur Morphologie der Gattung *Lycopodium*. *Bot. Zeit.*, 30.

HEGELMAIER, F., 1874: Zur Kenntniss einiger *Lycopodien*. *Bot. Zeit.*, 32.

HEGELMAIER, F., 1897: Zur Kenntnis der Polyembryonie von *Allium odorum*. *Bot. Zeit.*, 55, 133.

HEINRICHER, E., 1888: Beeinflust das Licht die Organanlage am Farnembryo? *Mitt. Bot. Inst. Graz.*, 2.

HERSH, A. H., 1941: Allometric growth: the ontogenetic and phylogenetic significance of differential rates of growth. *Growth* (suppl.), 113.

HILL, A. W., 1938: The monocotyledonous seedlings of certain dicotyledons, with special reference to the Gesneriaceae. *Ann. Bot.*, N.S., 2, 127.

HILL, T. G., 1908: The germination of *Gnetum gnemon* L. *Jour. Roy. Hort. Soc.*, 34, 1, 2.

HILL, T. G. and DE FRAINE, E., 1906: On the seedling structure of gymnosperms. *Ann. Bot.*, 20, 471.

HILL, T. G. and DE FRAINE, E., 1908: On the seedling structure of gymnosperms. I. *Ann. Bot.*, 22, 689.

HILL, T. G. and DE FRAINE, E., 1909: On the seedling structure of gymnosperms. II. *Ann. Bot.*, 23, 189.

HILL, T. G. and DE FRAINE, E., 1909: On the seedling structure of gymnosperms. III. *Ann. Bot.*, 23, 433.

HILL, T. G. and DE FRAINE, E., 1910: On the seedling structure of gymnosperms. IV. Gnetales. *Ann. Bot.*, 24, 319.

HIORTH, G., 1926: Zur Kentniss der Homozygoten-Eliminierung und der Pollenschlauch Konkurrenz bei *Oenothera*. *Zeitschr. Indukt. Abstamm. u. Vererb.*, 43, 171.

HIRMER, M., 1927: *Handbuch der Palaobotanik*. Munich.

HODGSON, R. W. and CAMERON, S. H., 1938: Effects of reproduction by nucellar embryony on clonal characteristics in *Citrus*. *Jour. Hered.*, 29, 417.

HOFMEISTER, W., 1851: *Vergleichende Untersuchungen*. Leipzig.

HOFMEISTER, W., 1855: Notes embryologiques. *Ann. Sci. Nat. Bot.*, 3, 209.

HOFMEISTER, W., 1857: Beiträge zur Kenntniss der Gefasskryptogamen. II, 607.

HOFMEISTER, W., 1858: Neuere Beobachtungen über Embryobildung der Phanerogamen. *Jahrb. wiss. Bot.*, 1, 82.

HOFMEISTER, W., 1859: Neue Beiträge zur Kenntnis der Embryobildung der Phanerogamen. I. Dikotyledonen mit ursprünglich, einzelligen, nur durch Zelltheilung wachsendem Endosperm. *Abh. Königl. Sächs. Gesell. Wiss.*, 5, 535.

HOFMEISTER, W., 1861: Neue Beiträge zur Kenntnis der Embryobildung der Phanerogamen. II. Monokotyledonen. *Abh. Königl. Sächs. Gesell. Wiss.*, 7, 629.

HOFMEISTER, W., 1862: *Higher Cryptogamia*. Ray Soc., London.

HOLLOWAY, J. E., 1909: A comparative study of the anatomy of six new species of *Lycopodium*. *Trans. New Zealand Inst.*, 42, 356.

HOLLOWAY, J. E., 1915: Studies in the New Zealand species of *Lycopodium*. Part I. *Trans. New Zealand Inst.*, 48, 253.

HOLLOWAY, J. E., 1917: The prothallus and young plant of *Tmesipteris*. *Trans. New Zealand Inst.*, 50, 1.

HOLLOWAY, J. E., 1921: Further studies on the prothallus, embryo and young sporophyte of *Tmesipteris*. *Trans. New Zealand Inst.*, 53, 386.

HOLLOWAY, J. E., 1930: The experimental cultivation of the gametophytes of *Hymenophyllum pulcherrimum* Col. and of *Trichomanes reniforme* Forst. f. *Ann. Bot.*, 44, 269.

HOLLOWAY, J. E., 1939: The gametophyte, embryo and young rhizome of *Psilotum triquetrum*, Swartz. *Ann. Bot.*, N.S., 3, 24.

HOLLOWAY, J. E., 1944: The gametophyte, embryo, and developing sporophyte of *Cardiomanes reniforme* (Forst.) Presl. *Trans. Roy. Soc. New Zealand*, 74, 196.

HOWARTH, W. O., 1927: The seedling development of *Festuca rubra* L. var. *tenuifolia* Mihi., and its bearing on the morphology of the grass embryo. *New Phytol.*, 26, 46.

HURD, A. M., 1920: Effect of unilateral monochromatic light and group orientation on the polarity of germinating *Fucus* spores. *Bot. Gaz.*, 70, 25.

HUTCHINSON, J., 1926: *The families of flowering plants*. Vol. I., *Dicotyledons*. Macmillan, London.

HUTCHINSON, J., 1934: *The families of flowering plants*. Vol. II. *Monocotyledons*. Macmillan, London.

HUXLEY, J. S., 1932: *Problems of relative growth*, London.

HUXLEY, J. S. and DE BEER, G. R., 1934: *Elements of experimental embryology*. Cambr. Univ. Press.

HUXLEY, J. S. and TESSIER, G., 1936: Terminology of relative growth. *Nature*, 137, 780.

HUXLEY, J. S., NEEDHAM, J. and LERNER, I. M., 1941: *Nature*, 148, 225.

IVANOV, M. A., 1938: Experimental production of haploids in *Nicotiana rustica* L. *Genetica*, 20, 295.

IWANOWSKAYA, E. V., 1946: Hybrid embryos of cereals grown on artificial nutrient medium. *Compt. Rend. (Doklady) Acad. Sci. U.R.S.S.*, 54, 445.

IYENGAR, M. O. P., 1932: *Fritschiella*, a new terrestrial member of the Chaetophoraceae. *New Phytol.*, 31, 229.

JÄGER, L., 1889: Beiträge zur Kenntniss der Endospermbildung und zur Embryologie von *Taxus baccata* L. *Flora*, 86, 241.

JAKOVLEV, M. S., 1937: On the number of fibro-vascular bundles in the coleoptile of barleys and oats. *Compt. Rend. (Doklady) Acad. Sci.*, U.R.S.S., 17, 69.

JANCZEWSKI and ROSTAFINSKI, 1875: Prothalle de l'*Hymenophyllum*. *Mem. Soc. Cherbourg*.

JEFFREY, E. C., 1895: Polyembryony in *Erythronium americanum*. *Ann. Bot.*, 9, 537.

JEFFREY, E. C., 1899: The development, structure and affinities of the genus *Equisetum*. *Mem. Boston. Soc. Nat. Hist.*, 5, 5.

JOHANSEN, D. A., 1945: A critical survey of the present status of plant embryology. *Bot. Rev.*, 11, 87.

JOHANSEN, D. A., 1950: *Plant embryology*. Chronica Botanica Co., Waltham, Mass.

JOHNSON, A. M., 1936: Polyembryony in *Eugenia Hookeri*. *Amer. Jour. Bot.*, 23, 83.

JOHRI, B. M., 1935: Studies in the family Alismaceae. I. *Limnophyton obtusifolium* Miq. *Jour. Indian. Bot. Soc.*, 14, 49.

JOHRI, B. M., 1934/5: Studies in the family Alismaceae. II. *Sagittaria sagittifolia*. L. *Proc. Ind. Acad. Sci.*, B. I, 340.

JOHRI, B. M., 1935/6: Studies in the family Alismaceae. III. *Sagittaria guayanensis*, H.B.K., and *S. latifolia*. Willd. *Proc. Ind. Acad. Sci.*, B, 2, 33.

JOHRI, B. M., 1935b: Life-history of *Butomopsis lanceolata*. Kunth. *Nature*, 136, 338.

JOHRI, B. M., 1936: The life-history of *Butomopsis lanceolata* Kunth. *Proc. Ind. Acad. Sci.*, 4, 139.

JOHRI, B. M. and KAPIE, R. N., 1953: Contribution to the morphology and life history of *Acalypha indica* L. *Phytomorph.*, 3, 137.

JOHRI, B. M. and TIAGI, B., 1952: Floral morphology and seed formation in *Cuscuta reflex*. Roxb. *Phytomorph.*, 2, 162.

JØRGENSEN, C. A., 1928: The experimental production of heteroploid plants in the genus *Solanum*. *Jour. Genet.*, 19, 133.

JULIANO, J. B., 1934: Origin of embryos in the strawberry mango. *Philippine Jour. Sci.*, 54, 553.

JULIANO, J. B., 1937: Embryos of carabao mango, *Mangifera indica* L. *Philippine Agr.*, 25, 749.

JUST, T., 1945: The proper designation of the vascular plants. *Bot. Rev.*, 11, 299.

KASHYAP, SHIV R., 1914: Structure and development of the prothallus of *Equisetum debile*. Roxb. *Ann. Bot.*, 28.

KATAYAMA, Y., 1932: Haploid formation by X-rays in *Triticum monococcum*. *Cytologia*, 5, 235.

KATAYAMA, Y., 1935: Karyogenetic studies on X-rayed sex cells and their derivatives in *Triticum monococcum*. *Agr. Coll. Jour. Tokyo Imp. Univ.*, 13, 333.

KENT, N. and BRINK, R. A., 1947: Embryonic growth in vitro of immature *Hordeum* embryos. *Amer. Jour. Bot.*, 43, 601.

KENT, N. and BRINK, R. A., 1947: Growth in vitro of immature *Hordeum* embryos. *Science*, 106, 547.

KHAN, R., 1943: Contributions to the morphology of *Ephedra foliata* Boiss. II. Fertilisation and embryogeny. *Proc. Nat. Acad. Sci.*, India, 13, 357.

KIESSELBACH, T. A., 1949: The structure and reproduction of corn. *Univ. Nebraska Agric. Exp. Sta. Res. Bull.*, 161, 1–96.

KIHARA, H., 1936: A diplo-haploid twin plant in *Triticum durum*. *Agri. and Hort.* (Tokyo), 11, 1425.

KIHARA, J., 1940: Formation of haploids by means of delayed pollination in *Triticum monococcum*. *Bot. Mag. Tokyo*, 4, 178.

KIHARA, J. and KATAYAMA, Y., 1932: On the progeny of haploid plants of *Triticum monococcum*. *Kwagau*, 2, 408.

KILLIAN, K., 1914: Über die Entwicklung einiger Florideen. *Zeit. f. Bot.*, 6, 209.

KLEBS, G., 1916: Zur Entwicklungsphysiologie der Farnprothallien. *Sitz. Heidelb. Akad. Wiss.*, Sect. B.

KLEIN, G., 1930: Der Wandel des Stickstoff in der grunen Pflanze. *Ergebn. Agr. Chem.*, 2, 143.

KNAPP, E., 1931: Entwicklungsphysiologische Untersuchungen an Fucaceen-Eiern. *Planta*, 14, 731.

KNIEP, H., 1907: Beiträge zur Keimungsphysiologie und Biologie von *Fucus*. *Jahr. Wiss. Bot.*, 44, 635.

KNUDSON, L., 1932: The use of amino compounds by orchid embryos. *New York Agric. Exp. Sta.* (*Cornell*) *Rept.*, 111–112.

KOGL, F. and HAAGEN-SMIT, A. J., 1936: Biotin und Aneurin als Phytohormone. Ein Beitrag zur Physiologie der Keimung. *Zeitschr. Phys. Chem.*, 243, 209.

KOSTOFF, D., 1929: An androgenic *Nicotiana* haploid. *Zeitschr. f. Zellforsch. u. Mikros. Anat.*, 9, 640.

KOSTOFF, D., 1930: Ontogeny, genetics and cytology of *Nicotiana* hybrids. *Genetica*, 12, 33.

KOSTOFF, D., 1941: The problem of haploidy (cytogenetic studies on *Nicotiana* haploids and their bearings to some other cytogenetic problems). *Bibl. Genetica*, 13, 1.

KRUYT, W., 1952: *Proc. Koninkl. Nederlandse Akad. Wetensch.*, Ser. C, 55, 503.

KUHN, E., 1930: Pseudogamie und Androgenesis bei Pflanzen. *Zuchter*, 2, 124.

KYLIN, H., 1917: Über die Keimung der Florideensporen. *Arkiv. f. Bot.*, 14, 22.

LAIBACH, F., 1925: Das Taubwerden der Bastardsamen und die künstliche Aufzucht früh absterbender Bastardembryonen. *Zeitschr. f. Bot.*, 17, 417.

LAIBACH, F., 1929: Ectogenesis in plants: methods and genetic possibilities of propagating embryos otherwise dying in the seed. *Jour. Hered.*, 20, 201.

LAIBACH, F., 1932: Pollenhormon und Wuchsstoff. *Ber. deutsch bot. Ges.*, 50, 383.

LAIBACH, F., 1934: Zum Wuchsstoffproblem. *Der Zuchter*, 6, 49.

LAM, H. J., 1948: Classification and the new morphology. *Acta Biotheoretica.*, 8, 107.

LAMMERTS, W. E., 1942: Embryo culture an effective technique for shortening the breeding cycle of deciduous trees and increasing germination of hybrid seeds. *Amer. Jour. Bot.*, 29, 166.

LAND, W. J. G., 1904: Spermatogenesis and oogenesis in *Ephedra trifurca*. *Bot. Gaz.*, 38, 1.

LAND, W. J. G., 1907: Fertilisation and embryogeny in *Ephedra trifurca*. *Bot. Gaz.*, 44, 273.

LAND, W. J. G., 1923: A suspensor in *Angiopteris*. *Bot. Gaz.*, 75, 421.

LANG, A., 1944: Entwicklungsphysiologie. *Fortschr. Bot.*, 11, 282.

LANG, A., 1949: Entwicklungsphysiologie. *Fortschr. Bot.* (Gaumann and Renner), 12, 340. Springer, Berlin.

LANG, W. H., 1902: On the prothalli of *Ophioglossum pendulum* and *Helmintho-stachys zeylanica*. *Ann. Bot.*, 16, 23.

LANG, W. H., 1905: On the morphology of *Cyathodium*. *Ann. Bot.*, 19, 411.

LANG, W. H., 1907: On the sporogonium of *Notothylas*. *Ann. Bot.*, 21, 201.

LANG, W. H., 1910: On a suspensor in *Helminthostachys*. *Ann. Bot.*, 24, 611.

LANG, W. H., 1914: The embryo of *Helminthostachys*. *Ann. Bot.*, 28.

LANG, W. H., 1915: Studies in the morphology of *Isoetes*. II. The analysis of the stele of the shoot of *Isoetes lacustris* in the light of mature structure and apical development. *Mem. Proc. Manchester Lit. Phil. Soc.*, 59, 29.

LANG, W. H., 1915: Phyletic and causal morphology. Pres. Addr. (Sect. K), Brit. Assoc., Adv. Sci.

LANKESTER, E. R., 1870: On the use of the term homology in modern zoology and the distinction between homogenetic and homoplastic agreements. *Ann. Mag. Nat. Hist.*, 4, ser. 6.

LARUE, C. D., 1936: The growth of plant embryos in culture. *Bull. Torrey Bot. Club*, 63, 365.

LARUE, C. D. and AVERY, G. S., 1938: The development of the embryo of *Zizania aquatica* in the seed and in artificial culture. *Bull. Torrey Bot. Club*, 65, 11.

LAWSON, A. A., 1907: The gametophyte, fertilisation and embryo of *Cephalotaxus drupacea*. *Ann. Bot.*, 21, 1.

LAWSON, A. A., 1917: *Phil. Trans. Roy. Soc. Edin.*, 51, 785.

LAWSON, A. A., 1926: A contribution to the life history of *Bowenia*. *Proc. Roy. Soc., Edin.*, 54, 357.

LEBÈGUE, A., 1949: Embryologie des Saxifragacées. Polyembryonie chez le *Bergenia delavayi* Engl. *Bull. Soc., Bot. France*, 96, 38.

LEBÈGUE, A., 1952: La polyembryonie ches les angiosperms. *Bull. Soc. Bot. France*, 99, 329.

LEBÈGUE, A., 1952: *Recherches embryogéniques sur quelques dicotyledones dialy-petalés*. Masson, Paris.

LEE, A. E., 1950: The growth in culture of intact seedlings and isolated seedling organs. *Amer. Jour. Bot.*, 37, 312.

LEE, A. E., 1952: The growth of excised immature sedge embryos in culture. *Bull. Torrey Bot. Club*, 79, 59.

LEITGEB, H., 1878: Zur Embryologie der Farne. *Sitz L.K. Akad. Wiss., Wien.*, 77.

LEITGEB, H., 1880: Studien über Entwicklung der Farne. *Sitz. Kais. Akad. Wiss. Math. Naturw.*, 80, 201.

LEROY, J. F., 1947: La polyembryonie chez les '*Citrus*' Son intérét dans la culture et amélioration. *Rev. Bot. Appl. et Agr. Trop.*, 301, 302; 483–495.

LEVRING, T., 1947: Remarks on the surface layers and the formation of the fertilisation membrane in the *Fucus* eggs. *Meddel. Göteborgs bot. trädg.*, 17, 97.

LEVRING, T., 1949: Fertilisation experiments with *Hormosira banksii* (Turn.) Dene. *Physiol. Plant.*, 2, 45.

LEVRING, T., 1952: Remarks on the submicroscopical structure of eggs and spermatozoids of *Fucus* and related genera. *Physiol. Plant.*, 5, 528.

LI, T. T., 1934: The development of the embryo of *Ginkgo biloba*. *Sci. Rept. Nat. Tsing Hua Univ.*, Ser. B, 2, 29.

LI, T. T. and SHEN, T., 1934: The effect of 'pantothenic acid' on the growth of the radical of *Ginkgo* embryo in artificial media. *Sci. Rept. Nat. Tsing Hua Univ.*, Ser. B, 2, 53.

LIEBIG, J., 1930–1931: Ergänzungen zur Entwicklungsgeschichte von *Isoetes lacustris* L. *Flora*, 125 (N.F. 25), 321.

LILLIE, F. R., 1909: Polarity and bilaterality of the annelid egg. Experiments with centrifugal force. *Biol. Bull.*, 16, 54.

LILLIE, R. S., 1945: *General biology and philosophy of organism*. Univ. Chicago Press.

LOOBY, W. J. and J. DOYLE., 1937: Fertilization and proembryo formation in *Sequoia*. *Sci. Proc. Roy. Dublin Soc.*, 21, 457.

LOOBY, W. J. and DOYLE, J., 1939: The ovule, gametophytes and proembryo in *Saxegothaea*. *Sci. Proc. Roy. Dublin Soc.*, 22, 95.

LOOBY, W. J. and DOYLE, J., 1940: New observations on the life-history of *Callitris*. *Sci. Proc. Roy. Dublin Soc.*, 22, 241.

LORCH, W., 1931: *Anatomie der Laubmoose*. Linsbauer's *Handbuch der Pflanzenanatomie*, 7A, 113.

LOWRANCE, E. W., 1937: Effect of temperature gradients upon polarity in eggs of *Fucus furcatus*. *Jour. Cell. and Comp. Physiol.*, 10, 321.

LOTSY, J. P., 1890: Contribution to the life-history of the genus *Gnetum*. *Ann. Jard. Bot. Buitenzorg*, 2, 1, 46.

LUDWIGS, K., 1911: Untersuchungen zur Biologie der *Equiseten*. *Flora*, N.F., 103, 385.

LUND, E. J., 1923: Electrical control of organic polarity in the egg of *Fucus*. *Bot. Gaz.*, 76, 288.

LYON, F. M., 1904: A study of the gametophyte of *Selaginella apus* and *S. rupestris*. *Bot. Gaz.*, 37.

LYON, H. L., 1904: The embryogeny of *Ginkgo*. *Minn. Bot. Stud.*, 3, Ser. 4, 275.

LYON, H. L., 1905: A new genus of Ophioglossaceae. *Bot. Gaz.*, 40, 455.

MACVICAR, R. and BURRIS, R., 1947: *63rd Ann. Report of Director, Wis. Agric. Exp. Sta.*, 57.

MAHESHWARI, P., 1937: A critical review of the types of embryo sacs in angiosperms. *New Phytol.*, 26, 359.

MAHESHWARI, P., 1940: The rôle of growth hormones in the production of seedless fruits. *Science and Culture*, 6, 85.

MAHESHWARI, P., 1945: The place of angiosperm embryology in research and teaching. *Jour. Indian Bot. Soc.*, 24, 25.

MAHESHWARI, P., 1950: *An introduction to the embryology of angiosperms.* McGraw-Hill, New York.

MAHESHWARI, P., 1950: Contacts between embryology, physiology and genetics. *Proc. 37th Indian Sci. Cong., Bot. Sect., Pres. Addr.*

MAHESHWARI, P., 1952: Polyembryony in angiosperms. *Palaeobotanist*, 1, 319.

MAHESHWARI, P. and JOHRI, B. M., 1941: The embryo sac of *Acalypha Indica* L. *Beihefte bot. Centbl.*, 61A, 125.

MAHESHWARI, P. and SRINIVASAN, A. R., 1944: A contribution to the embryology of *Rudbeckia bicolor* Nutt. *New Phytol.*, 43, 135.

MALPIGHI, M., 1687: Opera Omni; seu thesaurus locupletissimus botanico-medico-anatomicus. 2 vols. Lugduni Batavorum.

MANEVAL, W. E., 1914: The development of *Magnolia* and *Liriodendron*, including a discussion of the primitiveness of the Magnoliaceae. *Bot. Gaz.*, 57, 1.

MANTON, I., 1950: *Problems of cytology and evolution in the pteridophytes.* Cambridge Univ. Press.

MARRÈ, E. and MURNEEK, A. E., 1953: The effects of fertilisation and growth-regulating substances (hormones) on carbohydrate and hexose-phosphate metabolism during the early stages of growth of corn kernels (fruit). *Science*, 117, 661.

MATHER, K., 1948: Nucleus and cytoplasm in differentiation. *Symp. Soc. Exper. Biol.*, 2, 196. Cambr. Univ. Press.

MAURITZON, J., 1933: Studien über die Embryologie der Familien Crassulaceae und Saxifragaceae. Diss. Lund.

MAURITZON, J., 1934: Die Embryologie einiger Capparidaceen sowie von *Tovaria pendula. Arkiv. for Bot.*, 26A, 1.

MCCALL, M. A., 1934: Developmental anatomy and homologies in wheat. *Jour. Agric. Res.*, 48, 283.

MCLEAN, S. W., 1945: New hybrids with the aberrant species *Datura ceratocaula*, secured by embryo dissection. *Genetics*, 30, 14.

MCNAUGHT, H. L., 1929: Development of the sporophyte of *Marchantia chenopoda. Bot. Gaz.*, 88, 400.

MEDAWAR, P. B., 1945: Size, shape and age. *Essays on growth and form.* Oxford Univ. Press.

MERRY, J., 1941: Studies on the embryo of *Hordeum sativum.* II. The growth of the embryo in culture. *Bull. Torrey Bot. Club*, 69, 360.

METCALFE, C. R., 1936: An interpretation of the morphology of the single cotyledon of *Ranunculus ficaria* based on embryology and seedling anatomy. *Ann. Bot.*, 50, 103.

METTENIUS, G., 1856: *Filices horti botanica lipsiensis.* Leipzig.

MEYER, K. J., 1929: Die Entwicklung des Sporogons bei *Fegatella conica. Planta*, 8, 36.

MEYER, K. J., 1931: Zur Entwickelungsgeschichte des Sporophyten einiger Marchantiales. *Planta*, 13, 193.

MEYER, K. J., 1931: Die Sporophytenentwickelung und die Phylogenie bei den Marchantiales. *Planta*, 13, 210.

MICHAELIS, P., 1925: Zur Cytologie und Embryoentwicklung von *Epilobium. Ber. deutsch. bot. Gesell.*, 43, 61.

MILNE-EDWARDS, H., 1867–1881: *Leçons sur la physiologie et l'anatomie compareés.* Paris.

MIRBEL, DE and SPACH, E., 1843: Notes sur l'embryogénie des *Pinus laricio* et *sylvestris*, des *Thuya orientalis* et *occidentalis* et du *Taxus baccata. Ann. Sci. Nat. Bot.*, II, 20, 257.

MITCHELL, M. R., 1915: The embryo sac and embryo of *Striga lutea*. *Bot. Gaz.*, 59, 124.

MODILEWSKI, J., 1925: Zur Kenntnis der Polyembryonie von *Allium odorum* L. *Bull. Jard. Bot. Kieff*, 2, 9.

MODILEWSKI, J., 1928: Weitere Beiträge zur Embryologie und Cytologie von *Allium*-Arten. *Bull. Jard. Bot. Kieff*, 7/8, 57.

MODILEWSKI, J., 1930: Neue Beiträge zur Polyembryonie von *Allium odorum* L. *Ber. deutsch. bot. Gesell.*, 48, 285.

MODILEWSKI, J., 1931: Die Embryobildung bei *Allium odorum* L. *Bull. Jard. Bot. Kieff*, 12/13, 27.

LA MOTTE, C., 1933: Morphology of the megagametophyte and the embryo sporophyte of *Isoetes lithophila*. *Amer. Jour. Bot.*, 20, 217.

LA MOTTE, C., 1937: Morphology and orientation of the embryo of *Isoetes*. *Ann. Bot.*, N.S., 1, 695.

MÜLLER, F., 1864: *Für Darwin*. Leipzig.

MÜLLER, K., 1951: *Die Lebermoose Europas*. Rabenhorst's *Kryptogamen Flora*, 6, 100.

MÜNTZING, A., 1937: Note on a haploid rye plant. *Hereditas*, 23, 401.

MÜNTZING, A., 1937: Polyploidy from twin seedlings. *Cytologie* (Fujii Jubl.), 211–227.

MÜNTZING, A., 1943: Characteristics of two haploid twins in *Dactylis glomerata*. *Hereditas*, 29, 134.

MURBECK, S., 1901: Parthenogenetische Embryobildung in der Gattung *Alchemilla*. *Lunds Univ. Arsskr.*, N.F. Avd., II, 36, 1.

MURNEEK, A. E., 1937: Recent advances in physiology of reproduction of plants. *Science*, 86, 43.

NAKAJIMA, G., 1935: Occurrence of a haploid in *Triticum turgidum*. *Jap. Jour. Genetics*, 11, 246.

NAST, C. G. and BAILEY, I. W., 1945: Morphology and relationships of *Trochodendron* and *Tetracentron*. II. Inflorescence, flower and fruit. *Jour. Arnold Arb.*, 26, 265.

NAYLOR, M., 1953: The life-history of *Marginariella urvilliana*. *Ann. Bot.*, N.S., 17, 493.

NEEDHAM, J., 1931: *Chemical embryology*. Cambr. Univ. Press.

NEEDHAM, J., 1942: *Biochemistry and morphogenesis*. Cambr. Univ. Press.

NÉMEC, B., 1910: Das Problem der Befruchtungsvorgänge und andere zytologischen Fragen. Berlin.

NETOLITZKY, F., 1926: *Anatomie der Angiospermen-Samen. Handbuch der Pflanzenanatomie*. Borntraeger, Berlin.

NISHIMURA, M., 1922: Comparative morphology and development of *Poa pratensis*, *Phleum pratense* and *Setaria italica*. *Jap. Jour. Bot.*, 1, 55.

NOGUCHI, Y., 1929: Zur Kenntnis der Befruchtung und Kornbildung bei den Reizpflanzen. *Jap. Jour. Bot.*, 4, 385.

NORDENSKIOD, H., 1939: Studies of a haploid rye plant. *Hereditas*, 25, 204.

NORNER, C., 1881: Embryoentwickelung der Gramineen. *Flora*, 64, 241.

OLIVER, F. W., 1890: On *Sarcodes sarguinea* Torr. *Ann. Bot.*, 4, 303.

OLSON, R. A. and BUY, H. G. DU, 1937: The rôle of growth substance in the polarity and morphogenesis of *Fucus*. *Amer. Jour. Bot.*, 24, 611.

OLTMANNS, F., 1904: *Morphologie und Biologie der Algen*. Vols. 1 and 2. Fischer, Jena.

OSAWA, I., 1912: Cytological and experimental studies in *Citrus*. *Jour. Col. Agr. Imp. Univ. Tokyo*, 4, 83.

VAN OVERBEEK, J., 1940: Auxin in marine algae. *Plant Physiol.*, 15, 291.

VAN OVERBEEK, J., 1942: Hormonal control of embryo and seedling. *Cold Spring Harbor Symp.*, 10, 126.

VAN OVERBEEK, J., CONKLIN, M. E. and BLAKESLEE, A. F., 1941: Factors in coconut milk essential for growth and development of very young *Datura* embryos. *Science*, 94, 350.

VAN OVERBEEK, J., CONKLIN, M. E. and BLAKESLEE, A. F., 1941: Chemical stimulation of ovule development and its possible relation to parthenogenesis. *Amer. Jour. Bot.*, 28, 647.

VAN OVERBEEK, J., CONKLIN, M. E. and BLAKESLEE, A. F., 1942: Cultivation *in vitro* of small *Datura* embryos. *Amer. Jour. Bot.*, 29, 472.

VAN OVERBEEK, J., SIU, R. and HAAGEN-SMIT, A. J., 1944: Factors affecting the growth of *Datura* embryos *in vitro*. *Amer. Jour. Bot.*, 31, 219.

OVERTON, J. B., 1913: Artificial parthenogenesis in *Fucus*. *Science*, N.S., 37, 841.

PEARSON, H. H. W., 1909: Further observations in *Welwitschia*. *Phil. Trans. Roy. Soc.*, London, B., 200, 331.

PEARSON, H. H. W., 1910: On the embryo of *Welwitschia*. *Ann. Bot.*, 24, 759.

PERCIVAL, J., 1921: *The wheat plant: a monograph*. London.

PERCIVAL, J., 1927: The coleoptile bundles of Indo-Abyssinian emmer wheat (*Triticum dicoccum*, Schübl.). *Ann. Bot.*, 41, 101.

PEROTTI, R., 1913: Contributions all'embryologia delle Dianthaceae. *Ann. Bot. Roma*, 11, 371.

PFEIFFER, W. M., 1912: The morphology of *Leitneria floridana*. *Bot. Gaz.*, 53, 189.

PIJL, L., 1934: Über die Polyembryonie bei *Eugenia*. *Réc. des Trav. Bot. Néerl.*, 31, 113.

POITEAU, A., 1809: Mémoire sur l'embryon des Graminées des Cyperacées et du *Nelumbo*. *Ann. Mus. Hist. Nat.*, 13, 381.

PRAT, H., 1945: Les gradients histo-physiologiques et l'organogènèse végétale. *Contrib. l'Inst. Bot. Univ. Montreal*, Canada, 58, 1.

PRAT, H., 1948: Histo-physiological gradients and plant organogenesis. *Bot. Rev.*, 14, 603.

PURI, V., 1941: The life-history of *Moringa oleifera* Lamk. *Jour. Ind. Bot. Soc.*, 20, 263.

RADFORTH, N. W., 1936: The development *in vitro* of the proembryo of *Ginkgo*. *Trans. Roy. Canad. Inst.*, 21, 87.

RANDALL, T. E. and RICK, C. M., 1945: A cytogenetic study of polyembryony in *Asparagus officinalis* L. *Amer. Jour. Bot.*, 32, 560.

RENDLE, A. B., 1925: *The classification of flowering plants*. II. Cambr. Univ. Press.

RANDOLPH, L. F., 1936: Developmental morphology of the caryopsis in maize. *Jour. Agr. Res.*, 53, 881.

RANDOLPH, L. F., 1945: Embryo culture of *Iris* seed. *Bul. Amer. Iris Soc.*, 97, 33.

RANDOLPH, L. F. and COX, L. G., 1943: Factors influencing the germination of *Iris* seed and the relation of inhibiting substances to embryo dormancy. *Amer. Soc. Hort. Sci. Proc.*, 43, 284.

RAO, V. S., 1938: The correlation between embryo type and endosperm type. *Ann. Bot.*, N.S., 2, 535.

RAPPAPORT, J., SATINA, S. and BLAKESLEE, A. F., 1950: Extracts of ovular tumors and their inhibition of embryo growth in *Datura*. *Amer. Jour. Bot.*, 37, 586.

RAU, M. A., 1951: Development of the embryo in some members of the Papilionaceae. *Phytomorph.*, 1, 80.

RAU, M. A., 1953: Some observations on the endosperm in Papilionaceae. *Phytomorph.*, 3, 209.

RAUCH, K. V., 1936: Cytologisch-embryologische Untersuchungen an *Scurrula atropurpurea* Dans. und *Dendrophthoe pentandra* Miq. *Ber. Schweiz bot. Ges.*, 45, 5.

REED, E. A. and WHITAKER, D. M., 1944: Polarised plasmolysis of *Fucus* eggs with particular reference to ultra-violet light. *Jour. Cell and Comp. Physiol.*, 18, 329.

REEDER, J. R., 1948: The embryo of *Streptochaeta* as additional evidence for the foliar nature of the coleoptile. (Abstract) *Amer. Jour. Bot.*, 35, 797.

REEDER, J. R., 1953: The embryo of *Streptochaeta* and its bearing on the homology of the coleoptile. *Amer. Jour. Bot.*, 40, 77.

REEVE, E. C. R. and HUXLEY, J. S., 1945: Some problems in the study of allometric growth. *Essays on growth and form.* Oxford Univ. Press.

REEVE, R. M., 1948: Late embryogeny and histogenesis in *Pisum*. *Amer. Jour. Bot.*, 35, 591.

RENNER, O., 1914: Befruchtung und Embryobildung bei *Oenothera lamarckiana* und einiger verwandten Arten. *Flora*, 107, 115.

REYNOLDS, L. G., 1924: The female gametophyte of *Microcycas*. *Bot. Gaz.*, 77, 391.

REZNIK, M. A., 1934: Étude anatomique de la plantule de Sorgo. *Rev. Gen. Bot.*, 46, 384.

RICHARDS, O. W. and KAVANAGH, A. J., 1943: *Amer. Nat.*, 77, 385.

RICHARDS, O. W. and KAVANAGH, A. J., 1945: The analysis of growing form. *Essays on growth and form.* Oxford Univ. Press.

RICHARDS, O. W. and RILEY, G. A., 1937: *J. Exper. Zool.*, 77, 159.

RIETSEMA, J., SATINA, S. and BLAKESLEE, A. F., 1953: The effect of sucrose on the growth of *Datura stramonium* embryos *in vitro*. *Amer. Jour. Bot.*, 40, 538.

RIJVEN, A. H. G. C., 1952: *In vitro* studies on the embryo of *Capsella bursa-pastoris*. N. Holland Publ. Co., Amsterdam.

ROBERTSON, A., 1904: Studies in the Morphology of *Torreya californica* Torrey. II. The sexual organs and fertilisation. *New Phytol.*, 3, 205.

ROBERTSON, A., 1907: The Taxodieae; a phylogenetic study. *New Phytol.*, 6, 92.

ROBYNS, W. and LOUIS, A., 1942: Beschouwingen over Polyembryonie en Polyspermie bij de Bedektzadigen. *Verh. kon. Vlaam. Acad. Wetensch.*, 4, 1–112.

ROCÉN, T., 1927: Zur embryologie der Centrospermen. Diss. Uppsala.

ROSE, D. H., 1915: A study of delayed germination in economic seeds. *Bot. Gaz.*, 59, 425.

ROSENVINGE, M. K. L., 1889: Influence des agents extérieurs sur l'organisation polaire et dorsiventrale des plantes. *Rév. Gen. Bot.*, 1, 53.

ROSTOWZEW, S., 1891: Recherches sur l'*Ophioglossum vulgatum* L. *Over. Kong. Danske Vidensk. Selsk.*, 54–83.

ROSTOWZEW, S., 1892: Beiträge zur Kenntniss der Ophioglosseen L. Moscow.

RUHLAND, W., 1924: *Musci*, in Engler and Prantl's *Die Natürlichen Pflanzenfamilien*. 2nd Ed., 10.

RYTZ, W., 1939: Beitrag zum Aneurin Stoffwechsel bei hoheren Pflanzen. *Ber. Schw. Bot. Ges.*, 49, 339.

SACHET, M., 1948: Fertilisation in six incompatible species crosses of *Datura*. *Amer. Jour. Bot.*, 35, 302.

SACHS, J., 1890: *A history of botany.* (English trans. by H. E. F. Garnsey, Oxford Univ. Press.)

SADEBECK, R., 1878: Entwickelung des Keimes der Schachtelhalma. *Pringsh. Jahrb. Wiss. Bot.*, 59.

SADEBECK, R., 1879: *Handbuch der Botanik.* Schenk, I, 231.

SADEBECK, R., 1900: Equisetaceae. Engler and Prantl, *Nat. Pflanzenfamilien*, 1, 4.

SAHNI, B., 1921: Note on the presence of a 'tent-pole' in the seed of *Cephalotaxus pedunculata*. *Ann. Bot.*, 35, 297.

SAHNI, B., 1921: On the structure and affinities of *Acmopyle pancheri* Pilzer. *Phil. Trans. Roy. Soc.*, B, 210, 253.

SAMPSON, K., 1916: Note on a sporeling of *Phylloglossum* attached to a prothallus. *Ann. Bot.*, 30, 605.

SANDERS, M. E., 1948: Embryo development in four *Datura* species following self and hybrid pollinations. *Amer. Jour. Bot.*, 35, 525.

SANDERS, M. E., 1950: Development of self and hybrid embryos in artificial culture. *Amer. Jour. Bot.*, 37, 6.

SANDERS, M. E. and BURKHOLDER, P. R., 1948: Effect of amino acids on growth of *Datura* embryos in culture. *Amer. Jour. Bot.*, 35, 797.

SANDERS, M. E. and BURKHOLDER, P. R., 1948: Influence of amino acids on growth of *Datura* embryos in culture. *Proc. Nat. Acad. Sci.*, Wash., 34, 516.

SARGANT, E. and ARBER, A., 1915: The comparative morphology of the embryo and seedling in the Gramineae. *Ann. Bot.*, 29, 161.

SATINA, S. and BLAKESLEE, A. F., 1935: Fertilisation in the incompatible cross *Datura stramonium* × *D. metel*. *Bull. Torrey Bot. Club*, 62, 301.

SAXTON, W. T., 1913: Contributions to the life-history of *Actinostrobus pyramidalis*. *Ann. Bot.*, 27, 321.

SAXTON, W. T., 1934: Notes on Conifers. VIII. The morphology of *Austrotaxus spicata* Compton. *Ann. Bot.*, 48, 411.

SAXTON, W. T., 1936: Notes on conifers X. Some normal and abnormal structures in *Taxus baccata*. *Ann. Bot.*, 50, 519.

SCHAEPPI, H. and STEINDL, F., 1942: Blütenmorphologische und embryologische Untersuchungen an Loranthoideen. *Zeitschr. naturf. Ges. Zurich*, 87, 301.

SCHAFFNER, J. H., 1897: Contribution to the life history of *Sagittaria variabilis*. *Bot. Gaz.*, 23, 252.

SCHECHTER, V., 1934: Electrical control of rhizoid formation in the red alga, *Griffithsia bornetiana*. *Jour. Gen. Physiol.*, 18, 1.

SCHECHTER, V., 1935: The effect of centrifuging on the polarity of an alga, *Griffithsia bornetiana*. *Biol. Bull.*, 68, 172.

SCHLEIP, W., 1929: Die Determination der primitiv Entwicklung. *Akad. Verlag.*, Leipzig.

SCHNARF, K., 1929: *Embryologie der Angiospermen*. *Handbuch der Pflanzenanatomie*, II, 2. Borntraeger, Berlin.

SCHNARF, K., 1933: *Embryologie der Gymnospermen*. *Handbuch der Pflanzenanatomie*, II, 2. Borntraeger, Berlin.

SCHNEIDER, G. W., 1953: Megagametogenesis and embryology in a diploid and aneuploid apple. *Amer. Jour. Bot.*, 40, 196.

SCHOUTE, J. C., 1925: La nature morphologique du bourgeon féminin des *Cordaites*. *Rec. Trav. Bot. Néer.*, 12, 113.

SCHUEPP, O., 1926: *Meristeme*. Linsbauer's *Handbuch der Pflanzenanatomie*, 4. Berlin.

SCHWARITZ, F., 1935: Beiträge zur Analyse der pflanzlichen Polarität. *Bech. Bot. Centralbl.*, 54A, 520.

SCOTT, D. H., 1923: *Studies in fossil botany*, Vol. II; 3rd Edn., London.

SEDGWICK, P. J., 1924: The life-history of *Encephalartos*. *Bot. Gaz.*, 77, 300.

SEIFRIZ, W., 1935: The structure of protoplasm. *Biol. Rev.*, 1.

SEIFRIZ, W., 1936: *Protoplasm*. New York.

SEIFRIZ, W., 1938: Recent contributions to the theory of protoplasmic structure. *Science*, 88.

SHATTUCK, C. H., 1905: A morphological study of *Ulmus americana. Bot. Gaz.*, 40, 209.

SILOW, R. A. and STEPHENS, S. G., 1944: 'Twinning' in cotton. *Jour. Hered.*, 35, 76.

SILVA, B. L. T. DE, and TAMBIAH, M. S., 1952: A contribution to the life-history of *Cycas rumphii* Miq. *Ceylon Jour. Sci.*, 12, 223.

SINGH, B., 1952: A contribution to the floral morphology and embryology of *Dendrophthoe falcata* (L.f.). Ettingsh. *Jour. Linn. Soc.*, Lond., 53, 449.

SINGH, B., 1952: Studies on the structure and development of seeds of the Cucurbitaceae. I. Seeds of *Echinocystis Wrightii.* Cogn. *Phytomorph.*, 2, 201.

SKIRM, G. M., 1942: Embryo culturing as an aid to plant breeding. *Jour. Hered.*, 33, 210.

SKOVSTED, A., 1939: Cytological studies in twin plants. *Compt. Rend. des Trav. Carlsberg Lab.*, Ser. Physiol., 22, 427.

SMART, C., 1952: The life-history of *Tupeia* Cham. et Schl. (Loranthaceae). *Trans. Proc. Roy. Soc. New Zealand*, 79, 457.

SMITH, L., 1946: Haploidy in einkorn. *Jour. Agr. Res.*, 73, 291.

SMITH, P. G., 1944: Embryo culture of a tomato species hybrid. *Proc. Amer. Soc. Hort. Sci.*, 44, 413.

SMITH, W. G., 1938: *Cryptogamic botany.* Vol. II. *Bryophytes and pteridophytes.* McGraw-Hill, New York.

SOLOMON, B., 1950: Inhibiting effects of autoclaved malt preventing the *in vitro* growth of *Datura* embryos. *Amer. Jour. Bot.*, 37, 1.

SOUÈGES, R., 1916: Les premières divisions de l'oeuf et l'origine de l'hypophyse chez le *Capsella bursa pastoris* Moench. *C.R. Acad. Sci.*, Paris, 163.

SOUÈGES, R., 1919: Les premières divisions de l'oeuf et les differenciations du suspenseur chez le *Capsella bursa pastoris* Moench. *Ann. Sci. Nat.*, Ser. Bot. 10, 1, 1.

SOUÈGES, R., 1924: Embryogénie des Euphorbiacées. Développement de l'embryon chez l'*Euphorbia esula* L. *C.R. Acad. Sci.*, Paris, 179, 989.

SOUÈGES, R., 1924: Embryogénie des Graminées. Développement de l'embryon chez le *Poa annua* L. *Compt. Rend. Acad. Sci.*, Paris, 178, 860.

SOUÈGES, R., 1925: Développement de l'embryon chez l'*Euphorbia exigua* L. *Bull. Soc. Bot. France*, 72, 1018.

SOUÈGES, R., 1934: *L'embryologie végétale: résumé historique.* I and II. Hermann, Paris.

SOUÈGES, R., 1936: *La segmentation.* Hermann, Paris.

SOUÈGES, R., 1936: *La differenciation.* Hermann, Paris.

SOUÈGES, R., 1937: *Les lois du développement.* Hermann, Paris.

SOUÈGES, R., 1938, 1939, 1948, 1951: *Embryogénie et classification.* Hermann, Paris.

SOUÈGES, R., 1947: Le principe de la corrèspondence des formes. *C.R. Acad. Sci.*, 224, 312.

SPEMANN, H., 1936: *Experimentelle Beiträge zu einer Theorie der Entwickelung.* Springer, Berlin.

SPEMANN, H., 1938: *Embryonic development and induction.* Yale Univ. Press.

SPOERL, E., 1948: Amino acids as sources of nitrogen for orchid embryos. *Amer. Jour. Bot.*, 35, 88.

SPRINGER, E., 1935: Über apogame Sporogone an bivalenten Rasse des Laubmoses *Phascum cuspidatum. Zeits. Ind. Abst. Vererb.*, 69, 249.

SRIVASTAVA, R. K., 1952: Contribution to the embryology of Indian Euphorbiaceae. I. *Euphorbia rothiana* Spreng. *Ann. Bot.*, N.S., 16, 505.

STAHL, E., 1885: *Ber. deutsch. bot. Gesell.*, 3, 334.

STEBBINS, G. L. and JENKINS, J. A., 1939: Aposporic development in the North American species of *Crepis*. *Genetica*, 21, 1.

STEIL, W. N., 1918: Studies of some new cases of apogamy in ferns. *Bull. Torrey Bot. Club*, 45.

STEIL, W. N., 1939: Apogamy, apospory, and parthenogenesis in the pteridophytes. *Bot. Rev.*, 5, 433.

STERN, C., 1936; Genetics and ontogeny. *Amer. Nat.*, 70, 29.

STERN, C., 1938: During which stage in the nuclear cycle do the genes produce their effects in the cytoplasm? *Amer. Nat.*, 72, 350.

STERN, C., 1939: Recent work on the reaction between genes and developmental processes. *Growth* (suppl.), 19.

STEWARD, F. C. and THOMPSON, J. F., 1950: The nitrogenous constituents of plants with special reference to chromatographic methods. *Ann. Rev. Plant. Physiol.*, 1, 233.

STEWARD, F. C. and CAPLIN, S. M., 1952: Investigations on growth and metabolism of plant cells. IV. Evidence on the rôle of the coconut-milk factor in development. *Ann. Bot.*, N.S., 16, 491.

STIER, H. L. and DU BUY, H. G., 1938: Influence of phytohormones on flower and fruit production of tomato. *Proc. Amer. Soc. Hort. Sci.*, 36, 723.

STINGL, G., 1907: Experimentelle Studie über die Entstehung von pflanzenlichen Embryonen. *Flora*, 97, 308.

STOKEY, A. G. and ATKINSON, L. R., 1952: The gametophyte of *Stenochlaena palustris* (Bicrm.) Bedd. *Phytomorph.*, 2, 1.

STOKEY, A. G. and ATKINSON, L. R., 1952: The gametophyte of *Acrostichum speciosum* Willd. *Phytomorph.*, 2, 105.

STOKEY, A. G. and ATKINSON, L. R., 1952: The gametophyte and young sporophyte of *Matonia pectinata* R. Br. *Phytomorph.*, 2, 138.

STONE, E. C. and DUFFIELD, J. W., 1950: Hybrids of sugar pine by embryo culture. *Jour. For.*, 48, 200.

STRASBURGER, E., 1872: *Die Coniferen und die Gnetaceen.*

STRASBURGER, E., 1878: Über Polyembryonie. *Jenaische Zeit. Naturw.*, 12, 647.

STRASBURGER, E., 1897: *Die Angiospermen und die Gymnospermen.* Fischer, Jena.

STRASBURGER, E., 1900: Einige Bemerkungen zur Frage nach der doppelten Befruchtung bei Angiospermen. *Bot. Ztg.*, II, 58, 293.

STRASBURGER, E., 1904: Anlage des Embryosackes und Prothalliumbildung bei der Eibe nebst anschliessenden Erorterungen. (Festschrift von Ernst Haeckel.) *Denkschr. med-naturw. Ges.*, Jena, 11, 1.

STREET, H. E., 1949: Nitrogen metabolism of higher plants. *Adv. Enz.*, 9, 391.

STUDHALTER, R. A., 1938: Independence of the sporophyte in *Riella* and *Sphaerocarpus*. *Ann. Bryol.*, 11, 153.

SUGIHARA, Y., 1938: Fertilisation and early embryogeny of *Chamaecyparis pisifera* S. et. Z. *Sci. Rep. Tokohu Imp. Univ. Ser. IV, Biol.*, 13, 9.

SUGIHARA, Y., 1939: Embryological observations of *Thujopsis dolabrata* var. *honda* Makino. *Sci. Rep. Tokohu Imp. Univ.*, Ser. IV, Biol., 14, 291.

SUSSENGUTH, K., 1923: Über Pseudogamie bei *Zygopetalum mackayi* Hook. *Ber. deutsch. bot. Gesell.*, 41, 16.

SWAMY, B. G. L., 1943: Gametogenesis and embryogeny of *Eulophea epidendraea* Fischer. *Proc. Nat. Inst. Sci. India*, 9, 59.

SWAMY, B. G. L., 1948: Agamospermy in *Spiranthes cernua*. *Lloydia*, 11, 149.

SWAMY, B. G. L., 1946: Inverted polarity of the embryo sac of angiosperms and its relation to the archegonium theory. *Ann. Bot.*, 9, 171.

SWAMY, B. G. L., 1946: The embryology of *Zeuxine sulcata* Lindl. *New Phytol.*, 45, 132.

SWAMY, B. G. L., 1948: Post-fertilization development of *Trillium undulatum*. *Cellule*, 52, 7.

SWAMY, B. G. L., 1949: Further contributions to the morphology of the Degeneriaceae. *Jour. Arnold Arb.*, 30, 10.

SWAMY, B. G. L. and BAILEY, I. W., 1949: The morphology and relationships of *Cercidiphyllum*. *Jour. Arnold Arb.*, 30, 187.

SWINGLE, W. T., 1927: Seed production in sterile *Citrus* hybrids—its scientific explanation and practical significance. *Mem. Hort. Soc. N.Y.*, 3, 19.

TAHARA, M., 1940: Embryogeny of *Torreya nucifera*. *Bot. Mag. Tokyo*, 54, 469. (In Japanese.)

TAYLOR, W. R., 1921: The embryogeny of *Cyrtanthus parviflorus* Baker. *Amer. Jour. Bot.*, 8, 502.

THATHACHAR, T., 1952: Morphological studies in the Euphorbiaceae. I. *Acalypha lanceolata* Willd. *Phytomorph.*, 2, 197.

THIESSEN, R., 1908: The vascular anatomy of the seedling of *Dioon edule*. *Bot. Gaz.*, 46, 357.

THOMAS, A. P. W., 1901: Preliminary account of the prothallium of *Phylloglossum*. *Proc. Roy. Soc. London.*, 69, 285.

THOMAS, H. H., 1932: The old morphology and the new. *Proc. Linn. Soc.*, London, 145, 117.

THOMPSON, D'ARCY, W., 1917, 1942: *On growth and form* (1st and 2nd edns.). Cambr. Univ. Press.

THOMPSON, R. H., 1942: The morphology of *Riella affinis*. II. Development of the sex organs, fertilisation, and development of the sporophyte. *Amer. Jour. Bot.*, 29, 275.

THOMPSON, W. P., 1916: The morphology and affinities of *Gnetum*. *Amer. Jour. Bot.*, 3, 135.

THOMSON, R. B., 1927: Evolution of the seed habit in plants. *Proc. and Trans. Roy. Soc. Canada*, 21, Sec. V, 229.

THOMSON, R. B., 1934: Modification of the form of the haustorium in *Marsilea* on development in culture fluid. *Trans. Roy. Can. Inst.*, 20, 69.

THOMSON, R. B. and HULL, K. L., 1933: Physical laws and the cellular organisation of plants. *Bot. Gaz.*, 95, 511.

THOMSON, W. A., 1949: A natural hybrid of *Loranthus micranthus* and *Tupeia antarctica*. *Trans. Roy. Soc.*, New Zealand, 77, 208.

THURET, G., 1854: Rechèrches sur la fécondation des Fucacées. *Ann. Sci. Nat. Bot.*, IV, 2, 197.

TIAGI, B., 1951: A contribution to the morphology and embryology of *Cuscuta hyalina* Roth. and *C. planiflora* Tenore. *Phytomorph.*, 1, 9.

TIAGI, B., 1951: Studies in the family Orobanchaceae. III. A contribution to the embryology of *Orobanche cernua* Loeffl. and *O. aegyptiaca* Pers. *Phytomorph.*, 1, 158.

TIAGI, B., 1951: Studies in the family Orobanchaceae. I. A contribution to the embryology of *Cistanche tubulosa* Wight. *Lloydia*, 15, 129.

TIAGI, B., 1952: Studies in the family Orobanchaceae. II. A contribution to the embryology of *Aeginetia indica* Linn. *Bull. Torrey Bot. Club*, 79, 63.

VAN TIEGHEM, P., 1872: Observations anatomiques sur le cotyledon des Graminées. *Ann. Sci. Nat. Bot.*, 5, 15, 236.

VAN TIEGHEM, P., 1897: Morphologie de l'embryon et de la plantule chez les Graminées et les Cypéracées. *Ann. Sci. Nat. Bot.*, 8, 3, 259.

TIWARY, N. K., 1926: On the occurrence of polyembryony in the genus *Eugenia*. *Jour. India Bot. Soc.*, 5, 124.

TRETJAKOW, S., 1895: Die Beteilung der Antipoden in Fällen der Polyembryonie bei *Allium odorum*. *Ber. deutsch. bot. Gesell.*, 13, 13.

TREUB, M., 1881: Observations sur les Loranthacées. *Ann. Jard. Bot. Buit.*, 2, 54.

TREUB, M., 1883: Observations sur les Loranthacées. 3. *Viscum articulatum*. 4. *Loranthus pentandrus*. *Ann. Jard. Bot. Buit.*, 3.

TREUB, M., 1884: Études sur les Lycopodiacées: le prothalli de *Lycopodium cernuum* L. *Ann. Bot. Jard. Buit.*, 4, 107.

TREUB, M., 1885: Observations sur les Loranthacées: 1. Développement des sac embryonnaires dans le *Loranthus sphaerocarpus;* 2. Embryogénie du *L. sphaerocarpus*. *Ann. Jard. Bot. Buit.*, 2.

TREUB, M., 1886: Études sur les Lycopodiacées: le prothalli de *L. phlegmaria* L. *Ann. Bot. Jard. Buit.*, 5, 87.

TREUB, M., 1890: Études sur les Lycopodiacées. *Ann. Bot. Jard. Buit.*, 8, 1.

TROLL, W., 1950: Zur Klarung der Polaritätsverhaltnisse des Pteridophytenembryos. *Akad. Wiss. u. Lit. Mainz. Math. naturw.*, 10.

TROLL, W. and WETTER, C., 1952: Beiträge zur Kenntnis der Radikationsverhältnisse von Farnem. *Akad. Wiss. u. Lit.., Mainz*, 1.

TSI-TUNG LI, 1934: The development of the embryo of *Ginkgo biloba*. *Sci. Rep. Nat. Tsing Hua Univ.*, Ser. B, 2, 41.

TUKEY, H. B., 1933: Artificial culture of sweet cherry embryos. *Jour. Hered.*, 24, 7.

TUKEY, H. B., 1937: Growth patterns of plants developed from immature embryo in artificial culture. *Bot. Gaz.*, 99, 630.

TUKEY, H. B., 1944: The excised-embryo method of testing the germinability of fruit seed with particular reference to peach seed. *Proc. Amer. Soc. Hort. Sci.*, 45, 211.

TURING, A. M., 1952: The chemical basis of morphogenesis. *Phil. Trans. Roy. Soc.*, B, 237, 37.

VEH, R. VON, 1936: Eine neue Methode der Anzucht von Sämlingen unabhängig von Ruheperioden and Jahreszeit (bei Apfeln, Birnen, Quitten, Pflaumen, Kirschen). *Der Züchter*, 8, 145.

VIRTANEN, A. I. and LINKOLA, H., 1946: Organic nitrogen compounds as nitrogen nutrition for higher plants. *Nature*, 158, 515.

VLADESCO, M. A., 1931: Polyembryonie chez les fougères. *Bull. Soc. Bot. France*, 78, 325.

VLADESCO, M. A., 1935: Recherches morphologiques et expérimentales sur l'embryogénie et l'organogénie des fougères leptosporangiées. *Rev. Gén. Bot.*, 47, 422.

VÖCHTING, H., 1878, 1884: *Über Organbildung in Pflanzenreich*.

VOUK, 1877: Die Entwicklung das Embryo von *Asplenuim shepherdi*. *Sitz. der K.K. Akad. L. Wiss.*, Wien, 76.

WALKER, R. I., 1947: Megasporogenesis and embryo development in *Tropaeolum majus* L. *Bull. Torrey Bot. Club*, 74, 279.

WALTON, J., 1940: *An introduction to the study of fossil plants*. Black, London.

WALTON, J., 1953: The evolution of the ovule in the pteridosperms. Pres. Addr. (Sect. K), Brit. Assoc. Adv. Sci. *Adv. Sci.*, 10, 223.

WAND, A., 1914: Beiträge zur Kenntniss des Scheitelwachstums und der Verzweigung bei *Selaginella*. *Flora*, 106, 237.

WARD, M., 1950: Fertilisation and morphogenetic variations of the embryo of *Polypodium aureum* L. Unpubl. Thesis, Harvard University.

WARDLAW, C. W., 1925: Size in relation to internal morphology. *Trans. Roy. Soc. Edin.*, 54, 281.

WARDLAW, C. W., 1943: Experimental and analytical studies of pteridophytes. I. Preliminary observations on the development of buds on the rhizome of the ostrich fern (*Matteuccia struthiopteris* Tod.). *Ann. Bot.*, N.S., 7, 171.

WARDLAW, C. W., 1944: Experimental and analytical studies of pteridophytes. 3. Stelar morphology: the initial differentiation of vascular tissue. *Ann. Bot.*, N.S., 8, 173.

WARDLAW, C. W., 1945: Experimental and analytical studies of pteridophytes. 6. Stelar morphology: the occurrence of reduced and discontinuous vascular systems in the rhizome of *Onoclea sensibilis*. *Ann. Bot.*, N.S., 9, 383.

WARDLAW, C. W., 1947: Experimental investigations of the shoot apex of *Dryopteris aristata* Druce. *Phil. Trans. Roy. Soc.*, B, 232, 343.

WARDLAW, C. W., 1948: Experimental and analytical studies of pteridophytes. 13. The shoot apex of a tree fern, *Cyathea Manniana*. *Ann. Bot.*, N.S., 12, 371.

WARDLAW, C. W., 1949a: Further experimental observations on the shoot apex of *Dryopteris aristata* Druce. *Phil. Trans. Roy. Soc.*, B, 233, 415.

WARDLAW, C. W., 1949b: Experiments on organogenesis in ferns. *Growth*, (Suppl.), 9, 93.

WARDLAW, C. W., 1950: The comparative investigations of apices of vascular plants by experimental methods. *Phil. Trans. Roy. Soc.*, B, 234, 583.

WARDLAW, C. W., 1951a: Experimental and analytical studies of pteridophytes. 18. The nutritional status of the apex and morphogenesis. *Ann. Bot.*, N.S., 16.

WARDLAW, C. W., 1951b: Organisation in plants. *Phytomorph.*, 1.

WARDLAW, C. W., 1952: *Phylogeny and morphogenesis*. Macmillan, London.

WARDLAW, C. W., 1953: A commentary on Turing's diffusion-reaction theory of morphogenesis. *New Phytol.*, 52, 40.

WARDLAW, C. W., 1953: Experimental and analytical studies of pteridophytes. XXIII. The induction of buds in *Ophioglossum vulgatum* L. *Ann. Bot.*, N.S. 17.

WARDLAW, C. W., 1953: Comparative observations on the shoot apices of vascular plants. *New Phytol.*, 53.

WARDLAW, C. W., 1954: Experimental and analytical studies of pteridophytes. XXVI. *Ophioglossum vulgatum*. Comparative morphogenesis in the embryo and in induced buds. *Ann. Bot.*, N.S. 18.

WARDLAW, C. W. and ALLSOPP, A., 1948: Experimental and analytical studies of pteridophytes. 12. The effect of different concentrations of oxygen on inactive and active meristems of ferns. *Ann. Bot.*, N.S., 12, 157.

WARMING, E., 1879–80: Forgreningen og Bladstillingen Hos Slaegten *Nelumbo*. Kjøbenhavn Naturhist. Forening Vidensk. Meddel., 31–32, 444.

WEATHERWAX, P., 1920: Position of the scutellum and homology of coleoptile in maize. *Bot. Gaz.*, 69, 179.

WEBBER, J. M., 1938: Cytology of twin cotton plants. *Jour. Agr. Res.*, 57, 155.

WEBBER, J. M., 1940: Polyembryony. *Bot. Rev.*, 6, 575.

WEBBER, H. J. and BATCHELOR, L. D., 1943: *The citrus industry*. Vol. I. Berkeley.

WEIS, H. G., 1934: Der Mechanismus des Wuchsstofftransportes II. *Réc. Trav. Bot. Néer.*, 31, 810.

WEISS, P., 1939: *Principles of development*. Holt, New York.

WEISS, P., 1947: The problem of specificity in growth and development. *Yale Jour. Biol. and Med.*, 19, 235.

WEISS, P., 1950: Perspectives in the field of morphogenesis. *Quart. Rev. Biol.*, 25, 177.

WENIGER, W., 1927: Development of embryo sac and embryo in *Euphorbia preslii* and *E. splendens*. *Bot. Gaz.*, 63, 266.

WENT, F. W. and THIMANN, K. V., 1937: *Phytohormones.* Macmillan, New York.

WENT, F. W. and WHITE, R., 1939: Experiments on the transport of auxin. *Bot. Gaz.,* 100, 465.

WETMORE, R. H., 1950: Tissue and organ culture as a tool for studies in development. *Proc. 7th Internat. Bot. Congr.,* Stockholm.

WETMORE, R. H. and MOREL, G., 1951: Sur la culture *in vitro* de prothalles de *Lycopodium cernuum. Comp. Rend. Acad. Sci.,* Paris, 233, 323.

WETMORE, R. H. and MOREL, G., 1951: Sur la culture du gametophyte de *Selaginella. Comp. Rend. Acad. Sci.,* Paris, 233, 430.

WETMORE, R. H. and WARDLAW, C. W., 1951: Experimental morphogenesis in vascular plants. *Ann. Rev. Plant Physiol.,* 2, 269.

WETTER, C., 1952: Beitrag zum Polaritätsproblem bei leptosporangiate Farne. *Biol. Zentralb.,* 71, 109.

WETTSTEIN, R., 1903–1908, 1911: *Handbuch der systematischen Botanik.* Leipzig.

WHITAKER, D. M., 1931: Some observations on the eggs of *Fucus* and upon their mutual influence in the determination of the developmental axis. *Biol. Bull.,* 61, 294.

WHITAKER, D. M., 1937a: The effect of hydrogen ion concentration on the induction of polarity in *Fucus eggs.* I. Increased hydrogen ion concentration and the intensity of mutual inductions by neighbouring eggs of *Fucus furcatus. Jour. Gen. Physiol.,* 20, 491.

WHITAKER, D. M., 1937b: The effect of hydrogen ion concentration on the induction of polarity in *Fucus* eggs. 2. The effect of diffusion gradients brought about by eggs in capillary tubes. *Jour. Gen. Physiol.,* 21, 57.

WHITAKER, D. M., 1937c: Determination of polarity by centrifuging eggs of *Fucus furcatus. Biol. Bull.,* 73, 249.

WHITAKER, D. M., 1938: The effect of hydrogen ion concentration on the induction of polarity in *Fucus* eggs. 3. Gradients of hydrogen ion concentration. *Jour. Gen. Physiol.,* 21, 833.

WHITAKER, D. M., 1940a: Physical factors of growth. *Growth* (Suppl.).

WHITAKER, D. M., 1940b: The effect of shape on the developmental axis of the *Fucus* egg. *Biol. Bull.,* 78, 111.

WHITAKER, D. M., 1940c: The effects of ultra-centrifuging and of pH on the development of *Fucus* eggs. *J. Cell. and Comp. Physiol.,* 15, 173.

WHITAKER, D. M., 1941: The effect of unilateral ultra-violet light on the development of the *Fucus* egg. *Jour. Gen. Physiol.,* 24, 263.

WHITAKER, D. M. and CLANCY, C. W., 1937: The effect of salinity upon the growth of eggs of *Fucus furcatus. Biol. Bull.,* 73, 552.

WHITAKER, D. M. and LOWRANCE, E. W., 1936: On the period of susceptibility in the egg of *Fucus furcatus* when polarity is induced by brief exposure to white light. *J. Cell. and Comp. Physiol.,* 7, 417.

WHITAKER, D. M. and LOWRANCE, E. W., 1940: The effect of alkalinity upon mutual influences determining the developmental axis in *Fucus* eggs. *Biol. Bull.,* 78, 407.

WHITE, P. R., 1934: Potentially unlimited growth of excised tomato root tips in a liquid medium. *Plant. Physiol.,* 9, 585.

WHITE, P. R., 1939: Controlled differentiation in a plant tissue culture. *Bull. Torrey Bot. Club,* 66, 507.

WHITE, P. R., 1943: *A handbook of plant tissue culture.* Jaques Cattell Press, Lancaster, Penn.

WIELAND, G. R., 1906: *American fossil cycads.* Publ. 34, Carnegie Inst., Wash.

WIGER, J., 1930: Ein neuer Fall von autonomer Nuzellarembryonie. *Bot. Notiser,* 368–370.

WIGGLESWORTH, G., 1907: The young sporophytes of *Lycopodium complanatum* and *L. clavatum*. *Ann. Bot.*, 21, 211.

WILLIAMS, S., 1931: An analysis of the vegetative organs of *Salaginella grandis* Moore, together with some observations on abnormalities and experimental results. *Trans. Roy. Soc., Edin.*, 57, 1.

WILLIAMS, S., 1938: Experimental morphology. (Verdoorn's *Manual of pteridology*, 105. The Hague.)

WINKLER, H., 1908: *Über Parthenogenesis und Apogamie im Pflanzenreiche*. Jena.

WINKLER, H., 1934: Fortpflanzung der Gewächse. VII. Apomixis. (*In Handwörter-buch der Naturwissenschaft*.) 2nd ed. Jena. Vol. 4, 451–461.

WITHNER, C. L., 1942: Nutrition experiments with orchid seedlings. *Amer. Orch. Soc. Bull.*, 11, 112.

WITTWER, S. H., 1943: Growth hormone production during sexual reproduction of higher plants. *Missouri Agr. Exp. Sta. Res. Bull.*, 371.

WOODGER, J. H., 1929: *Biological principles*. Kegan Paul, London.

WOODGER, J. H., 1930, 1931: The 'concept of organism' and the relation between embryology and genetics. *Quart. Rev. Biol.*, 5, 1; 6, 178.

WOODGER, J. H., 1945: On biological transformations. *Essays on growth and form*. Oxford Univ. Press.

WOODGER, J. H., 1948: Observations on the present state of embryology. *Symp. Soc. Exper. Biol.*, 2, 351. Cambr. Univ. Press.

WOODWORTH, R. H., 1930: Cytological studies in the Betulaceae. III. Parthenogenesis and polyembryony in *Alnus rugosa*. *Bot. Gaz.*, 89, 402.

WORSDELL, W. C., 1897: On the development of the ovule of *Christisonia*, a genus of Orobanchaceae. *Jour. Linn. Soc.*, London, 31, 576.

WORSDELL, W. C., 1916: The morphology of the monocotyledonous embryo and of that of the grass in particular. *Ann. Bot.*, 30, 509.

YAMAMOTO, Y., 1936: Über das Vorkommen von triploiden Pflanzen bei Mehrling-skeimlingen von *Triticum vulgare* Vill. *Cytologia*, 7, 431.

YASUDA, S., 1932: Physiological researches on the fertility in *Petunia violacea*. II. On the effect of temperature upon self-fertilisation. *Bot. Mag. Tokyo*, 46, 679; *Bull. Imp. Coll. Agr. and For.*, Japan, 20, 1 (1934).

YASUDA, S., 1933: On the behaviour of pollen tubes in the production of seedless fruits, caused by inter-specific pollination. I. (Japanese with English resumé.) *Jap. Jour., Genetics.*, 8, 239.

YASUDA, S., 1934: On the behaviour of the pollen tubes in the production of seedless fruits by interspecific pollination. 2. (Japanese with English resumé.) *Jap. Jour. Genetics*, 9, 118.

YASUDA, S., 1934: Parthenocarpy caused by the stimulus of pollination in some plants of the Solanaceae. (Japanese with English resumé.) *Agr. and Hort.*, 9, 647.

YASUDA, S., 1936: Some contributions on parthenocarpy caused by the stimulation of pollination. (Japanese with English resumé.) *Bull. Sci. Fakult. Terkul.* Kjusu Imp. Univ., 7, 34.

YASUDA, S., 1940: A preliminary note on the artificial parthenogenesis induced by application of growth promoting substance. *Bot. Mag.*, Tokyo, 54, 506.

YASUDA, S., INABA, T. and TAKAHASHI, Y., 1935: Parthenocarpy caused by the stimulation of pollination in some plants of the Cucurbitaceae. *Agr. and Hort.*, 10, 1385.

YASUI, K., 1911: On the life-history of *Salvinia natans*. *Ann. Bot.*, 25.

YUNG, C. T., 1938: Developmental anatomy of the seedling of the rice plant. *Bot. Gaz.*, 99, 786.

ZIEBUR, N. K., BRINK, R. A., GRAF, L. H. and STAHMANN, M. A., 1950: The effect of casein hydrolysate on the growth of immature *Hordeum* embryos. *Amer. Jour. Bot.*, 37, 144.

ZIEBUR, N. K. and BRINK, R. A., 1951: The stimulative effect of *Hordeum* endosperms on the growth of immature plant embryos *in vitro*. *Amer. Jour. Bot.*, 38, 253.

INDEX